Understanding

Arithmetic

Alice Ambrose and Morris Lazerowitz
FUNDAMENTALS OF SYMBOLIC LOGIC

Ross A. Beaumont and Richard W. Ball
INTRODUCTION TO MODERN ALGEBRA AND MATRIX THEORY

Jack R. Britton
CALCULUS

Jack R. Britton and L. Clifton Snively
ALGEBRA FOR COLLEGE STUDENTS, *Revised*
COLLEGE ALGEBRA
INTERMEDIATE ALGEBRA

Howard Eves
AN INTRODUCTION TO THE HISTORY OF MATHEMATICS

Howard Eves and C. V. Newsom
AN INTRODUCTION TO THE FOUNDATIONS AND FUNDAMENTAL CONCEPTS
      OF MATHEMATICS

Casper Goffman
REAL FUNCTIONS

Richard E. Johnson, Neal H. McCoy, and Anne F. O'Neill
FUNDAMENTALS OF COLLEGE MATHEMATICS

Burton W. Jones
THE THEORY OF NUMBERS

Lucien B. Kinney and C. Richard Purdy
TEACHING MATHEMATICS IN THE SECONDARY SCHOOL

Harold D. Larsen
RINEHART MATHEMATICAL TABLES
RINEHART MATHEMATICAL TABLES, FORMULAS, AND CURVES, *Enlarged*

Horace C. Levinson
THE SCIENCE OF CHANCE

Neal H. McCoy and Richard E. Johnson
ANALYTIC GEOMETRY

Kenneth S. Miller
ENGINEERING MATHEMATICS

William K. Morrill
PLANE TRIGONOMETRY, *Revised*

John A. Northcott
MATHEMATICS OF FINANCE
PLANE AND SPHERICAL TRIGONOMETRY, *Revised*

Lewis M. Reagan, Ellis R. Ott, and Daniel T. Sigley
COLLEGE ALGEBRA, *Revised*

Paul R. Rider and Carl H. Fischer
MATHEMATICS OF INVESTMENT

Robert L. Swain
UNDERSTANDING ARITHMETIC

Gerhard Tintner
MATHEMATICS AND STATISTICS FOR ECONOMISTS

Walter W. Varner
COMPUTING WITH DESK CALCULATORS

Robert L. Swain

Professor of Mathematics
State University of New York

Understanding Arithmetic

Rinehart & Company, Inc., New York

To My Wife

Preface

As here presented, the drama of *number* will be for most readers neither a "remake" nor a variation on an old theme, but a tale essentially new and fresh.

The adult who seeks to *understand arithmetic* has little to gain from repetitious review and drill. The rambling structure in his mind that he labels "arithmetic" may be likened to a house that is rickety and askew—shall he just patch the holes and shore up the sagging beams? We propose with this book to help him lay a new foundation and build more soundly. The original construction project was lengthy and difficult, for it was a child who labored on it. As an adult now, of age twenty, or sixty, he will find that the re-erection of the arithmetical structure may proceed more swiftly and easily than he would have supposed possible.

What price computational skill? Has the individual who is already "good at figures" much to gain from improving his understanding of arithmetic? We may remind him that several hundred thousand machines now resting on office desks have computational speed and accuracy far exceeding his. In what ways may a person show himself superior to the machine? Only the person can analyze a real life situation and pick out the significant factors that are involved in it. He alone can relate these factors to numerical quantities and set up equations or other relations containing them. He *or* the machine may then manipulate or calculate. But he again must carry out the final task of making use of the "answers" to help him cope with the original problem situation.

Whenever anyone employs simple arithmetic in connection with his everyday pursuits, he must go through the steps just described. So must the expert who applies advanced mathematics in his technical work. On any level, a person's mathematical efforts can be effective only if his training is broadly based, with the routine skills appropriately fitted within a framework of conceptual understanding.

"How do you add $\frac{2}{3}$ and $\frac{3}{4}$? Multiply 673 by 26? Extract the square root of 463?" Questions like these call for rote demonstrations of techniques. Most of us can "go through the motions," as we learned them in school, and put down the work asked for. But how many of us can make much headway with the following questions?

Why do 2 and 2 make 4? Why do we "carry" when we add? If 3 and 4 make 7, why should 2 and 5 also make 7? Is there a reason why 24 times 53 equals 53 times 24? Why do we add, subtract, and so on, in the ways we do? Are ours the best ways? Are ⅔ and ⅚ the same or different numbers? How may multiplication by zero be explained? Why do we count by tens instead of by eights or twelves? When two people count the same group, why do they get the same answer? Just what *is* a number? Are $\sqrt{2}$ and -3 as "real" as 4 and 5? What is the relationship between the statements *2 + 3 = 5* and *2 inches + 3 inches = 5 inches*: Are either or both of these universally true?

Such questions have to do with the nature of the number concept and with the logic or meaning of arithmetic. It is our aim in this book to aid the reader or the student to comprehend the subject in these broad terms. In our treatment, we must rebuild the structure of arithmetic from the ground up, taking advantage, to be sure, of the reader's earlier school acquaintance with materials and techniques, but without actually depending upon the quantity and quality of this training in any important way.

Further, we must give the reader some opportunity to appreciate the human setting of our subject, its relationship to man and society. Like other liberal studies, mathematics has deep roots in the dim past. It is important for us to realize how social and cultural developments have set the course of mathematical growth, and vice versa. There are many parallels, too, between the genesis of ideas, mathematical or otherwise, in the individual and in the race, so that a historical perspective is valuable for the kind of understanding that we aim toward. Here are a few questions of the sort we may consider:

Is our arithmetic a gift of the ancients or has it evolved as have the sciences? How did peoples of earlier times write and use numbers? What mechanical aids did they contrive to facilitate computation? How have number discoveries upset philosophies and changed our world outlook? Is the language of numbers actually more abstract than the language of words? To what factors may we attribute the extraordinary successes won by mathematics in practical application—to science and technology as well as to the ordinary affairs of home, shop and office?

Though useful to a broad class of readers, in or out of college classrooms, this book is particularly addressed to the future teachers of arithmetic in the elementary and early secondary grades. It could well have been titled *What Every Teacher Ought to Know about Arithmetic*. Yet the road to understanding of a subject may be jointly traveled by all—by office worker, shopkeeper, craftsman, lawyer, engineer, teacher, and the rest. The general reader or the "general student" need not feel like an intruder should he "sit in" along with the teacher as our tale unfolds.

Writers on mathematical education generally agree that teachers need some sort of a specialized or "professionalized" background course in arithmetic, with the emphasis put upon "meaning" rather than upon the operative procedures as such, or even upon the formal logic underlying them. (See, for example, "Mathematical Background Needed by Teachers of Arithmetic," by C. V. Newsom, pages 232–250, *Fiftieth Yearbook of the National Society For the Study of Education, Part II, The Teaching of Arithmetic,* University of Chicago Press, Chicago, 1951.) Various colleges and universities have introduced such courses into their curricula during the past decade, and a few texts have been published. The same topics run through these books, but arrangements and treatments differ widely.

We place special emphasis upon the idea of a collection, or *set,* of objects. We regard a natural number (1, 2, 3, . . .) as a kind of "size tag" labeling such a set. From this principle we derive number properties and basic rules of operation. We strive to make this conception an integral part of the student's way of thinking, so that it will become for him a mental tool of broad power and lifelong utility. The set concept is especially valuable for the teacher, in that the child's development of number ideas must be in part based on it. (See, for example, *The Child's Conception of Number,* by Jean Piaget, International Library of Psychology, Philosophy and Scientific Method, Routledge and Paul, London, 1952.)

Chapter 11, "Using Units," provides some background for understanding mathematical application. On the whole, however, the book deals with the principal topics of "pure" rather than "applied" arithmetic. It is the subject matter of pure arithmetic, viewed in historical perspective and rendered both logical and meaningful, which is absolutely essential for the teacher, at *all* grade levels. Certain additional applied and analytical topics are important for the teacher of the upper grades: ratio and proportion, formulas and equations, functions, graphs, informal geometry and mensuration, consumer and business arithmetic, probability and statistics. These topics demand emphasis upon manipulation and "problem solving." They also represent a mathematical area important for everyone's "general education." Whether future teacher or businessman or housewife, a student ought to have acquired proficiency in that area quite early, in high school or in his freshman college year. So we do not treat those topics here.

This book is based upon previous mimeographed versions used, over a period of six years, with nearly 1500 students who have enrolled in the author's course "Numbers" at the State University Teachers College at New Paltz, New York. Half a dozen instructors on our staff and from other colleges and universities have given the course, to future and present teachers seeking certification at levels from kindergarten to high school grades.

Our experience has shown that future teachers are strongly motivated toward this type of course, particularly during their *junior and senior college years*, after they have had a chance to "observe and participate" in elementary or secondary school classrooms. Not only do they recognize the professional value of the work, but they find it inherently interesting and stimulating. They are ready for the most part to suspend any previous antagonisms felt toward the area of mathematics, and to approach the material with a fresh mind and an attitude spiced with curiosity. Middle-aged graduate teachers have frequently entered the course with some apprehension, yet have achieved superior performance.

In the three-hour, one-semester course at New Paltz, we cover the first nine chapters quite thoroughly. Problem sets are spaced throughout the text so that each set usually corresponds to a single class hour. The distribution of class time thus follows the pattern shown in the table at the right. This plan leaves time for just a few topics selected from Chapters 10, 11, and 12. For high-school mathematics teachers, in training or in service, a complete coverage is desirable, possibly with certain supplementations.

Chapter	Number of Problem Sets
1	4
2	5
3	6
4	3
5	6
6	4
7	5
8	4
9	3
	40
10	4
11	4
12	5
	53

For the most part, the material of the first nine chapters is sequentially arranged. Some sections and their problem sets are starred (*), indicating that they may be omitted without loss of continuity. (Individual problems of more than average difficulty are also starred.) Chapters 10, 11, and 12 are largely independent of each other.

Certain text matter is printed in smaller type. This includes supplementary material regarded as less important than that of the main text, also various explanatory and illustrative side comments, as well as some material of more than average technical difficulty. Being woven integrally with the text and often forming part of its continuity, these "asides" should not be regarded as mere footnotes.

Conceptual understanding is not easily won. In treating arithmetic on a mature level, we have probed deeply enough into the subject to challenge the mind of the intelligent reader or the better student. Some material is new, for example, the treatment of "accuracy" in §10–11 of Chapter 12. Some material is drawn from areas of mathematics usually classified as "advanced." The author has zealously labored to adapt this material and to present it as simply as it is in his power to do, so that it may be mastered by those whose mathematical background is weak. Technical terminology and notation have been held to a minimum. Terms loved only by pedants, like "minuend" and "involution," have been avoided. A few short abstract proofs have been included. In most cases, however, it has been found possible to convey the essential ideas behind the proof procedures by suitably arranged numerical demonstrations.

Thanks are gratefully extended to the students, faculty, and administration of the State University Teachers College at New Paltz for the continuous stimulation, cooperation and support given by them to the development of the course "Numbers." To Dr. C. V. Newsom, President of New York University, is due special appreciation for his long encouragement of the author's writing efforts and for the influence he has had upon the arrangement and treatment of the book. Thanks are also due the personnel of Rinehart & Company for their helpful and pleasant cooperation. Above all, the author is happy to acknowledge here his general debt to Professor F. L. Griffin, President Emeritus of Reed College, and Professor R. L. Moore, of the University of Texas, who chiefly guided his undergraduate and graduate mathematical studies, respectively. Some sections of the book reflect the influence of study and work pursued by the author while holding a fellowship grant, 1955–1956, from the Fund for the Advancement of Education.

ROBERT L. SWAIN

New Paltz, New York
March, 1957

A Word to the Teacher
of Arithmetic

Young children like numbers. They love to "count." They are quick to compare numbers of candies, pencils, marbles, and the like. They chant number rhymes and delight in number games. For some children arithmetic is ever a pleasant pursuit. But for others what once was sweet turns bitter. Arithmetic brings them annoyance and frustration, as it is converted from a charming pastime to a hateful and dreaded discipline.

Mental tastes differ, to be sure. No subject is universally liked or universally disliked. Yet it would seem that mathematics draws more than its fair share of pupil aversion. This is a sad and serious state of affairs. We live in a highly complex society. Man or woman, a citizen who has not mastered the basic arithmetical skills is a drag on the rest of us and is himself gravely handicapped.

Day by day, with mechanization becoming more widespread, business and industry rely less upon routine clerical procedures and less upon the use of unskilled and semiskilled labor. There are fewer and fewer places open to the mathematically illiterate. Technology invades our homes to a growing extent. And as we "do it ourselves," we must plan, measure, and figure.

We are budget, insurance, pension, and tax conscious. Our family finances are complicated by installment buying, wage deductions, premiums, discounts, and so on. Our newspapers are littered with numerical data, with ratios, percentages and rates, per capita citations, cost-of-living indices, tables, and graphs. From family circle to world sphere, the problems with which we must deal are always as much "quantitative" as they are "qualitative." To dislike arithmetic, in our modern era, is to visit upon oneself continual frustration.

We would wish of the ideal teacher that she should develop a true affection not only for every child who comes under her aegis, but also for every subject in which she gives instruction. As an alter-parent, her attitudes are bound to rub off upon her pupils. The pupils of the ideal teacher would by and large agree with her that "mathematics can be fun," and would regard their work in arithmetic as a stimulating and worth-while activity.

To achieve this latter end, of course, the teacher must bring more than favorable attitudes into the classroom. She must bring a full mind as well as a full heart. It is her prime duty *not to be ignorant.*

As a child passes through the grades, each of his teachers in turn will likely be weak in some area. Where the child's progress is thus slowed, perhaps in art or music, even in history or geography, he will normally be able to continue successfully under later instruction. In the case of mathematics, however, the consequences of teacher ignorance are much more severe.

A teacher who lacks an adequate conceptual grasp of arithmetic is forced to teach by rule and rote. She may drill per pupils so thoroughly that they become quite proficient at carrying through many complex processes, like that of long division. Yet these pupils may find their "skill" useless in practical application because they are unable to recognize the situations calling for its use—or they may apply the process blindly, say in dividing 200 into 8000! Skills so acquired, furthermore, are ephemeral—growths without root. A process that is *understood* can be recaptured after the memory of it fades. But when a process is seen as but a sequence of meaningless steps, then to forget one step is to lose the whole. In the passage of a summer, most of a year's learning may vanish. Next year's teacher may be able to patch up some of the gaps—or she too may be "ignorant," and then the pupil is in for a bad time. A child can suffer being taught by rote for a limited period. But mathematics is a "sequential" subject, each new unit of learning depending upon those previously mastered. There will come a time when the child will be blocked from going on. His shaky foundation will no longer support new learnings, at first along perhaps just a few mathematical directions, but finally along nearly all. As his frustrations mount, he will likely become so hostile to mathematical study as to pass beyond the point of possible rescue, despite efforts of later, more enlightened teachers.

The teacher should be familiar with important everyday uses of arithmetic. She should have some slight acquaintance with several types of mathematical application on the technical and scientific level. Also, she should know a little of the history of mathematics and of science, not considered in isolation, but in relation to man and society. A teacher prepared in these ways may be said to have some "appreciation of the role of mathematics in our culture." A teacher who lacks such a background will be likely to undervalue, hence to underteach, the subject. She will find it hard to give her pupils the motivations needed to stimulate their learning efforts. She will be unable to help them see how mathematics is related to other subjects. Her pupils will likely come to regard mathematics as dreary and dull, and will be hindered in their advance toward careers in technology, engineering, and the sciences. Many, and not only the less able, will turn away toward vocational paths actually less suitable for them.

To the teacher of arithmetic we address the plea that she gear her efforts toward higher goals than our schools now set. During the past few years, leaders from many fields, from science, from government, from business and industry, have become disturbed about the generally low standard of mathematical education in our country. They tell us, for example, that Soviet Russia is forging far ahead of us in the production of engineers, technicians, and scientists. A Soviet youngster in the fifth through the tenth grades spends over 40 per cent of his school hours upon science and mathematics—and he spends half again as many hours in school as does an American child. (See "The Challenge of Soviet Education," by former Senator William Benton, inserted into the *Congressional Record*, Mar. 19, 1956, by Sen. J. William Fulbright.)

We need not look across the seas to find evidence of our deficiencies. Any home owner can testify as to the difficulty of locating adequately trained plumbers, electricians, carpenters, and other expert craft workers. How many plumbers can cope with the intricacies of modern heating and air-conditioning systems? How many builders can apply physical-science principles to help them solve problems of grade drainage or of protection against condensation in insulated thin-wall construction? How many former radio repairmen can be trusted to deal with color TV and hi-fi installations? In our era of rapid technological change, the training received by these technicians of our homes, ten, twenty, thirty, forty years ago, in school and on the job, has not met the test of time. With a stronger school foundation in basic mathematics and science, our semi-technical craft workers could better adapt themselves to the needs of new times.

With respect to mathematics as well as to other subjects, *motivations* must be linked to a child's interests or "needs," present or evokable. On the other hand, the *content* of the mathematical curriculum must be linked to interests and needs of the future adult. What will be the nature of the world of that adult, the world of 1980, even 2000, A.D.?

In its particular aspects, the character of the future world is scarcely foreseeable. Surely it will be different. A new Rip Van Winkle who would learn today how to fix an automobile motor or a TV set, how to build a house or fly a plane, even how to be an accountant or factory manager, would awake to find his generation-old skills nearly useless. For a fresh start in the new era, he would have to fall back upon his schooling in basic mathematics and in the other liberal arts and sciences.

The awakened sleeper would find even this basic training sadly deficient, to be sure. We can be certain that there will be a much greater dependence upon mathematics in the future world than in the world of today, in all spheres of life, from home, farm, and office to laboratory and conference table. Many social scientists, for example, will find it necessary to take undergraduate and graduate college mathematical work to the extent that the physical scientist does today.

The teacher should remind herself from time to time that it is this new world in which her pupils will eventually have to make their way. Shall she teach mathematics at a level sufficient only unto yesterday when her pupils will need that which is adequate for tomorrow?

Contents

7 Number Structure — 113

8 Fractions — 135

9 Decimals — 155

Understanding

Arithmetic

1

Numbers and
Numerals

§1. PRIMITIVE NUMBER SCHEMES

Word and Number—these twin creations blaze the trail of human progress. To the degree that man has mastered their use, to this degree he controls the world about him.

Where the extent of man's mastery over Nature is slim, his number system reflects his ineptitude:

1.	*Neecha*	(1)
2.	*Boolla*	(2)
3.	*Boolla Neecha*	(2 + 1)
4.	*Boolla Boolla*	(2 + 2)

A primitive chant? The sequence furnishes a fine accompaniment to the boom-boom drone of the tom-tom. Yet it is actually the complete *counting system* of a native Australian tribe (*Bourke, Darling River*). It provides two basic number names from which other number names are compounded and is accordingly termed a "base two" or *binary* system.

The material culture of the Australian aborigines is among the most "backward" to be found in the world today. It is surely a simple way of life for which the number scheme described above may prove adequate. Posing to ourselves the questions "How big? How far? How many? How much?" a hundred times a day, we can scarcely imagine what it would be like to face the world around us with mental tools so crude and blunt.

Certain Greenland Eskimos use a more elaborate system:

1.	*atauseq*	
2.	*machdlug*	
3.	*pinasut*	
4.	*sisamat*	
5.	*tadlimat*	
6.	*achfineq-atauseq*	(Other Hand 1)
7.	*achfineq-machdlug*	(Other Hand 2)

8.	*achfineq-pinasut*	(Other Hand 3)
9.	*achfineq-sisamat*	(Other Hand 4)
10.	*qulit*	
11.	*achqaneq-atauseq*	(First Foot 1)
12.	*achqaneq-machdlug*	(First Foot 2)
13.	*achqaneq-pinasut*	(First Foot 3)
14.	*achqaneq-sisamat*	(First Foot 4)
15.	*achfechsaneq*	
16.	*achfechsaneq-atauseq*	(Other Foot 1)
17.	*achfechsaneq-machdlug*	(Other Foot 2)
18.	*achfechsaneq-pinasut*	(Other Foot 3)
19.	*achfechsaneq-sisamat*	(Other Foot 4)
20.	*inuk navdlucho*	(A Man Ended)

This is a "quinary-vigesimal" system. The counting proceeds by groups of five up to twenty, then goes on by twenties.

A striking feature of the system—and there are others like it—is its literal incorporation of the idea of counting on the fingers and toes. When a child counts on his fingers, he is perpetuating an association between the human hand and human number notions that is a basic element in cultural history. It is surely this association that has given us our *tens*, or *decimal*, system of counting. There is no natural advantage in counting by tens. We might just as well have learned to count by sixes, say, or eights, or twelves. Yet the major number systems of history have all been on a scale of ten or of a multiple of ten, such as 20, 40, or 60. If we had twelve fingers, would we not count by twelves? We will explore this possibility in Chapter 6.

In the meantime, let us regard our counting by tens as evidence that the concepts and structures of mathematics are at least in part of very *human* origin, and that they evolve and change as do all other works of man.

§2. OUR NUMERAL SYSTEM

In this chapter we will survey some numeral systems of earlier times, and will wish to contrast them with our own. It will be helpful to review the significant features of our own system before delving into the past.

We form our number symbols, or **numerals,** out of the ten basic numerals called the *digits*: 0, 1, 2, 3, 4, 5, 6, 7, 8, 9. A numeral is a succession of digits. Consider the numeral 237. This is commonly read "two hundred thirty-seven" or "two thirty-seven" or "two three seven." The digits occupy positions with the following place values:

Hundreds	Tens	Units
(100)	*(10)*	*(1)*
2	3	7

The digit 7 contributes 7 × 1, or 7 units, to the value of the numeral. The digit 3 contributes 3×10, or 3 tens. The digit 2 contributes 2×100, or 2 hundreds. Thus

$$237 \quad = \quad 2 \times 100 \quad + \quad 3 \times 10 \quad + \quad 7 \times 1$$
$$= \quad 200 \quad + \quad 30 \quad + \quad 7$$

The value of any numeral is the *sum* of the values that the digits contribute by virtue of their *position* in the numeral. Our system of number expression is therefore **additive** and is based upon the conception of **place value.**

In right-to-left order, each place has a value ten times larger than the one before. Hence the place values are the successive powers of ten, listed below. We count not just by tens, but by *powers of ten.*

Place Name	Place Value	Power of Ten
Units	1	
Tens	10	10^1
Hundreds	100	10^2
Thousands	1,000	10^3
Ten Thousands	10,000	10^4
Hundred Thousands	100,000	10^5
Millions	1,000,000	10^6

You and I have an accurate intuitive sense of the "size" of the number 237, acquired over years of experience. A Roman citizen of the early A.D.'s, displaced into modern times, would find it hard to develop this sense that we take for granted.

But the Roman would readily grasp our scheme of coinage. He could come to grips with the place value feature of our numeral system by watching a counting operation in which pennies, dimes, and dollars are used as tokens to keep track of the count.

Imagine that a long line of people file through a gateway. As each person passes, we lay a penny on our counting table. Lacking a place value scheme, we would end the counting with just a large pile of pennies on the table. Instead, as the tenth penny goes down, we scoop up the group and put down a dime in exchange. The next ten pennies are replaced by a second dime. This goes on until the tenth dime is put down, whereupon we clear the table and put down a dollar bill. If when the counting is done there lie on the table

2 dollar bills, 3 dimes, 7 pennies,

then we have counted to the number denoted by our numeral 237.

(Some primitives count merely by groups or multiples, instead of by powers, of ten. Counting that way, we would be limited to pennies and dimes, ending with 23 dimes and 7 pennies.)

The function of any numeral system is to provide a systematic and efficient way of *naming* the numbers that are used in counting. In addition to "word" names, like *thirty-seven*, the system usually provides special symbolic expressions, like 37. These number "names" are called *numerals.* They are what we write or say when we refer to numbers. A numeral *denotes* (or "designates," or "stands for") a number. Hence a numeral is a linguistic entity, whereas a number is a mathematical entity. (An object, say a stone, is quite unlike the *word* "stone" by which we denote it for the purpose of communication.)

This important distinction between "number" and "numeral" sometimes escapes notice, because the term "number" is widely used to refer to either concept. In this book we shall make the distinction whenever it seems wise to do so, but at other times we shall follow the common practice. At present our attention is chiefly upon *numerals;* in Chapter 2, it will be turned toward *numbers.*

§3. THE ABACUS

In our offices and in our laboratories the electrons spin our number wheels—and our engineers slide their numbers on a stick. Thus we depute the burden of our arithmetic to the unprotesting machine.

Our forebears were no less ingenious. From earliest times calculation has been aided by devices of one sort or another, most often by some form of **abacus.**

Etymological skirmishes have been waged over the origin of the word "abacus." According to one version, it evolved through the Greek word *abax* (slab) from a Semitic word meaning "dust." This would make an abacus a "dustboard," or table covered with dust or sand, on which one could mark with a stylus and erase by smoothing with the fingers. Such a form of abacus was indeed among those used by the Greeks, Romans, and Hindus.

The most popular historical form was the *line abacus.* To construct a model, rule several equally spaced lines on a sheet of paper and give them the successive values 1, 10, 100, 1000, . . . , as in Figure 1. Numbers may be represented by laying "counters" (pennies, buttons, etc.) on the lines. The number 237 is shown represented in the figure. The rule for using this abacus is that a "double-handful" (ten) of counters on a line is equivalent to a single counter on the next higher valued line.

To *count* on the line abacus, successively lay counters on the units (1) line until a double-handful are down. Then "exchange" by

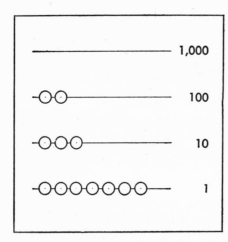

Fig. 1   Line Abacus
The number 237 is represented.

scooping these up and laying a single counter on the tens (10) line. Continue to lay counters on the units line until a double-handful are down, then exchange again. This process goes on indefinitely, occasionally interrupted by a higher order exchange, such as the replacement of a double-handful on the tens line by one counter on the hundreds line.

To *add* two numbers on the line abacus, represent them both separately, then treat the combination as the representation of a single number, simplifying by exchanges. Figure 2 indicates the procedure, applied to the sum 237 + 75 = 312.

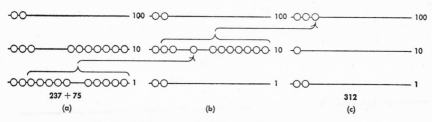

Fig. 2   Adding, on a Line Abacus, 237 + 75 = 312

In (a) above, 237 is represented on the left, 75 on the right portion of the abacus. The ten counters on the units (1) line beneath the "brace" (⏜) are taken off the abacus, and a single counter is placed on the tens (10) line, as the arrow indicates (b). A similar exchange of one hundred (100) for ten tens gives the final result (c).

To *subtract* on the line abacus, it may be necessary to exchange in reverse, or "borrow." Figure 3 shows how this may be done in the case of the difference 312 − 75.

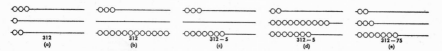

Fig. 3   Subtracting, on a Line Abacus, 312 − 75 = 237

The first step is to put 312 on the abacus, as shown in (a) above. In a reverse exchange, one counter is taken off the tens line, and a double-handful (ten) are laid on the units line (b). Now 5 can be taken away (c), leaving 70 to go, i.e., 7 on the tens line yet to be taken off. Again a reverse exchange is performed. A hundreds counter is removed and a double-handful are placed on the tens line (d); 7 of them are taken off, and the work is ended (e).

Modern abacuses are of the rod-and-bead variety. A simple form is shown in Figure 4, a rectangular wooden frame bearing several rods strung with ten sliding beads per rod. Numbers may be represented by sliding the appropriate beads to registering position at the right.

The rule for operating the rod abacus is similar to that for the line abacus: Ten registering beads on a rod may be slid back, and a single bead on the next higher valued rod slid forward to replace them. Suppose that 75 is to be added to the 237 shown. Begin to add the 5, counting *1, 2, 3* and sliding over a units bead at each count. At the count of 3 all

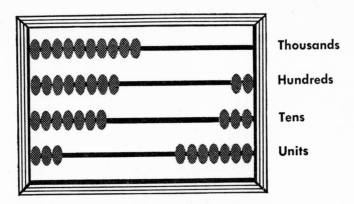

Fig. 4   Rod Abacus
The number 237 is shown represented.

units beads are at the right. Exchange by drawing them back and moving a tens bead over. Then finish the count, *4, 5,* ending with 2 units beads in registering position. Move to the tens rod and repeat the procedure, this time counting to 7.

A more efficient way of operating the rod abacus is as follows. With 237 on the abacus, we propose to add 75, as before. First, 5 is to be added to the 7 already on the abacus in the units row. It is noted that there are

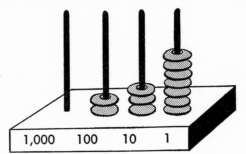

Fig. 5   A Form of Line Abacus
The number 237 is shown represented.

not 5 beads left to be moved to registering position. But to add 5 is the same as to *take away 5 and add 10* (5 = 10 − 5). Move 5 units beads back and move 1 tens bead over to the right. What shows on the abacus is now 242, and 70 is yet to be added. To add 7 is the same as to take away 3 and add 10 (7 = 10 − 3). Therefore, move 3 tens beads back and move 1 hundreds bead over to the right.

An interesting form of line abacus can be made by inserting several vertical rods or heavy wires into a flat base, as in Figure 5. Loose beads may be dropped onto or taken off the rods. This device is useful for displaying numeral structure, as well as for computing.

In connection both with numerical work and with the discussion of arithmetical principles, we shall from time to time use abacus illustrations or direct the student to employ an abacus. The student should keep some pennies, checkers, poker chips, tiddlywinks, or other counters handy for line-abacus practice. He may purchase a rod abacus at a toy store, but will do better to make his own. The abacus vanished from American schoolrooms some years ago, but is now reappearing in them in various forms—from hand models to large demonstration types with vertical rods and spring-inset colored beads which stay put wherever they are slid.

PROBLEM SET 1 (§1–§3)

1.   How could the Australian tribe in §1 have continued to count: "five," "six"?

2.   On what scale is our succession of common liquid measures, from "cup" to "gallon"?   *Answer:* Binary

3.   Read each number in words: (a) 37,207; (b) 5,653,024.

4.   Name the place value associated with each digit of each number: (a) 37,207; (b) 5,653,024.

5.   Explain the difference between counting by tens and by powers of ten. Use the number 542 in illustration.

6.   Explain the distinction between number and numeral. What is the relation between a person and his name?

7.   The relation $237 = 2 \times 100 + 3 \times 10 + 7 \times 1$ appears in §2. Write similar relations for (a) 360, (b) 2107, (c) 37,207.

8.   How many exchanges (dime for 10 pennies, dollar for 10 dimes) must you perform when counting a group of 328 people passing through a gate by using pennies, dimes, and dollars to keep the tally?   *Answer:* 35

9.   Construct a line abacus as described in §3 (several lines ruled on a sheet of paper). Count to 13; to 41.

10.   Add, on your line abacus:

(a) $8 + 6$	(d) $52 + 43$	(g) $238 + 85$
(b) $17 + 23$	(e) $88 + 34$	(h) $829 + 461$
(c) $10 + 20$	(f) $84 + 62$	(i) $573 + 427$

11.   Subtract, on your line abacus:

(a) $8 - 3$	(d) $38 - 15$	(g) $502 - 222$
(b) $13 - 9$	(e) $72 - 48$	(h) $1063 - 581$
(c) $20 - 7$	(f) $140 - 82$	(i) $3462 - 1886$

12.   Construct a rod abacus, and carry out the additions in Problem 10 on it. (A crude representation of a rod abacus can be fixed up just by distributing 40 pennies in four rows. The pennies can be slid a few inches to the right to "register.")

13.   Carry out the subtractions in Problem 11 on a rod abacus (or crude representation of one).

14.   How can you find 2×43 on a line abacus? 3×43?

15. Try to discover an efficient scheme for computing 23 × 46 on a line abacus. (*Hint:* 23 = 20 + 3.)

§4. EGYPTIAN NUMERALS

Unlike our contemporary nomadic Australian natives, the ancient Egyptians possessed a material (and a religious) culture of some complexity. The pyramids stand as monuments to their engineering ability. Traders as well as builders and surveyors, they needed accurate means to represent and handle large numbers.

As early as 3000 B.C., the Egyptians had developed an effective numeral system. Stone was then their writing medium. We can today inspect their numerals in *hieroglyphic* or picture-symbol form, carved on the walls of their tombs. For the powers of ten from one to one million, the hieroglyphs look like this, the forms being simplified and the appended interpretations uncertain:

EGYPTIAN HIEROGLYPHIC NUMERALS						
1	10	100	1,000	10,000	100,000	1,000,000
Stroke	Arch	Coiled Rope	Lotus Flower	Pointed Finger	Tadpole	Astonished Man

Just as we group several coins and bills to make up a given sum, the Egyptians could put together several symbols whose values added up to a given number. They represented our number 23,529 as:

Sometimes they carved the symbols in descending order of value, as above (from left to right), and sometimes in ascending order. However, they could have scattered them about in as disorderly a way as they pleased without affecting the value of the group. Each of the following three expressions, for example, represents the same number (10,210):

There is no hint here of such notions as those of digits and position value.

Adding Egyptian numerals is easy. The separate hieroglyphic symbols appearing in the given numbers may be grouped together. The result may be simplified wherever possible—for example, by replacing 13 strokes by 3 strokes and an arch. *Subtracting* is easy too, but multiplying and dividing offer some difficulties. The Egyptian multiplication method will be mentioned in Chapter 5.

The Egyptians made clever use of fractions and were able to use some simple algebra as early as the time of the "Middle Kingdom," from 2000 to 1800 B.C. A "handbook" of their methods is preserved in the British Museum: the celebrated *Rhind papyrus*, compiled by the scribe Ahmes about 1650 B.C., from earlier sources. This and other Egyptian mathematical texts are primarily concerned with such practical applications of mathematics as might ordinarily be encountered by surveyors, builders, traders, and administrative officials—areas, volumes, quantities of money and materials.

It is painful to follow through the work schemes used by the Egyptians in solving simple problems. Handling fractions was a task for an expert. One looks in vain for *general methods*, always our principal concern today. Egyptian geometry, for example, was largely a collection of area and volume formulas, some right and some wrong. With their attention focused too narrowly on what seemed "practical," the Egyptians failed to see the need for developing any basic *theory*. They were empiricists.

When they began to write on papyrus in place of stone the Egyptians abandoned the colorful but cumbersome hieroglyphs in favor of a script form called *hieratic* ("priestly"). There was also a form called *demotic* ("popular"). Much computation and problem work seem to have been carried out in script form. The Egyptians may also have used abacuses made by ruling lines on stone or by tracing grooves in sand.

§5. BABYLONIAN AND GREEK NUMERALS

Before 3000 B.C., the Sumerians in southern Mesopotamia wrote by pressing the ends of cylindrical rods into clay tablets. Their numeral characters were like little moons and half-moons. Later, the end of the rod was sharpened to prism form, and this stylus was used to produce two types of *cuneiform* ("wedgy") characters, a "single-tailed" and a "two-tailed" form (Fig. 6). By the time of the first Babylonian dynasty (Hammurabi, *ca.* 1800 B.C.), into which the Sumerians were absorbed, an extensive body of mathematical knowledge and an effective positional numeral system had been developed.

The single-tailed character, written vertically, stood for the unit, 1; the two-tailed character, written horizontally, stood for 10. Figure 6(a) depicts two numerals constructed from the symbols. Up to 60, the numerals were constructed in this straightforward way. Now a surprise: The Babylonian was a "sexagesimal" system, based on 60, so that the numerals 1, 2, 3, . . . , 59 were just the *digits* of the system. (Hence our seconds and minutes units for time and angle, based on 60.) Babylonian numerals were successions of such "digits," even as are our own numerals. Thus in Figure 6(b), the "digit" 1 is followed by the "digit" 23, so that the value is

$$1 \times 60 \quad + \quad 23 \quad = \quad 83.$$

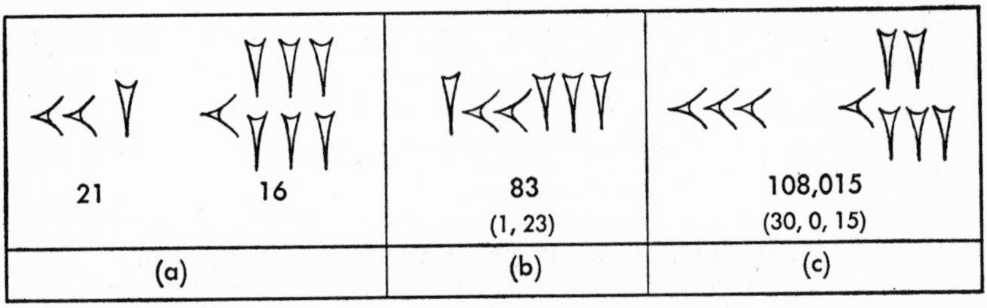

		83 (1, 23)	108,015 (30, 0, 15)
21	16		
(a)		(b)	(c)

Fig. 6   Examples of Babylonian Numerals

The Babylonian scheme was much like ours in structure, therefore, except for two important features. First, the Babylonians lacked a bonafide conception of *zero*. When a place value was "missing," as in Figure 6(c), they originally just made a wider separation between characters. Later they put in a special character, but as a "separatrix" rather than as a true zero symbol, as indicated by the fact that it was never written at the *end* of the numeral. Second, they lacked a "decimal point" conception. The value of their numerals had to be told from the context of the discussion. We labeled the numeral in Figure 6(b) with the value 83 = 1 × 60 + 23. But we might just as logically have taken it to mean

$$4980 \quad = \quad 1 \times 60^2 \quad + \quad 23 \times 60,$$

or to mean

$$1\frac{23}{60} \quad = \quad 1 \quad + \quad 23 \times \frac{1}{60}.$$

With their superior numeral system and an effective arithmetic based upon it, the Babylonians made excellent progress, pretty much covering that part of mathematics taught in our schools through the ninth grade. It was evidently they who discovered the form of the famous "Pythagorean" theorem—the square relation between the legs and the hypotenuse of the right triangle. In this and in other ways they revealed knowledge of some "general methods." But as with the Egyptians, their turn of mind was more "practical" than "theoretical." So it was left to the Greeks to invent the conception of *proof* and to develop mathematical *theory*.

But the Greeks, intellectual giants though they were, failed to appreciate the virtues of the Babylonian arithmetic. In the time of the first known Greek mathematician, Thales, about 600 B.C., the Greeks used letter symbols for numerals in much the same way as the Romans were to do several centuries later. Structurally, this early Greek scheme was like the Egyptian, but with extra symbols for 5, 50, etc., inserted between those for the powers of ten, giving more compact expressions. These "five-multiples" were constructed by hanging each power-of-ten symbol from a gibbet. At least it looks that way to us—but the "gibbet" or "gallows" is actually but an old form of the capital "pi," Π. (NOTE TO THE STUDENT: Do not memorize the Greek numeral values unless you are specifically instructed to do so. There is a risk that you will confuse the symbols for 1,000 and 10,000 with our present X and M, which as Roman numerals have different values.)

GREEK NUMERALS (Old Form)				
1	10	100	1,000	10,000
I	△	H	X	M
5	50	500	5,000	50,000
Γ	Γ△	ΓH	ΓX	ΓM

Like the Egyptian, the Greek scheme is based on an additive principle. A number is represented by the minimum group of symbols whose values add up to the number:

$$X X \, Γ \! H \, H \, H \, H \, Γ \, △△ \, Γ \, | \, | \; = \; 2{,}977$$

2000 + 500   + 400   +   50 + 20 + 5 + 2

Perhaps a hundred years later, the Greeks developed a second numeral scheme, patterned after the Egyptian hieratic and demotic forms. Values were assigned to all the letters of their alphabet, and special devices were employed for denoting very large numbers and for denoting fractions. The Hebrews employed a similar alphabetical numeral system. These alphabetical schemes will be referred to in Chapter 7 when certain mystical ideas that have been associated with numbers are discussed. The two systems of the Greeks, the literal and the alphabetical, continued in use concurrently.

The student who wishes to explore more deeply into the mathematics of antiquity will find many standard older works available, such as *History of Mathematics*, vol. II, by David Eugene Smith, Ginn, New York, 1925. These recent books are especially authoritative, interesting, and stimulating:

Science Awakening, by B. L. Van Der Waerden, Noordhoff, Holland, 1954
The Exact Sciences in Antiquity, by O. Neugebauer, Princeton University Press, 1952
An Introduction to the History of Mathematics, by Howard Eves, Rinehart, New York, 1953

Most of our knowledge of Babylonian mathematics has been acquired within the last twenty-five years, as a result of extensive researches carried out by Neugebauer and a few others. Thousands upon thousands of clay tablets have been unearthed since the mid-1800's. A typical tablet may be about ¾ in. thick and bear twenty to thirty lines of characters on a 3-in. by 4-in. face. The first two books listed above contain photographs.

The impact of mathematics and of mathematical thought upon our society is described in a nontechnical, yet masterly way, in Morris Kline's *Mathematics in Western Culture*, Oxford University Press, New York, 1953.

PROBLEM SET 2 (§4–§5)

1. Represent each number in Egyptian hieroglyphs:

    (a)   3   (d)   26   (g)   307   (j)   23,640
    (b)   30   (e)   274   (h)   1040   (k)   508,006
    (c)   300   (f)   620   (i)   3002   (l)   2,672,873

2. How many symbols are needed to represent 620,987 in hieroglyphs?

    Answer: $6 + 2 + 9 + 8 + 7 = 32$

3. Represent in hieroglyphs, then add:

    (a) $23 + 42$ (c) $174 + 258$
    (b) $28 + 46$ (d) $582 + 733$

4. Represent in hieroglyphs, then subtract:

    (a) $46 - 34$ (c) $384 - 321$
    (b) $23 - 9$ (d) $1023 - 768$

5. Why is it that we need a zero to write 306, whereas the Egyptians did not?
6. Has the hieroglyphic notation any advantages over ours?
7. What is needed to convert your homemade line abacus of §3 for use with Egyptian hieroglyphs?
8. The Egyptian hieroglyphic numeral system is based upon an "additive" principle. Explain this statement.
9.* Neugebauer represents Babylonian sexagesimal numerals by writing successive "digit" values from 1 to 59 in parentheses, separated by commas. Thus the value of (1,42,20) is

$$1 \times 60^2 \quad + \quad 42 \times 60 \quad + \quad 20 \quad = \quad 6140.$$

Represent each number in parts (a) to (l) of Problem 1 by this sexagesimal device.

10.* Using the representations found in Problem 9, write the corresponding Babylonian cuneiform numerals.

11.* If a semicolon is used as a "sexigesimal point," then (5;20) may be taken to mean

$$5 \times 1 \quad + \quad 20 \times \frac{1}{60} \quad = \quad 5\frac{1}{3}.$$

What is the value of each of the following?

(a) (0;30)   (c) (2,50;12)
(b) (4;3,30)   (d) (10,10;4,20)   *Answer:* (d) $610\frac{13}{180}$

12.* Represent each number in parts (a) to (j) of Problem 1 in Greek numeral form.

§6. ROMAN NUMERALS

Roman numerals are still in use. They are inscribed on public buildings, on memorial tablets and cornerstones. Ornamental clock faces display them. In books they designate chapter numbers, or prefatory page numbers.

Since the Romans used large numbers infrequently, their symbols for 1,000 and higher numbers remained unstandardized. A common form for 1,000 was CIↃ; the D symbol for 500 may have evolved from the "half" of this form (IↃ). The M symbol for 1,000 was seldom used in combination with lower numerals. Not until medieval times did the M attain wide use. A bar symbol placed over a numeral to indicate multiplication by 1,000 also appeared in the Middle Ages ($\bar{I} = 1{,}000$; $\bar{X} = 10{,}000$; $\bar{C} = 100{,}000$; $\bar{\bar{I}} = 1{,}000{,}000$).

There is an extensive literature on the Roman notation: what forms were used by the Romans; how they were used; where they came from; how they were modified in medieval times and after the Renaissance; etc., etc. The mathematician takes a dim view toward the Romans, because their total contribution to mathematics and the sciences was nearly negligible. But the Roman numerals lingered long in history, and their structure has interesting features which we will wish to examine here.

As now used, the Roman numerals are shown at the top of page 14. Numbers may be written according to the additive principle, just as with Egyptian hieroglyphs, the basic numeral symbols being strung out in descending size order:

$$\text{M D C C C C L V I I I I} = 1959.$$

MODERN ROMAN NUMERALS			
1	10	100	1,000
I	X	C	M
5	50	500	
V	L	D	

It is easy to add and to subtract numbers written as Roman numerals. It is unnecessary to refer to the table of values cited above. Instead, use the following *addition table* for *handfuls* and *pairs:*

$$I\ I\ I\ I\ I = V \qquad\qquad V\ V = X.$$
$$X\ X\ X\ X\ X = L \qquad\qquad L\ L = C.$$
$$C\ C\ C\ C\ C = D \qquad\qquad D\ D = M.$$

To add two numbers, group the basic numeral symbols in them together, then simplify according to this table.

Example 1.   Add: MDCCCLXII + CXXXXIIII.

Work.
$$MDCCCLXII + CXXXXIIII$$
$$= MDCCCCLXXXXXIIIIII$$
$$= MDCCCCLLVI$$
$$= MDCCCCCVI$$
$$= MDDVI$$
$$= MMVI$$

Subtraction can be a direct "take away" procedure, except that some numerals may need to be broken down into lower order ones to make the taking away possible.

Example 2.   Subtract: MDV − CCLXII.

Work.
$$MDV - CCLXII$$
$$= MCCCCCIIIII - CCLXII$$
$$= MCCCIII - LX$$
$$= MCCLLIII - LX$$
$$= MCCLIII - X$$
$$= MCCXXXXXIII - X$$
$$= MCCXXXXIII$$

It is somewhat shocking to reflect that Roman numerals were used in Europe as late as A.D. 1600 for many ordinary purposes of business: bookkeeping, banking, etc. One reason is that our modern Hindu-Arabic numerals did not become standardized in typographical form until after the invention of printing. Roman numerals were less subject to misreading and to forging.

The general populace, moreover, was poorly educated. You and I may regard the adding of Roman numerals as an awkward procedure. Yet it is far *simpler* and requires much less training to master than our own familiar process. The "handful" and "pairs" table is quickly learned. Our children, on the other hand, spend several school years learning more than a hundred addition and subtraction "facts," such as "4 and 7 make 11." And our children must cope with the place value notions of "carrying" and "borrowing." Our smaller tradesmen do much paper figuring, whereas the merchants of earlier times used the *counting table* as a concrete computational aid. A type of line abacus, this device was even easier to use in conjunction with the Roman notation than with our own.

In modern times we employ a *subtractive* as well as an *additive* principle in writing Roman numerals. Both the Babylonians and the Romans occasionally used the subtractive idea. Why did it not become popular? For one thing, only numerals in additive form can readily be put on an abacus or added and subtracted.

It has been said that the Romans may have avoided the use of IV for 4 because these are the initial letters of the name of the god IVPITER. The Babylonians, Hebrews, and others are known to have avoided certain numeral combinations for like reasons.

According to the subtractive principle, when a numeral symbol precedes one that it would ordinarily follow, its value is subtracted instead of added. In practice, only these "four" and "nine" combinations were used:

IV = IIII	XL = XXXX	CD = CCCC
IX = VIIII	XC = LXXXX	CM = DCCCC

More extensive use of the principle can lead to confusion or ambiguity. Thus, should IVX mean 4 or 6? Take your choice.

To add or to subtract Roman numerals that contain a subtractive combination, first rewrite them in purely additive form.

Roman *fractions* were not decimal but *duodecimal*, having multiples of 12 for their denominators. They will be referred to in Chapter 6.

§7. THE COUNTING TABLE

As noted in §3, the "line abacus" has an ancient history. Herodotus wrote that the Egyptians "reckoned with pebbles." A Greek abacus consisting of a ruled marble slab is displayed in an Athens museum. That the use of pebbles for counters was common in Roman times is suggested by the etymology of our word "calculate," which derives from the Latin *calculare* and this in turn from *calculus,* which means "pebble."

In its most widespread use, the line abacus took the form of the medieval **counting table.** Merchants or accountants sat before this counting table or "counter" (whence our term *counter,* over which we trade in stores). Either the table itself or a cloth laid over it was ruled with lines valued according to the ascending powers of ten: I, X, C, M. The spaces between the lines were assigned the values V, L, D. The shopkeepers then "laid their sums" and reckoned "on the lines," using loose counters for the purpose. The well-known "Court of the Exchequer" of twelfth-century England took its name from the *exchequer* itself, which was simply a large counting table.

The student may construct his own counting table by ruling lines on a large sheet of paper and laying pennies for counters. The number 782 is shown "laid out" in Figure 7.

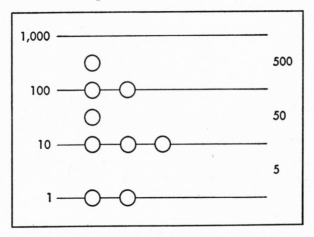

Fig. 7   The Counting Table (Schematic)
The number 782 is shown "laid out."

The rules for using the counting table are

1. A handful of counters on a line may be replaced by a single counter on the space above.
2. A pair of counters in a space may be replaced by a single counter on the line above.

Hence if 53 is to be added to the 782 of the illustration, a single "50" counter and three "1" counters are laid out, and then the resulting handful of "1's" may be replaced by a "5," and the pair of "50's" by a single new "100." (This is the exchange or *carrying* process.) A few minutes of practice will lead to one's becoming fairly adept at adding or subtracting on the counting table. With chalk in one hand and eraser in the other, the student may also carry out the work effectively at the blackboard, marking and erasing instead of putting down and picking up counters.

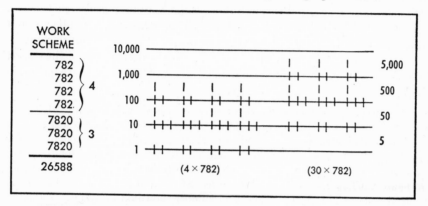

Fig. 8   34 × 782
Each vertical dash represents one counter.

Multiplication and division are lengthier processes. Suppose that 782 is to be multiplied by 34. This means that 782 is to be multiplied by 4, then by 30, and the results summed. Multiplication by 4 is effected by laying out 782 four separate times (left portion of Fig. 8). Note now that multiplication by ten (7820) may be accomplished just by laying the original 782 pattern of counters a *full line higher* on the table. So to multiply by 30, do this three times (right portion of Fig. 8). At this stage, the counters on the table represent the desired product, 34 × 782, and the rest of the work consists in simplifying according to the "handful" and "pair" rules. Work from bottom up, as shown in Figure 9.

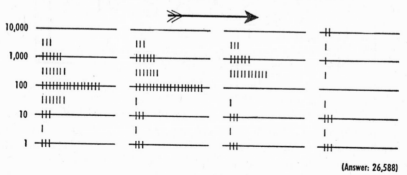

(Answer: 26,588)

Fig. 9   34 × 782 = 26,588
Some steps of simplification. (Initial array shown in Fig. 8.)

The student will find the above procedure to be an easy one if he will but "lay and seize" correctly, as European boys were admonished in fifteenth-century schools.

The multiplication process just illustrated is a kind of *repeated addition*, as indicated in the "work scheme" set down at the left in Figure 8. Division may be carried through in a similar way by *repeated subtraction*. These techniques will be explained further in Chapter 5. The abacus that reposes beneath the counter in many of our Chinese laundry shops is operated much like the counting table: On it the deft fingers of the expert may compute more rapidly than may the swiftest of us with pen and paper.

The design of a Roman abacus of late origin is shown in Figure 10. This is of "rod" rather than "line" type (§3). Made of bronze, the abacus was grooved for the pebbles or counters, shown in the diagram as circles. The grooves or slots are labeled with the appropriate Roman numerals, except those for fractions, which are shown tagged with our own symbols to help the student who wishes to figure out how they were used. Counters at the lower ends of the slots are in neutral or nonregistering position. The number shown on the abacus is 1852⅔.

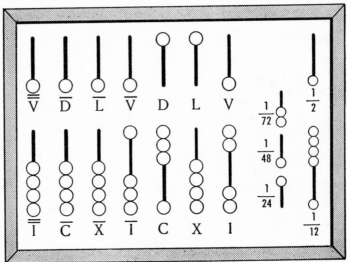

Fig. 10   Roman Abacus
Schematic diagram.

In modern use, the abacus takes several forms. The *s'choty*, Figure 11, is specifically adapted to the monetary system of Russia, and is still used throughout that country. The Chinese *suan pan* (Fig. 12) and the Japanese *soroban* (Fig. 13) are more efficient computing devices. On their lower rods the beads are worth 1, 10, 100, etc., and on the upper 5, 50, 500, etc. On the soroban, the distance toward the center crosspiece that the beads must be moved to register is less than finger width, so that an expert may operate the instrument just by stabbing with his finger tips.

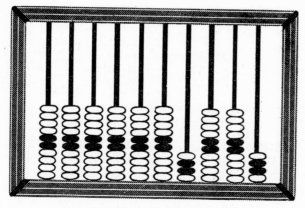

Fig. 11 Russian S'choty

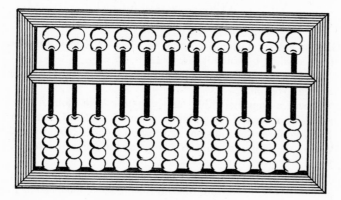

Fig. 12 Chinese Suan Pan

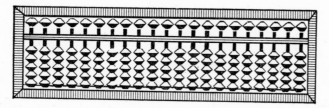

Fig. 13 Japanese Soroban

PROBLEM SET 3 (§6–§7)

1. Express each number in Roman numerals, without subtractive combinations:

(a) 7	(d) 48	(g) 372	(j) 1949
(b) 9	(e) 49	(h) 819	(k) 1956
(c) 16	(f) 53	(i) 970	(l) 1990

2. Same as Problem 1, using subtractive combinations.

3. Add. Check by converting to our own numerals.

(a) XIII + IIII	(e) CCCVI + CLXXXXVII
(b) XVII + III	(f) MDXII + DCVIII
(c) LXXV + XXV	(g) MCCL + DCCL
(d) CLI + L	(h) DLVI + DLVI

4. Subtract. Check by converting to our own numerals.

(a) XVIII − XII	(e) C − X
(b) XV − III	(f) DC − CCLXII
(c) X − VII	(g) MCCVI − DCLXIII
(d) LXXV − XXXIII	(h) MMDX − CCXXXVI

5. Give an interpretation according to which IVX means our number 6. Give another according to which it means 4.

6. What advantages has the Roman numeral system over the Egyptian? What advantages over ours?

7. Construct a counting table for computing with Roman numerals by ruling four lines on a sheet of paper, labeling them I, X, C, M, then labeling the spaces V, L, D. Perform the additions of Problem 3 on this counting table.

8. Perform the subtractions of Problem 4 on the counting table of Problem 7.

9. Modernize the counting table of Problem 7 by replacing the Roman with modern numeral labels, 1, 10, 100, 1000 on the lines and 5, 50, 500 in the spaces. Represent the following numbers:

(a) 27	(c) 78	(e) 566	(g) 2650
(b) 53	(d) 207	(f) 739	(h) 3896

10. Add, on the counting table of Problem 9:

(a) 12 + 4	(d) 27 + 46	(g) 508 + 674
(b) 13 + 9	(e) 78 + 27	(h) 673 + 327
(c) 18 + 6	(f) 232 + 459	(i) 888 + 888

11. Subtract, on the counting table of Problem 9:

(a) 10 − 3	(c) 100 − 27	(e) 1000 − 666
(b) 46 − 23	(d) 367 − 154	(f) 1271 − 338

12. Perform the following multiplications on the simple form of line abacus consisting of five lines labeled 1, 10, 100, 1000, 10,000:

(a)	3×42	(d)	32×42	(g)	76×83
(b)	30×42	(e)	32×68	(h)	234×308
(c)	300×42	(f)	32×265	(i)	208×417

13. Write abacus work schemes for these multi-plications:

Add

(a)	32×68	(c)	234×308
(b)	32×265	(d)	208×417

$Answer$ (b):

$$\left.\begin{array}{r}265 \\ 265\end{array}\right\}2$$

$$\left.\begin{array}{r}2650 \\ 2650 \\ 2650\end{array}\right\}3$$

$$\underline{}$$
$$8480$$

14. Perform the multiplications of Problem 12 on the counting table of Problem 9.

15. Practice multiplying 23×31 on the simple line abacus or on the counting table, repeating the work at least twenty times until you feel yourself proficient at it. Then time yourself. Next, time your pencil and paper performance on the same problem. Is the counting table a slow device?

§8. HINDU-ARABIC NUMERALS

As pointed out in §2, the central feature of our modern numeral system is the use of digits whose values are determined by their *position* in the sequence of digits which make up the numeral. This feature has enabled us to develop an efficient arithmetic.

This conception of place value is our heritage from the Babylonians and from the Hindus. The Hindus held the computational arts in high esteem. They were delighted by fanciful, poetically phrased problems involving large numbers. Such problems were fashionable in their court circles and played an important role in the education of their princes.

The Hindus developed symbols for the positive digits 1, 2, . . . , 9. They assigned a name to each power of ten, continuing far into the upper number realms, as they sought to number the very atoms in the world. We ourselves name the powers only to the third: ten, hundred, thousand. Thereafter we name the powers of a thousand: million, billion, trillion, etc. The number which we read as "Two billion, three hundred seventy-one million, five hundred thirty-two thousand, one hundred sixty four" might have been read by a Brahman as:

2 *padmas*, 3 *vyarbudas*, 7 *kōtis*, 1 *prayuta*, 5 *laksas*, 3 *ayutas*, 2 *sahasra*, 1 *sáta*, 6 *daśan*, 4

From such a rendition, it is a short step to omitting the place value names and just writing the digits in succession, as we do: 2,371,532,164. But this step could not be taken until a symbol was provided to indicate a *vacancy*. Else "2 *sahasra*, 3" and "2 *sáta*, 3 *daśan*" (2003 and 230) would both telescope into the same digital sequence, 23, resulting in hopeless confusion.

A "placeholder" symbol was needed to fill in such vacancies: the digit we now call **zero,** 0. Sometime prior to about A.D. 600, the symbol mysteriously showed up as a new tenth Hindu digit. The zero is surely one of the great inventions of human history. Once historians gave sole credit to the Hindus for it. The tale was impressive. It is nicely set forth in *Number, The Language of Science,* by Tobias Dantzig. But now there is evidence that the invention took place by gradual growth instead of by sudden discovery.

As we noted earlier, the Babylonians used a "zero mark" where it was needed to separate digits. This was a pure "placeholder" usage, indeed hardly more than a form of punctuation. In the late Greek period, the usage was extended. Ptolemy, in about A.D. 150, employed the sexagesimal scheme in his astronomical calculations. He used a zero symbol at the end of a succession of digits, as well as between digits. And he wrote the zero as a little circle (o, "omicron," initial letter of the Greek word ουδεν, "nothing"). It therefore seems likely that the Hindus borrowed both the idea and the symbol.

So we owe our present-day arithmetic to the achievements of at least three important cultural groups—Babylonian, Greek, and Hindu. If the Hindus were not the gifted mathematical innovators they were at one time held to be, at least it was they who completed the monumental task of framing our well-nigh perfect modern numeral notation.

The "golden age" of Greek mathematics extended from about 400 to 200 B.C. Why did the brilliant mathematicians of those times fail to develop the zero idea and to devise a sound arithmetic? No easy answer can be given to this query. An important factor seems to have been that their interest in computation was theoretical rather than practical and that they conceived exact computation to be possible only in geometric rather than in numerical terms. (The meaning of this statement will be developed further in §7 of Chapter 10.) The development of a sound arithmetic might well be supposed to have required a blend of practical and theoretical interests. "It takes all kinds of people to make a world"—from abstruse ivory-towerists to hard-headed down-to-earthers.

In the year 1050, the Hindu digits looked like this:

HINDU DIGITS (1050 A.D.)									
0	1	2	3	4	5	6	7	8	9
o	)	૨	૨	૪	૫	૬	૨	૭	૭

Our present digital forms evolved from these. So did some others that resemble ours very little, such as those of modern Sanskrit.

The Hindu arithmetic became known to the Arabs, themselves no mean mathematicians. Shortly before the year 1000, the Arabian mathematics, incorporating the Hindu, began to filter into Europe by way of Spain and other channels. Europe was then slowly awakening from her five-hundred-year cultural slumber (the "Dark Ages"). Several more centuries were to pass before the revival would be complete and European peoples ready to assume a leading role in secular activities—commerce, industry, the arts, the sciences, and mathematics.

By the thirteenth century, the intellectual awakening was fairly under way. Some respectable mathematics was done, an Italian named Fibonacci being outstanding for his work in that era. The true mathematical renaissance, however, came in the sixteenth century. The many excellent mathematicians of that period brought the subject to a stage at which the giants of the seventeenth century (Newton, Leibniz, Descartes, Pascal, Fermat, etc.) could take over, to lay the sturdy foundations of modern mathematics. The physical sciences ran their parallel course.

Over a five-hundred-year period terminating in the sixteenth century, a bloodless battle-royal had been waged between the "algorists" and the "abacists." The former championed the Hindu-Arabic arithmetic, the latter the abacus or counting-table form of computation. As we well know, the algorists' victory was complete. By the year 1600, arithmetic had substantially reached its present form.

In Chapters 4 and 5 we shall take up the development of the techniques or processes of elementary arithmetic for adding, subtracting, multiplying, and dividing, as they evolved from their Hindu-Arabic origins.

§9. MISCELLANEOUS FORMS

A variety of interesting and significant numeral systems have not been mentioned in the preceding account, many of them belonging to lines of evolutionary development separate from our own.

In Yucatan, for example, the Mayas used a clever symbol scheme which was essentially *vigesimal:* based on powers of twenty.

Oriental systems display interesting features. (See *A History of Japanese Mathematics*, by Smith and Mikami, Open Court, Chicago, 1914.) A curious Chinese development was a "monogram" form of numeral derived from diagrams drawn to show the positions of *rods* laid out for computing purposes. The Chinese computing rods passed to Japan and Korea. The abacus (*suan pan*) displaced the rods in China in about the thirteenth century. The *sangi* board of Japan, on which the rods were laid out for computation, gave way to the abacus (*soroban*) not long after the end of the seventeenth century. The Koreans tossed away their number rods in favor of the superior abacus only about forty years ago.

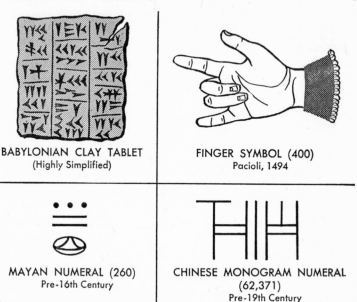

BABYLONIAN CLAY TABLET
(Highly Simplified)

FINGER SYMBOL (400)
Pacioli, 1494

MAYAN NUMERAL (260)
Pre-16th Century

CHINESE MONOGRAM NUMERAL
(62,371)
Pre-19th Century

Fig. 14

In addition to numeral systems designed for computational purposes, there have been a host of curious schemes for simple counting and for recording numbers. The Peruvian *quipu* was a great sheaf of colored cords, the strands bearing small and large knots representing numbers by units and tens. These were used to record census results and other public data.

In England, tally sticks served as official accounting records from the twelfth century to the early part of the nineteenth. Notches were cut into the sticks according to a decimal code signifying sums from pence to £1000. Parliament at last abolished the system in 1826. Several years later the great accumulation was put to the torch. The dry old sticks made a fine hot fire—too hot for the stoves. The Parliament buildings went up in flames along with the tallies. (For photographs of Exchequer tallies, see page 9 of *Number Theory and Its History*, by Oystein Ore, McGraw-Hill, New York, 1948. For an interesting account of the fire episode, see page 23 of *Number, The Language of Science*, by Tobias Dantzig, 2nd Edition, Macmillan, New York, 1933.)

§10. FINGER RECKONING

Finger ways of representing numbers presumably preceded all others, though we have no definite historical reference to finger symbolism until the fifth century B.C., when it was mentioned by the Greek historian Herodotus.

A common way to begin counting on the fingers is to place the right forefinger upon the little finger of the open left hand. In most systems of finger symbolism the number *one* was indeed represented by a folding inward of this left little finger. It became customary to represent the numbers from 1 to 99 on the left hand, the hundreds on the right. The Roman satirist Juvenal tells us, "Happy is he indeed who has postponed the hour of his death so long and finally numbers his years upon his right hand."

Finger symbolism flourished in pre-Renaissance Europe: It assisted barter between those of different tongues, served as a memory device, and aided in simple calculations.

Many of the more poorly educated peoples in Europe have used finger reckoning until quite recent times, some even today, as an agreeable substitute for learning the full "times" tables. Select any two of the digits 6, 7, 8, 9—or take one of them twice. The product may be found as follows.

Subtract 5 from each selected digit. Hold up as many fingers on each hand as given by the two resulting digits. The raised fingers count as *tens* toward the answer. Add to this the result of multiplying together the numbers of closed fingers on each hand.

Products like 7 × 3 can be found by decomposition:

$$7 \times 3 \quad = \quad 5 \times 3 \quad + \quad 2 \times 3.$$

Using this notion in conjunction with the finger method above, a poorly educated peasant could make out by learning the multiplication tables only up to 5 × 5.

The representation of the numbers on the fingers is perhaps the most primitive, yet the most intimate or personal way of all. This is of special interest to us, as we are in this text concerned with the *meaning* and *significance* of numbers rather than with their history as such. The capsule dose of numeral history provided in this chapter is intended primarily to aid the student to perceive the manifest variety of the possible ways of counting and numbering groups of things—particularly such concrete ways as are exemplified by the abacus in its many forms.

He who takes off by jet to soar into the stratosphere must needs have the certainty that the good firm earth remains below, that he may again return to it, whole and entire. As we deal with *abstractions* like number and number operations we may proceed surely and confidently only so long as we keep them linked in our minds to their *concrete* bases.

In the next chapter we deal with the idea of a group or "set" of objects. This is the firm ground on which our concept of *number* is based.

PROBLEM SET 4 (§8–§10)

1. How might the Hindus have read each number?

   (a)   302   (c)   25,006
   (b)   2,780   (d)   37,000,000

2.   Consult an encyclopedia or other source to find our names for the powers of one thousand (billion, trillion, etc.), then write our word form for this number:

$$600,750,017,064,802,500,003.$$

3.   In England, after a million, only the successive powers of one million are named, a million million being called a billion, and a million billion a trillion. How would an Englishman read the number in Problem 2?

4.   Are there any advantages in considering zero to be a *number?* Why not just use a dash (or other punctuation symbol) to indicate a vacant place, writing 2–8 for 208, 57– for 570, 6—3 for 6003, etc.?

5.   Try devising several codes for representing numbers from 1 to 1000, using as elements

   (a)   Toothpicks (like Chinese computing rods)
   (b)   Notches in a stick (like English tally sticks)
   (c)   Knots in a cord (like the Peruvian *quipu*)
   (d)   Hand and finger positions
   (e)   A choice of your own

6.   Multiply on your fingers, using the "times" table only up to 5×5, by the "European peasant" method of §10:

   (a) 6×6 (c) 6×8 (e) 7×7 (g) 7×9 (i) 8×9
   (b) 6×7 (d) 6×9 (f) 7×8 (h) 8×8 (j) 9×9

2

Sets and
Numbers

§1. BASIC NUMBER NOTIONS

Long before he enters a schoolroom, a child begins to form crude number notions. Playing with blocks, crayons, and other objects, he comes to recognize differences in sizes of groups as well as differences in sizes of individual objects. He may even learn to count a little. In these activities, he has begun to acquire *three* separate number conceptions.

"Size of an object" is a measurement conception. Eventually the child will learn to use a ruler and will gradually become acquainted with the idea of a continuous *number scale*. This is a fairly sophisticated conception. In our treatment we shall have little to do with it for some time to come (Chap. 10).

The other two primary number conceptions are termed **cardinal** and **ordinal**. A cardinal number tells the size of a group. An ordinal number is used in counting. (In common usage, "cardinal" means "most basic" or "most important." "Ordinal" is derived from a Latin word meaning "order.")

When are two groups alike in size? Sometimes an equality can be recognized instantly. When a child places his *hands* on his *ears*, he discovers that he has a like number of each, though he may not yet have learned to say "two." In any group of people there are surely as many mouths as there are heads, each mouth being associated with a particular head, and vice versa. Such a comparison process may be called *matching*.

It is thus the processes of *matching* and *counting* upon which our simplest number ideas, cardinal and ordinal, are based. Distinct as they are, these processes become so interlinked in application that it is hard to put our attention just to one of them without the other slyly intruding. No peoples of the earth appear to have developed the one approach to number without at the same time having developed the other.

§2. SETS

The English language displays a rich variety of collective words: set, collection, group, class, assembly, family, flock, herd, and many others. The mathematician prefers the simplest, the term **set,** though he may occasionally use a synonym, especially *collection.* The objects making up the set are said to be *in* it or to *belong* to it, and are called *members* or **elements** of the set.

One way to describe a set is to list its elements. Suppose, for example, that we wish to think about or to talk about seven things that are in a room. Three are people, named Bob, Dave, and Mary. There are also a dog, a book, a chair, and a sofa. We will employ this set of seven things in several illustrations.

In talking about the seven things, we will single out certain among them as we talk. Thus we may speak of the "people." These constitute a set of three objects, each an element of the original set of seven. This new set is part of the original. It is called a **subset** of the original set and is said to be *contained in* the original set. Here is a list of several such subsets, to be used in further discussion:

ILLUSTRATIVE SETS

Set A: Bob, Dave, Mary
Set B: Dog, Book, Chair
Set C: Bob, Dave, Mary, Dog
Set D: Chair
Set E: Chair, Sofa
Set F: Chair, Sofa, Book
Set G: Bob, Dave, Mary, Chair, Sofa
Set H: Dog, Book

The set conceptions now to be developed are of widespread application. They pervade our talk, our thought, and our action. Every noun that we use refers to some set of objects or "entities." We determine subsets of these sets whenever we qualify the nouns by adjectives. Active verbs describe choices of elements or subsets from sets of possible actions. And underlying the behavior of each one of us is the set of all his life experiences. From the elements of this basic reference set, one derives all his conceptions and avenues of action.

Example 1.   Discuss the statement "I see a yellow cat" in set terms.

Work.   The subject "I" can be thought of as representing a choice of a particular element from the gross set of all things known to the speaker. (Psychologically, it is probably a simpler choice, as between "I" and "somebody or something else"—or perhaps from the set of all things capable of seeing.) The phrase "a yellow cat" refers to some element of the set of all yellow cats, which is itself a subset of the set of all cats. There are many ways in which the objects designated by "I" and "a yellow cat" may be related. (Examples of phrases describing such relationships: "own," "am stroking," "was frightened by," "stepped on the tail of.") "See" refers to an element of this set of possible relationships.

§3. MATCHING SETS

Consider sets A and B of the list in §2:

Set A: Bob, Dave, Mary

Set B: Dog, Book, Chair

The elements of these two sets may be paired with each other: "Bob" with "Dog," "Dave" with "Book," "Mary" with "Chair." In this circumstance the sets are said to **match**. (A mathematician would say that a "one-to-one correspondence" has been set up between the sets.)

If Bob, Dave, etc., were present in person, we could construct a physical model of the matching by running a cord from Bob to the dog, another from Dave to the book, etc.—or we could have Dave hold the book, Mary seated in the chair, etc. It is important that the student should practice demonstrating "actual" matchings of sets in such ways, trivial as the procedure may seem, in order that the basic conception shall become part and parcel of his thinking (Fig. 15).

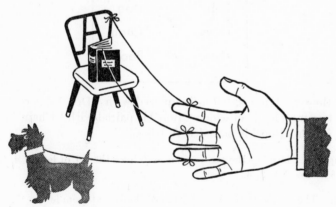

Fig. 15   "Demonstrating" a Matching

Here we see how a certain set of fingers matches set B (Dog, Book, Chair). The one-to-one association of elements of the sets is made physically evident by the imaginary (or real) cords linking corresponding elements.

Properly we should say that the two sets *match one-to-one* instead of just that they *match*. The simpler terminology will not usually be misleading, however, since we will in our treatment seldom have occasion to discuss a "many-to-one" or a "one-to-many" matching. An example of a one-to-many matching is that from a set of fathers to the set of their children, each father corresponding to his own children. We will occasionally use the symbol (1-1) as a shorthand for the term "one-to-one."

There are six different ways to exhibit a (1-1) matching between set A and set B. The one originally described may be shown in a table, like this:

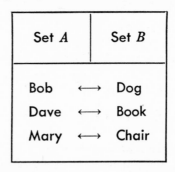

Set A	Set B
Bob ⟷ Dog
Dave ⟷ Book
Mary ⟷ Chair

We may instead pair "Dave" with "Chair" and "Mary" with "Book," obtaining another matching:

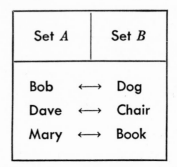

Set A	Set B
Bob ⟷ Dog
Dave ⟷ Chair
Mary ⟷ Book

In both these matchings, "Bob" is paired with "Dog." There will similarly be two matchings in which "Bob" is paired with "Chair," and two more in which "Bob" is paired with "Book."

Example 1.   Display the six ways of matching the set of letters a, b, c with the set of numbers 1, 2, 3.

Work.   The array at the top of page 31, looked at from left to right, shows a systematic way of deriving the matchings. The six matchings are shown in the boxes.

Example 2.   In how many ways can a matching be displayed between the set of letters a, b, c, d and the set of numbers 1, 2, 3, 4?

Work.   In the various matchings, the letter a can be paired with any of the *four* numbers. For each such pairing, the letter b can be paired with any one of the *three* remaining numbers. For each such pairings of a and b, the letter c can

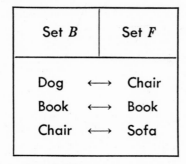

be paired with either of the *two* remaining numbers. With *a*, *b*, *c*, paired, *d* must be paired with the *one* remaining number. The total ways of matching are

$$4 \times 3 \times 2 \times 1 = 24.$$

Referring again to the list in §2, we may match set *A* and set *F*, or set *B* and set *F*, or set *E* and set *H*. Here, for example, is a matching between set *B* and set *F*. Note that we are unconcerned about the duplication of elements in these sets.

Set *B*	Set *F*
Dog ⟷	Chair
Book ⟷	Book
Chair ⟷	Sofa

Can we match sets *A* and *E*?

Set *A*:   Bob, Dave, Mary
Set *E*:   Chair, Sofa

If we try pairing "Bob" with "Chair," then we must pair "Dave" with "Sofa," and "Mary" is left dangling. In this futile attempt at matching the sets, what we have done is to match set *E* with a lesser part or "proper subset" of set *A*.

Our aim is to base the idea of number upon the idea of set. Two sets that *match* will have the *same* number associated with them. A set that matches a (proper) *subset* of another will have a *smaller* number associated with it.

PROBLEM SET 1 (§1–§3)

1. How can you demonstrate to a friend, without speaking or counting, that you have the same number of fingers on each hand?

2. When you buy a carton of a dozen eggs at a grocery store, do you have to count the eggs to tell if the dozen are there?

3. When an infantry platoon assembles for drill, can the platoon leader spot absences without counting?

4. When the dinner table has been arranged, need you count to tell if there are as many cups as saucers?

5. Discuss each statement in set terms (§2):

    (a) A white dog is in this room.

    (b) I hear a loud sound.

    (c) Ann and Josey are friends of mine.

    (d) Rich men pay high taxes.

6. Two particular (1-1) matchings of set A and set B (of the list in §2) were shown in §3. Make four similar diagrams showing the other four ways of matching these sets.

7. Same as Problem 6, for five other ways of matching set B and set F.

8. Show a one-to-one correspondence between set B and some subset of set C. In how many different ways could you do this?

9. Draw four circles (about 2 in. in diameter) in a row on a sheet of paper. Label them: a, b, c, d. Take four coins of different denominations: penny, nickel, dime, quarter. Put a coin in each circle, thus demonstrating a matching of the coins with the circles. If the penny is in circle a, the nickel in circle b, etc., you could describe this matching in "code": $(a1, b2, c3, d4)$. Now make all the 24 possible matchings, jotting down the code of each. Do the work systematically, on the pattern of Examples 1, 2 of §3.

10. Verify (by reasoning, as in Example 2, §3) that there are 120 ways of matching a set of five against a set of five.

11. There are 3,628,800 ways to match a set of ten people and the set of their noses. Can you verify this assertion? Which is the easiest one of these ways to describe?

12. Write out the various subsets of set A. Does their number agree with the formula $2^x - 1$, where x is the number of elements of the given set?

13. Same as Problem 12, using set C.

§4. NUMBER OF A SET

The notions of "set" and "matching of sets" are basic or *primitive* conceptions which are part and parcel of everyone's experience, from babyhood on. Out of these have grown our ideas about number.

Take some particular set, such as set A of the list in §2 (Bob, Dave, Mary). We may compare any other set with set A, then say of the new set either that it matches set A or that it doesn't, as the case may be.

Let us imagine that a tag or label is associated with set A. We will call this label a *number*. We will mentally attach this same label, or number, to *any* set that matches set A, but to no other set. (As children, of course, we "agreed"—upon persuasion from parents, teachers, books, etc.—to use the symbol "3" to stand for this particular number.)

DEFINITION OF NUMBER

To any given set is attached a label, called a number. The same label is attached to all those sets (and only those) that match (1-1) the given set.

Our fingers make handy basic sets with which to compare others. Extend your right forefinger and tell yourself that the number 1 is associated not only with the set consisting of that finger but also with every set whatsoever that matches it. Should you point the finger at this book, then this "matching" will show that 1 is also the number of the set consisting of this book. It is the number of set D of the list in §2.

Example 1. Myrtle Smudge used the fingers of her right hand as a basic set to which to attach the label "5". Ho San, in Shanghai, used the toes of his left foot. Show that Myrtle's conception of the number 5 is the same as Ho San's.

Work. Let F denote the set of the fingers of Myrtle's right hand, and T the set of toes of Ho San's left foot. We are told that F and T match, and we may picture in our minds a set of imaginary cords linking Myrtle's fingers to Ho San's toes, thumb to big toe, and so on (Fig. 16). Now suppose that S is any set which Myrtle would label "5." Then S matches F, and we may imagine a second set of cords linking the individual elements of S to Myrtle's fingers. Now think of the two sets of cords as one. The new set of cords joins the elements of S with Ho San's toes (*via* Myrtle's fingers). Hence S matches T, and Ho San would likewise apply the label "5" (in his own language terms) to the set S.

What we have shown so far is that every set labeled "5" by Myrtle is also labeled "5" by Ho San. By interchanging the roles of Myrtle and Ho San and repeating the argument, we can show that every set labeled "5" by Ho San will also be labeled "5" by Myrtle. The conceptions of the number 5 held by Myrtle and by Ho San are thus identical.

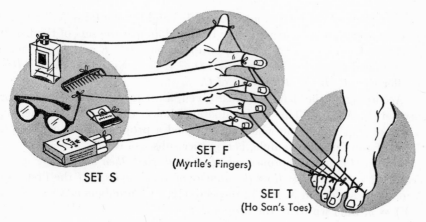

SET F
(Myrtle's Fingers)

SET S

SET T
(Ho San's Toes)

Fig. 16
Set S Matches Set T via Set F.

§5. NOTATION

We have begun to use capital letters to designate sets, and will continue this practice. For the time being, we will use small letters to denote numbers. Thus the number of a set X may be denoted by x. We will also use the abbreviation:

$$n(X) \qquad \text{for} \qquad \text{"The number of the set } X \text{."}$$

For short, we may read "$n(X)$" as "the number of X" or even just "n of X."

If X and Y both denote the *same set*, then we will write the equality:

$$X = Y.$$

It is important to distinguish carefully between number equality and set equality. Thus sets A and B of the list in §2 are different sets, so that $A \neq B$ (read: "A is not equal to B"). Yet these two sets have the same number, so that $n(A) = n(B)$.

It is often a matter of great practical importance to demonstrate that two sets, described in different ways, and therefore symbolized differently, are actually one and the same set. Set X, for example, may be "the gang who held up the Orangeville bank." Set Y may be "Toughy Johnson, Dick (the Drip) Murphy, and Bughead Jones." The district attorney may devote weeks of effort toward establishing the relation $X = Y$.

If every element of a set X is also an element of a set Y, then set X is called a **subset** of set Y. This *inclusion* relation is expressed by writing either

$$X \subset Y \qquad \text{or} \qquad Y \supset X.$$

These may be read "X is contained in Y" and "Y contains X," respectively. Several such inclusions may be found among the sets of the list in §2. Thus $A \subset C$ and $A \subset G$. The two relations $D \subset E$ and $E \subset F$ may be combined into a single expression: $D \subset E \subset F$. Note that though B is smaller than C, B is *not* a subset of C.

According to the definition just given, a set is a subset of itself: For any set X, $X \subset X$. This is a deliberate choice, convenient in practice. A subset that is not the whole set is called a **proper subset** of the set. Set E of the list, for example, is a proper subset of set F.

If one set matches a proper subset of another set, then the number of the first set is said to be less than the number of the second set. If the first and second sets are called X and Y, respectively, with numbers $n(X) = x$ and $n(Y) = y$, then we write the *inequality*:

$$x < y.$$

This is read "x is less than y." We can also write it the other way around and still mean the same thing:

$$y > x,$$

read "y is greater than x." *Examples:* $1 < 3$ and $3 > 1$.

Example 1. With reference to the list in §2, show that $n(F) < n(G)$.

Work. The following exhibit shows a matching between set F and a proper subset of set G:

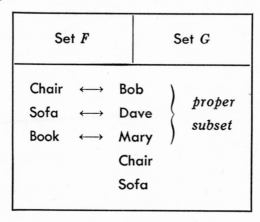

PROBLEM SET 2 (§4–§5)

1. Take the set of fingers of your right hand for a "given" or comparison set. Describe three sets having the same number associated with them.

2. Same as Problem 1, except that the described sets are to have smaller numbers.

3. Same as Problem 1, except that the described sets are to have larger numbers.

4. How does the number of the set of all automobiles in the United States compare with the number of the set of their steering wheels?

5. How does the number of the set of all automobiles in the United States compare with the number of the set of those automobiles that have automatic transmissions?

6. How does the number of the set of all automobiles in the United States compare with the number of the set of their automatic transmissions? (How does the analysis differ in this problem from that in Problem 5? See Example 1, §5.)

7. Describe a relationship between the set of all the automobiles in the United States and the set of all people who are at this instant driving one of these automobiles.

8. Describe a relationship between the set of all the automobiles in the United States and the set of all their windows (windshields included).

9.   Describe a relationship between a set of books and the set of pages of the books. Between a set of books and the set of their front covers.

10.   Describe a relationship between a set of children and a set of their mothers (living or dead).

11.   Select some convenient set on which Myrtle Smudge might base her conception of the number denoted by the numeral "2." Also pick a set which Xlazj/97B (a flying saucer visitor) might use for the same number. Show their conceptions of the number to be identical. (See the Example of §4.)

12.   Same as Problem 11, for the number 37.

13.   In general, if a set A matches a set B, and set B matches a set C, then set A matches set C. Show why this is so in the special case in which set B is a set of the fingers of a hand.

14.   Give a general argument to support the statement in Problem 13.

15.   Show how the statement in Problem 13 can be used to establish the following: Given the numbers x, y, z, if $x = y$ and $y = z$, then $x = z$.

16.   Devise an argument along the same lines as those you used in Problems 14 and 15, to establish the following: Given the numbers x, y, z, if $x < y$ and $y < z$, then $x < z$.

17.   Refer to the list of sets in §2. Which of the following statements are true (T), false (F), or meaningless (M)? (NOTE. A statement like "$2 \subset 5$" is neither true nor false, but is meaningless, because it is permissible to use the inclusion symbol $\subset$ only when the symbols on either side of it refer to sets.)

    (a) $A = B$ (c) $B \subset B$
    (b) $A = A$ (d) $D < E$

18.   As in Problem 17, designate as true (T), false (F), or meaningless (M):

    (a) $A \neq B$ (c) $F \supset E$
    (b) $B \subset C$ (d) $B \subset H$

19.   Designate as T, F, or M:

    (a) $n(A) = n(B)$ (c) $n(A) \neq n(D)$
    (b) $n(A) < n(C)$ (d) $n(E) > n(F)$

20.   Designate as T, F, or M:

    (a) $n(A) \subset n(G)$ (c) $n(D) = 1$
    (b) $C < A$ (d) $n(F) < n(G)$

21.   Designate as T, F, or M:

    (a) $nA = 3$ (c) $D \subset E \subset F$
    (b) $C = 4$ (d) $n(E) < n(F) < n(G)$

§6.   COUNTING

The inequality relationship defined in §5 enables us to arrange or *order* the numbers of sets in a systematic way.

The number 1 is the smallest. This is the number labeling the set S consisting of your right forefinger. Given any other set X, you may point to some element of it with your forefinger, and by this pairing demonstrate a matching between S and a subset of X. For every set X, therefore, $n(X) \geq 1$ (i.e., $n(X) > 1$ or $n(X) = 1$, read "n of X is greater than or equal to 1").

Extend the next finger to join the forefinger. We agree to use the symbol "2" for the number of the set composed of both fingers—as well as for the number of any matching set.

Extend the next finger to join the others, and you have a set whose number we write "3." This process can be continued *without end.* You will run out of fingers, to be sure, but may substitute tally marks on a sheet of paper—or just conceive mentally of this "and one more" succession as going on and on.

In this way we obtain an unending **basic sequence** of numbers:

$$1, 2, 3, 4, 5, 6, 7, 8, 9, 10, 11, \ldots \quad .$$

The three dots on the right indicate that the sequence continues without end. The numbers of the sequence are called **natural numbers.** They are the numbers of *finite* sets.

The set of all natural numbers is an infinite set. So is the set of all points of a line. We will have no concern with the numbers of infinite sets. There are no known "practical" applications of such *transfinite* numbers.

The basic sequence has this fundamental property:

Every natural number in the basic sequence is the number of the set of all the natural numbers up to and including it.

For example, 3 is the number of the set consisting of the numbers 1, 2, 3. Suppose we denote this set by S_3. Then $n(S_3) = 3$. Similarly, $n(S_1) = 1$, $n(S_2) = 2$, $n(S_4) = 4$, and so on. It may be helpful to visualize the basic sequence as a row of numbered blocks, so that S_3 is the set of the first three blocks, etc.

Example 1. Show that $5 < 8$.

Work. Consider the sets

$$S_5: \quad 1, 2, 3, 4, 5.$$
$$S_8: \quad 1, 2, 3, 4, 5, 6, 7, 8.$$

Since S_5 is a proper subset of S_8, $n(S_5) < n(S_8)$, or $5 < 8$.

Counting is a way of effecting a matching between an arbitrary finite set and one of the basic natural number sets S_1 or S_2 or S_3, etc.—whichever one turns out to match the given set.

Let us count set C of the list in §2. We show the counting by numbered tags affixed to the elements of C:

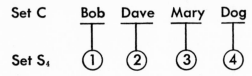

The counting has matched set C with the set S_4, which consists of the natural numbers 1, 2, 3, 4. Since $n(S_4) = 4$, this is the number of the set C. It is also the last number named in the counting procedure.

In general, as we count a set, at any stage of the counting we have accomplished a matching of the subset so far counted with the set of natural numbers up to and including the last one named. The final number named at the end of the count must therefore be the number of the whole set.

This argument proves that our common counting procedure is a correct way of finding the number of a set.

PROBLEM SET 3 (§6)

1. By comparing the basic sequence sets S_3 and S_5, show that $3 < 5$.
2. Compare S_6 and S_7, showing that $6 < 7$.
3. Compare S_{562} and S_{564}, showing that $562 < 564$.
4. Assuming that $n(S_5) = 5$ and using the definition $6 = 5 + 1$, prove that $n(S_6) = 6$.
5. Assuming that $n(S_m) = m$, where m is some natural number, prove that $n(S_{m+1}) = m + 1$. Use this result, in conjunction with $n(S_1) = 1$, to establish that $n(S_k) = k$ for every natural number k. (This process is called "mathematical induction.")
6. Explain how the result $n(S_k) = k$ establishes a connection between the number of a set (cardinal idea) and the counting process (ordinal idea).
7. In how many ways can a set of 3 objects be "counted"?
   Answer: $3! = 3 \times 2 \times 1 = 6$
8. In how many ways can a set of 8 objects be counted? *Answer:* 40,320
9. Why is it that two different ways of counting a given set must give the same result?
10. Is this a correct statement: $4 \leq 4$?

§7. MORE ABOUT SETS

In developing basic number ideas, we have referred in illustration and discussion to sets of various kinds of physical objects. The student has been urged to practice with such actual sets, so as to learn what "subset," "matching," etc., mean on the level of his physical sense experience.

In developing number ideas with children, it is surely even more important to make extensive use of sets of actual objects, objects that can be seen and handled—blocks, crayons, chairs, fingers. Furthermore, the objects in a given set should at first be physically grouped—placed close together in a heap or stack, for example.

Yet where important ideas are concerned, the concrete level of discussion is always only a beginning. Without generalization and abstraction, deep understandings cannot be attained.

A set element need not be a material object. It may be a thought, a fictional character, a perception. Set elements may be distant or dissimilar; they need not be grouped in time or space. Even in the schoolroom, the "grouped in space" restriction is soon abandoned. There may be several heaps of blocks in parts of the room. The teacher may ask the children to collect all the *red* blocks. This new set may be composed of blocks scattered among many heaps, and exists of itself before the gathering is done.

Anything that can be talked about is potentially a set element. Consider these items:

> A girl
> Her last night's dream
> A unicorn
> The Taj Mahal

Our very act of listing the items has already made them the members of a set. But can they *naturally* be grouped together in some context? We need but imagine the girl to say, "Last night I dreamed I rode on a unicorn before the Taj Mahal." It is usually easy to make up an imaginary conversation in which any given group of items are the ones talked about.

The formation of a set is thus a purely mental process, an arbitrary association of "things" of any sort—objects, activities, fancies, and conceptions. As we talk, we continually form and dissolve sets. In one sentence, a certain object may occur as an element of a set. In the next sentence, the same object may be referred to as an element of a different set—or the object may itself be treated as a set. (*Example:* "My house needs painting. Yet it is less than three years old. Look how the sideboards are wearing and those steps sagging!") Being a set element or a set, therefore, is not an absolute property of an entity: It becomes an element, or a set, or a subset of a set, or a set of sets, solely by virtue of the point of view from which we discuss it.

At the end of a day, a restaurant owner may contemplate a "set of sets of sets," namely the set whose three elements are the set of breakfasts, the set of lunches, and the set of dinners served. Each of these is a set of sets. For each meal served is itself a set of individual food servings (portion of peas, portion of pork chops, etc.). Incidentally, each meal is likewise a subset of the set of all individual food servings of the day. Furthermore, a biochemist may regard an individual food serving as a set whose chemical components he is to analyze.

The recognition that a set is *always* a mental conception will aid the student in answering various puzzling questions which may arise in his own mind or be put to him by others. Since the kind of existence or reality had by a set may be different from that had by its elements, a set may have properties which its elements do not, or cannot, have. A set of small towns may be large, though its elements are small. The American Indian may be vanishing, but no one Indian is vanishing! By virtue of his office, a judge has certain rights and powers which would be denied him as a plain person.

Set D of the list in §2 has the single element, Chair. Can the chair and set D be regarded as the same thing? The answer is no. An obvious reason is that the chair is a physical object, whereas the set is a mental conception. (But in the case of a set whose single element is a set, the simple argument just given can no longer be used, and real difficulties arise. The best solution seems to be to assume, as an axiom about sets, that no set can have itself as one of its own elements.)

In ordinary usage, sets are more often specified by *descriptions* rather than by direct listings of their elements. There probably nowhere exists a list of all the *red-haired men* in the United States, nor do we need the list in order to discuss the group. *Mammals* form a certain subset of the set of animals; this subset is quite satisfactorily defined by requiring its elements to be "animals whose females possess milk-secreting organs for suckling their young."

It frequently happens that a described set does not exist, by accident or by necessity. Up to the moment that a man reaches into his pocket for a pack of cigarettes, he may be unaware that the set of cigarettes in his pocket is a vacuous entity (because he left them at home). A girl's specifications for her husband-to-be may have narrowed her set of suitable men to a blank without her realizing it. What of the set of green-haired men? The set of voters in Washington, D.C.? The set of inhabitants of Mars?

The notion of a set without any elements is thus a perfectly ordinary notion, familiar to us all. Such a set is called an "empty set." In practice, it turns out to be unnecessary to conceive of more than one such set. Hence we speak of **the empty set,** and regard it as a subset of *every* set.

So long as there are any men over x years old, the "set of all men over x years old" is an actual subset of the "set of all men." It is reasonable to regard the subset relation as still holding even when x becomes so large, as $x = 200$, that "the set of all men over x years old" describes the empty set.

The number of the empty set is called **zero: 0.** Since the empty set is a proper subset of every other set, zero is less than any natural number N: that is, $0 < N$.

PROBLEM SET 4 (§7)

1. Make up a plausible sentence containing these terms:

     Oak tree   Love

     Boy Scout knife   Rain

2. Make up a plausible sentence containing these terms:

     Egg beater   Times Square

     Wizard of Oz   Cadillac

3. Team up with three other students. Write a term (word or phrase, as in Problems 1, 2) at the top of a slip of paper. Fold your writing under and pass the paper to the next student, who is to do the same. When all four have written a term, unfold and inspect. Each of you is now to compose a plausible sentence using the terms.

4. Each following list defines a set of playing cards (s = spades, h = hearts, d = diamonds, c = clubs). Which sets could also conveniently be defined by word descriptions, like "all red cards"?

     (a) $2h, 3s, Kd, Jc, 8s$

     (b) Qs, Qh, Qd, Qc

     (c) $2d, 3d, 4d, 5d, 6d, 7d, 8d, 9d, 10d, Jd, Qd, Kd, Ad$

     (d) Js, Qs, Ks, Jc, Qc, Kc

5. What are some advantages in defining sets by listing the elements instead of by word descriptions? By descriptions instead of lists?

6. Take a deck of cards, and separate the red cards from the black cards. You now have two packets: (1) the set of red cards, (2) the set of black cards. The number of the set of these two sets is 2. Now separate each packet according to suit (spades, clubs, . . .). What is the number of the new set of packets? Make up other ways of using the deck to form sets of sets.

7. To what sets does the object described by the term "my lunch" belong as it occurs in the following discussion? When is the term used in reference to a set? When to a subset?

"My lunch was poor indeed: a nearly raw egg, a limp and tasteless strip of bacon, burnt toast, and bitter coffee. I gave some of the bacon to the dog, who sniffed at it and walked away. The meals I've had in this hotel have been so miserable that I suspect the cook has a grudge against me."

8. The set of ways a card can be drawn from a deck numbers 52, and these "ways" are "equally likely." The set of ways a King can be drawn numbers 4. The *probability* of getting a King on a single draw is the ratio of these numbers: $\frac{4}{52} = \frac{1}{13}$. What is the probability of drawing a heart? A picture card ($J, Q,$ or K)? A red honor ($10, J, Q, K, A$)?

9. What is the probability that a tossed coin will fall heads? That two tossed coins will both fall heads? (*Answer:* $\frac{1}{4}$, the set of all ways of falling being HH, HT, TH, TT.) What is the probability that of three tossed coins, exactly two will fall heads? (*Answer:* $\frac{3}{8}$.)

10. If X denotes the set of all men over 100 ft. tall and Y denotes the set of all winged dogs, is $X = Y$? Describe the empty set in some other ways.

In Problems 11 and 12, designate each statement as true (T), *false* (F), *or meaningless* (M). *The letters* A *through* H *refer to the sets listed in* §2, *and the letters* I *through* L *refer to these additional sets:*

SET I: Set E, Chair   SET K: Set G, Dog
SET J: Set D, Chair   SET L: Set J, Set K

11. (a) $I \supset E$ (c) $n(I) = n(E)$
     (b) $J = D$ (d) $J \subset L$
12. (a) $n(K) = 6$ (c) $n(J) < n(K)$
     (b) $n(L) = 2$ (d) $D \subset I$

*§8.   LANGUAGE AND LOGIC

In the words of the psychologist William James, the world of the newborn babe is a "buzzing, blooming confusion." From birth on, Baby's chief task is learning how to straighten out this disorder, to sort and classify his sense impressions so as to create a rational and meaningful context for his living activities.

Language is the child's best tool for the job. Words provide tags with which to label experiences. The child runs against an object, upon which his mother exclaims, "That nasty *tree!*" Another day he trips over a branch, and again hears the word *tree*. His father shows him a pretty *tree* leaf. As the years pass, the word "tree" acquires many references for the child. It labels a large set of his experiences (vicarious as well as actual).

During this time, the child is also learning to conceive of an external, objective world which lies beyond the immediate realm of his personal experience. Hence he also comes to use the word "tree" as a label for a set of objects.

Language promotes "communication" in a very broad sense. It enables a person to trade and to share his experiences and his conceptions with others. (It also allows communication with oneself—the very substance of thought.) In the process, it is of the utmost importance that the "receiver" (hearer or reader) should formulate faithful copies of the conceptions held by the "transmitter" (speaker or writer). The science of *semantics* concerns itself with this problem.

In the case of a precisely definable term like "circle," it is easy to ensure that transmitter and receiver share similar conceptions. But abstractions like "loyalty," "beauty," and "mother-love" vary enormously in their significance from person to person. A Marxist and a liberal democrat may talk at length, speaking of "freedom" and of "peace," yet reach no meeting of minds because these terms signify for them such grossly different conceptions. To understand each other, they must mutually reveal the structure of their hidden conceptions. One way to do this is by a return to beginnings, each citing "experiences"—examples, cases, illustrations—associated by him with the terms. *Two conceptions are alike to the extent that they represent like sets of experiences.*

Mathematics is a special variety of language. Ordinary language makes use of a fixed dictionary. It employs some terms which are precise (e.g., "circle") and others which are vague or ambiguous (e.g., "freedom"). Without the inexact or ambiguous terms, language would lack sufficient scope for dealing with the immensely complex realm of worldly and human affairs. It is left to the users of language—the philosopher, the "common man," the reporter, the propagandist, the fictioneer, and the poet—to juggle the ambiguous terms so adroitly as to convey significant meaning. The rules for this procedure cannot be framed simply and explicitly.

Mathematics, on the other hand, has only a small fixed dictionary of terms, listing special technical words, numerals, symbols of operation, etc. For any given problem, a supplementary temporary dictionary is set up, giving the definition of symbols like x, y, z, etc., special to the problem. Mathematics also provides certain groups of procedural rules, which must be strictly obeyed. Only *precise* conceptions can be dealt with mathematically. This limits the usefulness of the language of mathematics, but has the virtue of ensuring accurate and correct results. Mathematics is thus not actually more "abstract" than ordinary language. It is a continually "new" language, whose symbolic terms (x, y, z, . . .) never have a chance to become permanently associated with any specific sets of personal experiences, and so must remain emotionally "cold" to the user of the language. The aesthetic appeal of mathematics is one of form instead of content—of pattern and design instead of color and texture.

Logic, "the art and science of correct reasoning," is kin to both language and mathematics. Logicians call the sets they deal with, "classes." Here is an illustration of a common type of argument involving class-terms, called a "syllogism":

> All cats are animals;
> All animals are living creatures.
> *Therefore:* All cats are living creatures.

We deal here with three sets ("classes"):

> C: The set of all cats
> A: The set of all animals
> L: The set of all living creatures

The statement "All cats are animals" asserts an inclusion relation, $C \subset A$, that set C is a subset of set A. Similarly, "All animals are living creatures" translates as $A \subset L$. From $C \subset A$ and $A \subset L$, we derive the conclusion $C \subset L$.

The above may be more easily understood with the aid of a diagram.

A circle or other curve may be used symbolically to bound the region of "all cats," etc. In Figure 17 the statement "All cats are animals" is portrayed by having the region corresponding to the set of all cats included within the region corresponding to the set of all animals. This latter is in turn included within the region corresponding to the set of all living creatures. But then we see that the "all cats" region is necessarily included within the "all living creatures" region, so that we may draw the conclusion: "All cats are living creatures."

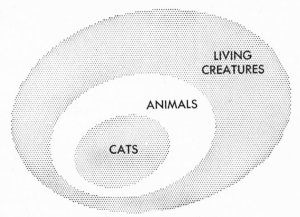

Fig. 17   An Inclusion Diagram

Example 1. What conclusion may be drawn from the following syllogistic premises?

> All our city councilors are Republicans;
> No Republicans are insane.

Work. The appropriate set diagram representing these premises is shown in Figure 18. A conclusion is:

> None of our city councilors is insane.

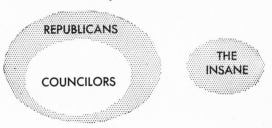

Fig. 18

The purpose of this section has been to give the student some inkling of the variety of ways in which set conceptions are applied, in mathematics and in everyday language and thinking activity. In learning about sets, he is acquiring a mental tool of wide utility, useful to him not only in connection with the understanding of numbers and with the teaching of arithmetic, but also in connection with the understanding and the use of language, of scientific method, and of common reasoning.

*PROBLEM SET 5 (§8)

1. Discuss the difference between "tree" as a label for a set of objects and as a label for a set of experiences.

2. Same as Problem 1, with respect to the term "my mother."

3. Why does a word like "loyalty" bear an emotional value, whereas a word like "chair" does not?

4. Why can't we agree on the meaning of "freedom"?

5. In technical and scientific fields, precise terminologies are employed. What is wrong with extending this notion of exact definition to language in general?

6. Use a set diagram to help you draw a conclusion from the following syllogistic premises:

> All God's chillun have wings.
> No winged creatures are men.

7. Same as Problem 6:

> Some men are journalists.
> All journalists lead a merry life.

8. Same as Problem 6:

> All college professors love to talk.
> Everyone who loves to talk is sometimes a nuisance.
> When a person is a nuisance, he should be scolded.

9. Is there any conclusion here? Draw a diagram.

> All Socialists are human beings.
> All Communists are human beings.

10.* Can you conceive of a way or ways in which our discussion of how concepts grow may have some bearing upon the theory of art appreciation?

3

Number
Operations

§1. ADDITION

If X and Y are any two sets, we will denote their **union** by the expression $X + Y$. We define this to be a set which consists of all those elements that belong either just to the one or just to the other or to both of the sets X, Y. (Briefly, an element belonging to either set also belongs to their union.)

Example 1. Suppose that Jones belongs to the Kiwanis and the Masons, while Smith belongs to the YMCA, the Kiwanis, and the Elks. The union of these two sets of clubs is the set of four elements consisting of the Kiwanis, the Masons, the YMCA, and the Elks.

Example 2. Consider the sets A, B, F of the list in §2 of Chapter 2:

> Set A: Bob, Dave, Mary
> Set B: Dog, Book, Chair
> Set F: Chair, Sofa, Book

The elements of $A + B$ and of $B + F$ are:

> $A + B$: Bob, Dave, Mary, Dog, Book, Chair
> $B + F$: Dog, Book, Chair, Sofa

Note that $n(B + F) = 4$, although $n(B) + n(F) = 6$, so that

$$n(B + F) \neq n(B) + n(F).$$

Yet $n(A + B) = n(A) + n(B)$. Why?

We wish to base our definition of a *sum* of whole numbers upon this notion of a *union* of sets which represent the numbers—even as a teacher shows a child how to add 2 and 3 by combining 2 blocks and 3 blocks into a single pile (union) of 5 blocks (Fig. 19).

46

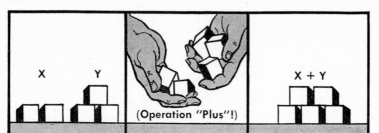

Fig. 19   Set Union (Concrete Illustration)

But first we must deal with a difficulty which turned up in Example 1 and in the case of $B + F$ in Example 2. When two sets share an element, this element gets counted twice when the sets are separately enumerated, yet only once in their union. In defining number addition in terms of set union, therefore, we will wish to deal only with sets which are "mutually exclusive" or "nonoverlapping." We will call a pair of sets **disjoint** if there is no element which belongs to both. Sets A and B of Example 2 are disjoint; sets B and F are not.

DEFINITION OF THE SUM OF TWO NUMBERS

Given any two natural numbers, consider a pair of *disjoint* sets which represent them. *The sum of the numbers is defined to be the number of the union of the sets.*

In symbols, the definition reads: Given two natural numbers, x, y, let X, Y be a pair of disjoint sets such that $n(X) = x$, $n(Y) = y$. Then $x + y = n(X + Y)$.

To illustrate the definition and to help us see that we can always find the required pair of disjoint sets, let us take the particular case: $3 + 4$. For the set X which is to represent $x = 3$, we take S_3, which in the notation of §6 of Chapter 2 denotes the set of the numbers 1, 2, 3 of the basic sequence of natural numbers. Then $n(X) = 3$. For the set Y which is to represent $y = 4$, we take the set of the numbers 4, 5, 6, 7 of the basic sequence, a set which matches S_4 but which is *disjoint* from $X = S_3$, as S_4 is not. Then $n(Y) = 4$. Now the set $X + Y$ is S_7, the set of the numbers 1, 2, 3, 4, 5, 6, 7. Hence

$$3 + 4 = x + y = n(X + Y) = 7.$$

The process is pictured in Figure 20. It is essentially the same process which a child uses to establish or to justify a basic "addition fact." It is a procedure of counting along the basic sequence:

$$\text{COUNT: } 1 - 2 - 3 - 1 - 2 - 3 - 4.$$
$$\qquad\quad 1 \quad 2 \quad 3 \quad 4 \quad 5 \quad 6 \quad 7.$$

In doing this with a child, it would be helpful to use numbered blocks to represent the basic sequence.

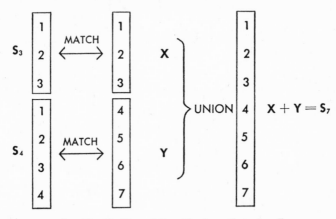

Fig. 20   The Sum of Two Numbers: $3 + 4 = 7$

In the above demonstration, we selected a particular pair of sets X, Y to represent the numbers 3, 4. We must show that the result, $3 + 4 = 7$, is always obtained no matter what sets are chosen. Let X', Y' denote any pair of disjoint sets which represent 3, 4, respectively. Then since $n(X') = n(X) = 3$, we know that X and X' match. So do Y and Y'. The three pairings between the individual elements of X and X' and the four pairings between the elements of Y and Y' all together provide a matching between the union sets $X + Y$ and $X' + Y'$. Hence $n(X' + Y') = n(X + Y) = 7$. It is suggested to the student that he try constructing a diagram to show the pattern of this argument, perhaps using sets F and C of the list in §2 of Chapter 2 for the sets X', Y'.

The various ways in which 7 is obtained as the sum of two natural numbers can be seen by partitioning the basic sequence in all six possible ways:

| 1 | 2 3 4 5 6 7 | $1 + 6 = 7$ |

| 1 2 | 3 4 5 6 7 | $2 + 5 = 7$ |

| 1 2 3 | 4 5 6 7 | $3 + 4 = 7$ |

| 1 2 3 4 | 5 6 7 | $4 + 3 = 7$ |

| 1 2 3 4 5 | 6 7 | $5 + 2 = 7$ |

| 1 2 3 4 5 6 | 7 | $6 + 1 = 7$ |

PROBLEM SET 1 (§1)

In Problems 8–15 below, we will make use of the list of sets of §2 of Chapter 2, augmented by those listed with Problems 11 and 12 of Problem Set 4 of Chapter 2. For convenience, the whole list is reproduced here:

A.	Bob, Dave, Mary	G.	Bob, Dave, Mary, Chair, Sofa
B.	Dog, Book, Chair	H.	Dog, Book
C.	Bob, Dave, Mary, Dog	I.	Set E, Chair
D.	Chair	J.	Set D, Chair
E.	Chair, Sofa	K.	Set G, Dog
F.	Chair, Sofa, Book	L.	Set J, Set K

1. Let U denote the set of fingers of your right hand, V the set of all your toes. What is the number of the union set $U + V$?   *Answer:* $n(U + V) = 15$

2. Let U denote the set of fingers of your right hand, V the set of your forefingers. What is the number of the union set $U + V$?

Answer: $n(U + V) = 6$

3. Find $n(U + V + W + Z)$, where U is the set of fingers on your right hand, V is the set of your thumbs, W is the set whose elements are your two hands, and Z is the set consisting of your right thumb, right little finger, right forefinger, and your left leg.   *Answer:* $n(U + V + W + Z) = 9$

4. A man, his wife, his sister, his mother-in-law, his mother-in-law's only daughter, his father, and his father's only two children climbed into the family car to take a trip. Was the car overloaded?   *Answer:* Probably not.

5. A group composed of men, women, and children contains an equal number of each. Everyone in it is either a Republican, a Democrat, or an Independent, and there are the same number of each. Everyone is to vote for a chairman. One candidate will receive the votes of all the men, also the votes of all the Republicans. Is he sure to be elected?

6. Let U denote the set of all girls in a class, V the set of all seniors in the class. Suppose that $n(U) = 15$ and $n(V) = 10$. What can you say about $n(U + V)$?   *Answer:* $15 \leq n(U + V) \leq 25$

7. A person is eligible to vote in a school election if either (a) he owns property in the district, or (b) he is the parent of a child attending school in the district. Let U be the set of people fulfilling condition (a), V the set fulfilling condition (b). Would you expect U and V to be disjoint? Describe $U + V$.

8. Designate each of the following as true (**T**), false (**F**), or meaningless (**M**):

     (a) $A + B \supset G$ (c) $D + C = G$

     (b) $E + F = F$ (d) $G + H = A + B + C + D + E + F$

9. Designate as **T**, **F**, or **M**:

     (a) $n(A + C) < n(G)$ (c) $n(A) + n(B) = n(A + B)$

     (b) $n(A) = n(D + E + F)$ (d) $n(F) + n(H) = n(F + H)$

10. Verify that $n(B + C) = 6$.

11. Verify that $G = A + E$.

12. Verify that $B + H = B$.

13.   Verify that $n(E) + n(F) \neq n(E + F)$.

14.   Verify that $n(H + K) = 3$.

15.   Verify that $n(I + J + E) = 4$.

16.   In §1 the addition of 3 and 4 was related to the union of the set S_3 and a set which matched set S_4. Repeat the demonstration for the addition of 5 and 2.

17.   In how many ways can 300 be obtained as the sum of two natural numbers?

§2.   LAWS OF ADDITION

From the symmetric way in which the union of two sets is defined, it is evident that the *order* of adding two numbers is inconsequential. Thus the expressions $2 + 1$ and $1 + 2$ must designate the same number (3). This important property has a technical name: It is called the **commutative law of addition.**

For a collection of sets in general, the union of all the sets of the collection is defined to be that set which consists of all the elements found in any set or sets of the collection. Consider these sets (§2, Chapter 2):

Set A: Bob, Dave, Mary
Set B: Dog, Book, Chair
Set C: Bob, Dave, Mary, Dog
Set D: Chair

Then according to the definition, the union set $A + B + C + D$ consists of:

$A + B + C + D$: Bob, Dave, Mary, Dog, Book, Chair.

Note that $A + B + C + D = A + B$.

For any three sets X, Y, Z, the following identity holds:

$$X + Y + Z = (X + Y) + Z = X + (Y + Z).$$

Note how the parentheses affect the meanings of the expressions. $X + Y + Z$ refers to the union of the three sets X, Y, Z, as just defined. But $(X + Y) + Z$ refers to the union of the *two* sets $X + Y$ and Z, as defined in §1.

The proof of the identity is simple, but lengthy. To show that $X + Y + Z = (X + Y) + Z$, for example, it is necessary to show that (1) any element e of $X + Y + Z$ is also an element of $(X + Y) + Z$, (2) any element e of $(X + Y) + Z$ is also an element of $X + Y + Z$. Considering only (1), if e belongs to $X + Y + Z$, it must belong to one of X, Y, Z. If to X, then it belongs to $X + Y$; hence to $(X + Y) + Z$. Similarly in the other two cases. It is a good exercise to write out the entire proof.

From the above set identity, the **associative law of addition** for whole numbers follows immediately:

$$x + y + z = (x + y) + z = x + (y + z).$$

This rule is used constantly in computation. To add 3, 2, and 4, for example, we may proceed from left to right, saying "3 + 2 gives 5. And 5 + 4 gives 9." In so doing we made use of the equality,

$$3 + 2 + 4 = (3 + 2) + 4,$$

for we "associated" the 3 with the 2, added these, then added 4 to the result. We could just as well have "associated" the 2 with the 4, added, and then have added the result to 3, according to the alternative form: 3 + (2 + 4).

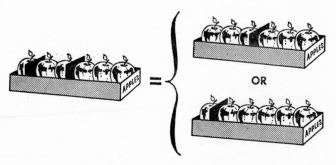

Fig. 21   The Associative Law of Addition (Concrete Illustration)
$$1 + 2 + 3 = (1 + 2) + 3 = 1 + (2 + 3)$$

Taken together, the commutative and associative laws tell us that in adding numbers "most anything goes." No matter how we mix up the numbers, we get the right answer. Thus the following 18 expressions all denote the same number (9):

2 + 3 + 4	(2 + 3) + 4	2 + (3 + 4)
2 + 4 + 3	(2 + 4) + 3	2 + (4 + 3)
3 + 2 + 4	(3 + 2) + 4	3 + (2 + 4)
3 + 4 + 2	(3 + 4) + 2	3 + (4 + 2)
4 + 2 + 3	(4 + 2) + 3	4 + (2 + 3)
4 + 3 + 2	(4 + 3) + 2	4 + (3 + 2)

Example 1.   Using the commutative and associative laws, show that $(2 + 3) + 4 = 3 + (4 + 2)$.

Work. $(2 + 3) + 4 = (3 + 2) + 4$ (Comm.)
                          $= 3 + (2 + 4)$ (Assoc.)
                          $= 3 + (4 + 2)$ (Comm.)

With four numbers, the sum may be expressed in 264 different ways! One of them is

$$1 + [(2 + 3) + 4].$$

This directs us to add 2 and 3, getting 5, to add 4 to this, getting 9, then

to add this 9 to 1, obtaining 10 as the final result. Note
that this is exactly the procedure in the *column addition*
of 2, 3, 4, 1, as indicated at the right.

Another form is

$$(2 + 3) + (4 + 1).$$

$$
\left.\begin{matrix} 1 \\ 4 \\ 3 \\ 2 \end{matrix}\right\} \quad \begin{matrix} \text{Add} \\ \text{upwards} \end{matrix}
$$
$$\overline{10}$$

This gives $5 + 5 = 10$, as before. (In adding columns of figures, we often
make such pairings, to save time or to relieve monotony.)

The two commutative and associative laws tell us that all 264 expressions denote the same number. If no such rules held, our arithmetic
would be complicated beyond measure. Because we do have the rules,
addition is so foolproof that we may easily tend to think of the rules,
when we are made aware of them at all, as possibly obvious or trivial.
They are neither. They are a magnificent tribute to the creative ingenuity
of man, who over a period of many centuries succeeded in abstracting
out of Nature that structure (the natural number system) which obeys
these most useful and simple rules of combination.

Generally speaking, the most useful mathematical quantities are those which
obey the simplest rules of combination. Such quantities have the best chance of
being suited to describe natural events of all sorts. For a given simple pattern is
likely to occur frequently in Nature, a given complex pattern rarely. (The term
"pattern" here refers to a system of relationships among natural phenomena.
In analogy, consider visual patterns. Simple designs—scattered dots, concentric
circles, parallel lines—will be encountered time and again, alone or as elements
within more complicated designs. A very complex design may be wholly unique.)
Many mathematical quantities obey the commutative and associative laws of
addition: ordinary numbers, complex numbers, vectors, matrices, etc. Transfinite
ordinal numbers do not.

PROBLEM SET 2 (§2)

1. Let X, Y, Z and X', Y', Z' denote the following sets:

X:	Abe, Bess, Carol	X':	Joan, Kitty, Lem
Y:	Dot, Eric, Fay	Y':	Joan, Mae, Ned
Z:	Gene, Harry	Z':	Kitty, Oscar

Show the construction of $X + Y + Z$ and $X + (Y + Z)$ in detail, verifying
that $X + Y + Z = X + (Y + Z)$. Similarly, $X + Y + Z = (X + Y) + Z$. Do
the same with respect to the nondisjoint set triple X', Y', Z'.

2. Put two pennies in your left hand and three in your right. Can you now
think of a simple and dramatic way to put the $3 + 2 = 2 + 3$ idea across to a
young pupil?

3. Put three piles of objects (pennies, blocks, . . .) on a table. In what
simple way can you now demonstrate the associative property of addition?

4. Use the following star (∗) diagram to help you explain $3 + 4 = 4 + 3$. (*Hint:* Consider two separate "partitionings" of the diagram, i.e., two different ways of separating the group of stars into two groups.)

∗   ∗   ∗   ∗   ∗   ∗   ∗

5. Use the following star diagram to help explain $(2 + 3) + 4 = 2 + (3 + 4)$.

∗   ∗   ∗   ∗   ∗   ∗   ∗   ∗   ∗

6. As in the Example of §2, use the commutative and associative laws to show that $2 + (4 + 3) = 4 + (3 + 2)$.

7. Use the laws to show that $1 + [(2 + 3) + 4] = (2 + 3) + (4 + 1)$. (*Hint:* An expression like $(2 + 3)$ can be thought of as symbolizing a single number. Hence $(1 + 4) + (2 + 3) = 1 + [4 + (2 + 3)]$, by the associative law.)

8. Use the laws to show that $(2 + 3 + 1) + 4 = [4 + (2 + 3)] + 1$.

9. In §2 the statement was made that the sum of four numbers could be expressed in 264 different ways. Can you verify this statement by a systematic inspection of the ways of placing parentheses? (*Hint:* $264 = 11 \times 24$.)

§3. MULTIPLICATION

If 300 people each pay 50¢ to see a show, and we wish to find the total amount collected from them, we must form the sum of three hundred 50's: $50 + 50 + \cdots + 50$ (300 terms). It is very awkward to deal with such an extended sum. Since situations of this kind occur quite frequently, it is natural to seek efficient ways of treating them.

The first step is to frame a new conception, called **multiplication.** Although at first we may think of multiplication as a kind of extended addition, we will later come to regard it as a *number operation* in its own right.

We define 3×2 as $2 + 2 + 2$, the sum of three two's. Similarly, 300×50 means $50 + 50 + \cdots + 50$, the sum of three hundred 50's. In general, if x and y are any natural numbers, we define their **product** xy as:

$$xy = y + y + \cdots + y \qquad (x \text{ of these } y\text{'s}).$$

The symbol xy may be read either as "eks wigh" or as "x times y." The form $x \times y$ is avoided, since the "times" symbol $\times$ is easily confused with the letter x. When expressions involve both letters and numerals, a dot symbol is often used: $2 \cdot 3$ and 2×3 both denote the product of 2 and 3.

The familiar and much used commutative and associative laws of multiplication are not obvious consequences of the definition given above. According to the definition,

$$3 \times 2 = 2 + 2 + 2, \qquad \text{while} \qquad 2 \times 3 = 3 + 3.$$

Is it obvious from an inspection of the *form alone* that $2 + 2 + 2 = 3 + 3$? (If so, then $2 \times 2 \times 2 = 3 \times 3$ should appear equally "obvious"!) It is true that when the indicated additions are carried out, the result 6 is obtained in both cases. Yet it is a long step from such an empirical or experimental verification in this and in other special numerical cases to a general proof of the commutative property for *every* pair x, y of natural numbers: $xy = yx$.

To see the pattern on which a general proof can be based, begin with the form $3 \times 2 = 2 + 2 + 2$, and represent the number $2 + 2 + 2$ by 3 groups (columns) of 2 stars each laid out as in this diagram:

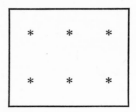

It is plain that the set of stars in the array represents not only the number 3×2, but also the number 2×3. For the set may also be regarded as composed of 2 groups (rows) of 3 stars each $(3 + 3)$. To establish $xy = yx$, we may mentally conceive of an array with x rows and y columns of stars.

This pictorial analysis suggests the possibility of developing the idea of multiplication directly in *set* terms, instead of basing it upon addition.

Given two sets X, Y, consider the set of all **couples** formed by pairing an element of X with an element of Y. Call this set of couples the **product** XY of the sets X, Y. In similar fashion, a product of three sets may be defined as a set of triples, etc.

In technical mathematics, the above type of set product is called the "combinatorial product" to distinguish it from another type called the "logical product" or "intersection." The order within the pairings is also taken into account, which we do not do. With this provision, the product of the x- and y-axes, for example, is the xy-plane (the x,y coordinates of a point giving a pairing).

Illustration. Let the elements of the set X be three boys: Bob, Dave, Ted. Let the elements of set Y be two girls: Mary, Joan. Then XY is the set of all six possible boy-girl couples, (Bob, Mary), (Bob, Joan), (Dave, Mary), (Dave, Joan), (Ted, Mary), (Ted, Joan). In the tabular array on page 55, the six starred spaces correspond to these pairings.

Now we may define number product in set terms. Given any two natural numbers, consider a pair of disjoint sets which represent them. *The product of the numbers is defined to be the number of the product of the sets.*

In symbols, if x and y are any two natural numbers, and X and Y a pair of disjoint sets such that $n(X) = x$ and $n(Y) = y$, then $xy = n(XY)$.

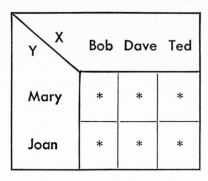

PROBLEM SET 3 (§3)

1. Lay out 12 pennies in a rectangular array to show that $3 \times 4 = 4 \times 3$ (where 3×4 means $4 + 4 + 4$ and 4×3 means $3 + 3 + 3 + 3$).

2. Try to convince a friend who affects to have forgotten the multiplication tables that $37 \times 53 = 53 \times 37$ by showing him how you could lay out pennies to prove it if you had enough of them.

3. A social club has 10 members, 4 boys and 6 girls. Every night, just one of the boys dates one of the girls, while the other 8 members stay home and watch TV. It is against the club rules for a boy to date a girl twice. How long will it be before they have to change the rules?

4. If the club in Problem 3 changes its rules so as to permit a boy to date a girl only so often as he takes her to a different place of entertainment, and the town provides just 8 such places, how long can the dating go on?

Answer: 192 nights

5. There are 3 roads from Podunk Center to Mudbank, and 5 roads from Mudbank on to Deville. By how many routes can one drive from Podunk Center to Deville?

6. If in Problem 5, there are also 2 roads which lead directly from Podunk Center to Deville, by-passing Mudbank, then among how many routes may one choose?

7. If in Problem 6, one may also take a plane to Mudbank, continuing on to Deville by taxi, how many choices are there in all?   *Answer:* 22

8. A combination lock has three dials, one bearing all the letters of the alphabet, the others each bearing all the digits. (*Example:* G–2–0 is one possible combination.) How many combinations are possible?   *Answer:* 2600

9. A signaler has five signal flags: white, black, yellow, red, green. Will he be able to arrange a code so that he can signal every number from 1 to 100 by showing three flags in succession?

10. How many one-foot-square floor tiles are needed to cover a rectangular floor of dimensions 8 ft. by 9 ft.?

§4. LAWS OF MULTIPLICATION

We have seen that a product xy can be represented by a rectangular array with x rows and y columns (or x columns and y rows). *Order* is thus inconsequential in multiplying as well as in adding. We have a **commutative law of multiplication:**

$$xy = yx.$$

Likewise, there is an associative law of multiplication, which tells us that we may *group* the factors of a product in any way we wish. For any three natural numbers, x, y, z:

$$xyz = (xy)z = x(yz).$$

To illustrate a method of proof of the associative law, let X, Y be the boy, girl sets of §3, and Z a set whose elements are Miss Prim and Miss Prude—elderly ladies who insist upon chaperoning the couples on their dates.

$$X: \quad \text{Bob, Dave, Ted}$$
$$Y: \quad \text{Mary, Joan}$$
$$Z: \quad \text{Prim, Prude}$$

Now XYZ is a set of 12 triples. A typical one of these is (Bob, Mary, Prim). Corresponding to this is an element of $(XY)Z$ which may be written [(Bob, Mary), Prim], a pair. Obviously the sets XYZ and $(XY)Z$ match **(1-1)**, so that $n(XYZ) = n[(XY)Z]$, or $xyz = (xy)z$.

An example may help to demonstrate the nontrivial nature of the associative rule. Suppose that we employ the subtractive principle with a triple combination of Roman numerals and use parentheses to avoid ambiguity. Then I(VX) will mean $5 - 1 = 4$. But (IV)X will mean $10 - 4 = 6$. The reason for this discrepancy is that *subtraction is not an associative operation:* $a - (b - c) \neq (a - b) - c$. What about division?

For any three natural numbers, the truth of the associative law of multiplication may be perceived by inspecting a star array of the following type, shown set up for the case $2 \times 3 \times 4$:

* *	* *	* *
* *	* *	* *
* *	* *	* *
* *	* *	* *

Consider the form $(2 \times 3) \times 4$. This is represented by the array, or set, because there are 2×3 squares of 4 stars each. Also, the form $2 \times (3 \times 4)$ is represented because there are 2 rows of squares, each row containing 3×4 stars.

In three dimensions, of course, a symmetrically distributed array can be formed. The elementary school teacher may use blocks in place of stars, stacking them to form a solid box whose "block dimensions" are 2 by 3 by 4, to illustrate how $2 \times 3 \times 4$ gives the number of blocks in the box (or gives its volume).

§5. LAWS OF ARITHMETIC

The **distributive law** links addition and multiplication:

$$x(y + z) = xy + xz.$$

The full name of this rule is "the distributive law of multiplication with respect to addition." The rule "distributes" the multiplication by x among both the added terms y and z. (Hence a "distributive law of addition with respect to multiplication" would read: $x + yz = (x + y)(x + z)$. This formula is true of numbers only if $x = 0$ or if $x + y + z = 1$, and so does not constitute a law of arithmetic. There is a form of the algebra of sets, however, in which the formula is always valid.) The student who remembers some algebra will recognize the distributive rule as a basic factoring formula, one of his most useful algebraic tools.

The following diagram shows the "why" of the rule for the numerical case $2 \times (3 + 4) = 2 \times 3 \quad + \quad 2 \times 4 = 14$.

It is left to the student to show how the set of stars in the diagram represents both $2 \times (3 + 4)$ and $(2 \times 3) + (2 \times 4)$. The rule can also be derived from the set identity $X(Y + Z) = XY + XZ$. (Work this relation out using the special sets X, Y, Z of §4, before trying to establish it in general.)

For future reference, we gather here the five basic laws of arithmetic (or algebra) which we have proved for natural numbers. For simplification, the forms $x + y + z$ and xyz are omitted. It will later be observed that these rules apply to all real numbers: negative, fractional, irrational.

FIVE BASIC LAWS OF ARITHMETIC

	Addition	Multiplication
Commutative Associative	$x + y = y + x$ $(x + y) + z = x + (y + z)$	$xy = yx$ $(xy)z = x(yz)$
Distributive	$x(y + z) = xy + xz$	

PROBLEM SET 4 (§4–§5)

1.   Suppose that you open a door, then cross the threshold. Can you reverse the order of these two operations? Give another example of a sequence of two operations in which reversing the order produces a different result. Also give an example in which the order is irrelevant.

2.   How would you arrange 72 cubical blocks to verify the associative relation $(3 \times 4) \times 6 = 3 \times (4 \times 6)$?

3.   Produce a "star" diagram like that in §4 to verify the associative relation $(2 \times 5) \times 3 = 2 \times (5 \times 3)$.

4.   Produce a "star" diagram like that in §5 to verify the distributive relation $3 \times (4 + 7) = 3 \times 4 + 3 \times 7$.

5.   When you mentally multiply 23 by 30, how do you make use of the associative law?

6.   When you mentally add 300 and 400, how do you make use of the distributive law?

7.   For the case in which $X = A$, $Y = E$, $Z = H$, where A, E, H are the sets listed in §2 of Chapter 2, verify the set identity $X(Y + Z) = XY + XZ$ by listing the elements of the set $X(Y + Z)$; also of the set XY; also of the set XZ.

8.   Prove the set identity $X(Y + Z) = XY + XZ$.

§6.   SUBTRACTION AND DIVISION

Mathematics is an active rather than a contemplative field. We think, for example, of proceeding from a pair of numbers to their sum, or to their product. Hence we regard *addition* and *multiplication* as number "operations"—as the *principal operations*, in fact, of arithmetic and algebra.

In mathematical discussion, the active tense is usually preferred to the passive. Given a pair of numbers, 2, 3, it can be said of them that they "have a sum, denoted by $2 + 3$, or 5." More commonly, however, we speak of "*adding* the 3 to the 2, to *obtain* the *result* 5." Instead of just observing that the expressions $2 + 3$ and $3 + 2$ denote the same number, we are apt to say that if we *add* the numbers in the other order, we *get* the same *result*. Rather than referring to the existence of a correspondence between two sets, we have felt it to be more vivid to speak actively of *matching* the sets.

In everyday life, after we have performed an operation, we frequently do it backwards, or undo it, getting back to where we started. Having opened a door, we may shut it again. Having switched on a light, we may switch it off. The "undoing" operation is called the **inverse** of the original.

In arithmetic, we may add the number 3 to the number 2, thus performing an operation of addition to get the result 5. This implies the "existence" of an *inverse operation* (involving the same number, 3) which we are to apply to 5 in order to get back to the 2 with which we began. This we call **subtraction**. We write $5 - 3 = 2$, and may refer to the expression $5 - 3$ as the **difference**, 5 *minus* 3. Thus $5 - 3 = 2$ *because* $2 + 3 = 5$. The following "operational diagram" shows the relationships involved:

ADD (+3)

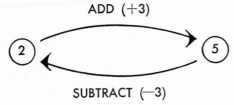

SUBTRACT (−3)

To emphasize the active character of the process, we may say that we subtract 3 from 5 to get 2, or even that we *take away* 3 from 5. This last mode of description suggests many physical illustrations of the operation, such as the actual removal of 3 oranges from a group of 5 oranges, the cutting of a 3-ft. length from a 5-ft. string, etc.

In set terms, if x and y are two natural numbers and $x < y$, then if Y is some set representing y, there will be some subset X of Y such that X represents x. We may define $y - x = n(Y - X)$, where $Y - X$ consists of all those elements of Y that do not belong to X.

The operation of multiplying 2 by 3 produces 6: $3 \times 2 = 6$. Hence we conceive of an inverse operation which when performed on 6 with 3 gives back the 2. This we call **division** and write $6 \div 3$ (6 divided by 3) or $\frac{6}{3}$ or $\%$ (the **quotient**, 6 "over" 3) to symbolize the operation. We have $6 \div 3 = 2$ *because* $3 \times 2 = 6$.

MULTIPLY (×3)

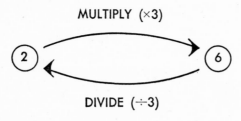

DIVIDE (÷3)

A set operation which corresponds to division by 3 is that of separating a set into 3 mutually matching sets. Another is that of separating a set into subsets of 3 elements each.

With respect to the system of the whole numbers, subtraction and division are limited operations. There is no whole number to which 7 can be added to give 5. Hence the operation indicated by $5 - 7$ cannot be performed. There is no whole number which when multiplied by 3 gives 8. The indicated operation $\frac{8}{3}$ cannot be performed. *With respect to the system of natural numbers*, therefore, the expressions $5 - 7$ and $\frac{8}{3}$ are *meaningless*. In physical set terms, seven people cannot be taken away from an original group of only five, and eight people cannot split up into teams of three. As we later proceed to enlarge the number system, we will increase the scope of the subtraction and division operations, until they are finally made universally possible (except that division by zero cannot be made a feasible operation in any respectable number system).

"Compound" operations are of some interest. Practice with them may aid the student to grasp the inverse operation concept more easily. A compound operation is a succession of addition, multiplication, subtraction, or division operations. Let $0(\ \ )$, for example signify the result of *subtracting* 3, then *multiplying by* 2, where these successive operations are to be applied to any number written in the parenthetical blank space. What is $0(12)$? Subtract 3 from 12, getting 9, then multiply this by 2, ending with 18. So $0(12) = 18$. Now let $0'(\ \ )$ symbolize the *inverse* operation. Obviously $0'(18) = 12$. What is $0'(8)$? Proceeding backwards, we must first *divide by* 2, then *add* 3. $0'(8) = 7$. The following operational diagram shows the various steps:

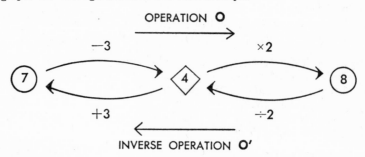

Subtraction and division are neither commutative nor associative:

$$7 - 5 \neq 5 - 7 \qquad\qquad 2 \div 1 \neq 1 \div 2$$
$$(10 - 4) - 2 \neq 10 - (4 - 2) \qquad (24 \div 6) \div 2 \neq 24 \div (6 \div 2)$$

To avoid ambiguity, it is often necessary to use parentheses when linking several terms by operational symbols. We conventionally understand that $10 - 4 - 2$ means $(10 - 4) - 2$ rather than $10 - (4 - 2)$, being accustomed to using the rule of subtracting in sequence, from left to right. It is also conventional that multiplications are performed before additions or subtractions, when there is just a string of terms, like $2 \times 3 + 4$. This expression means $(2 \times 3) + 4 = 6 + 4 = 10$, not $2 \times (3 + 4) = 2 \times 7 = 14$. *It is best not to employ any such conventions with the division symbol.* Write $(28 \div 4) + 3$ rather than $28 \div 4 + 3$. Write $(28/4) + 3$, or $\frac{28}{4} + 3$, rather than $28/4 + 3$. In general, with any expression, always use as many parentheses as seem needed to make the meaning clear.

PROBLEM SET 5 (§6)

1. Cite some everyday life illustrations of operations and their inverses.
2. What are the inverses of the following?

    (a)   Sit down   (d)   Move three feet west
    (b)   Get wet   (e)   Stretch to double length (a spring)
    (c)   Get cold   (f)   10° rise (temperature)

3. Lay two pennies on a table. Add three pennies to the two, demonstrating $2 + 3 = 5$. Now take the three pennies away again, leaving the original two, demonstrating the inverse operation $5 - 3 = 2$. Devise a similar procedure for showing how addition is inverse to subtraction.

4. Sketch an operational diagram for $6 + 8 = 14$ (taking the order $6 + 8$ as meaning that 8 is added to 6). What difference equation is associated with the inverse operation?

5.* Prove that the definition $y - x = n(Y - X)$, cited briefly in §6, is consistent with the definition of subtraction as inverse to addition, i.e., that $x + (y - x) = y$.

6. Sketch an operational diagram for $24 \div 6 = 4$. The inverse operation gives what multiplication?

7. As noted briefly in §6, dividing by 3 corresponds to the operation of separating a set into 3 mutually matching sets. Given the number 12, for example, we may take a set of 12 objects and separate it into 3 sets of 4, upon which we conclude $12 \div 3 = 4$. Upon the basis of the following array of stars can you give a general argument to show that this "partition" definition of division is equivalent to its definition as inverse to multiplication?

      *   *   *   . . .   *

      *   *   *   . . .   *   (3 rows of n stars each)

      *   *   *   . . .   *

8. Another "set definition" of division by 3 arises from the idea of separating a set into subsets of 3 elements each, the number of such subsets being the quotient of the number of the set by 3. Can you use the star diagram in Problem 7 to show that this definition is equivalent to the other set definition cited in Problem 7?

9. Explain the meaning of the following statement: "The expression $2 - 8$ is meaningless with respect to the system of the natural numbers."

10.   Same as Problem 9, but with "7 ÷ 2" in place of "2 − 8."

11.   Let $0(x)$ denote the operation of multiplying x by 5, then subtracting 3 from the result. Thus $0(4) = 5 \times 4 − 3 = 17$. Is this the same as first subtracting 3, then multiplying by 5?

12.   Let $0'(\ )$ denote the operation inverse to the operation $0(\ )$ of Problem 11.   Verify that $0'(27) = 6$, using an operational diagram as an aid. Find $0'(62)$. What about $0'(10)$?

13.   If 0 and 0′ are inverse operations, and $0(x)$ is the operation of adding 4 to x, then dividing the result by 3, find $0'(20)$.

14.   To demonstrate that subtraction and division are not associative operations, compute the values of these four expressions, showing each pair to have different values:

(a) $(12 − 5) − 2 = \ ?$ (b) $(36 ÷ 6) ÷ 3 = \ ?$
      $12 − (5 − 2) = \ ?$ $36 ÷ (6 ÷ 3) = \ ?$

15.   Is it true that $(48 ÷ 3) + 5 = 48 ÷ (3 + 5)$?

§7.   THE INTEGERS

The **integers** form a *two-way* sequence:

$$\ldots, -4, -3, -2, -1, 0, +1, +2, +3, +4, \ldots$$

A child begins to become accustomed to some of the ideas underlying the system of integers long before he meets the system in explicit form. There are many games in which the player both adds to and takes away from the score, others in which a marker is moved both forward and backward. A player may sometimes be ahead and sometimes behind, and may even end a game "in the red" or "in the hole." Red and black checkers could be used to keep score in such a game, the blacks indicating additions, the reds deductions. A surplus of *blacks* over reds would correspond to a *plus* score, a surplus of *reds* over blacks to a *minus* score.

Evidently we may express the conception of the system of the integers in terms of sets by considering sets that have two different kinds of elements. What these two kinds are will depend upon the specific application being made. They could be: male and female; living and dead; up and down; right and left; input and output; asset and liability. Whatever the case, we will term the two types *black* and *red*.

A given set may have an equal number of red and black elements. It will then be called a **null set,** and will have assigned to it the integer 0.

A nonnull set has a surplus of one element. The (*signed*) *number of the set* is defined to be the *number of the surplus elements*, with a *plus* or *minus* sign appended according as the surplus elements are *black* or *red*.

Consider a set with 5 black and 2 red elements. We will express its structure by the symbol [5B,2R]. The symbol will also be used to denote the integer which is the number of the set: [5B,2R] $= +3$. *Examples:*

$$[7B,4R] = [6B,3R] = [5B,2R] = [4B,1R] = [3B] = +3.$$
$$[3B,3R] = [2B,2R] = [1B,1R] = 0.$$
$$[4B,7R] = [3B,6R] = [2B,5R] = [1B,4R] = [3R] = -3.$$

We may define number addition in terms of set union just as in the case of the natural numbers, and may develop rules for adding and subtracting positive and negative integers.

Example 1.   Find: $-3 + 5$.

Work.   Select any black-red sets to represent -3 and 5. The simplest choices are [3R] and [5B]. For illustrative purposes, let us pick a less special pair, say [4B,7R] and [19B,14R]. The union of two such disjoint sets will contain $4 + 19 = 23$ *black* and $7 + 14 = 21$ *red* elements, and so will have the number $+2$. Hence: $-3 + 5 = +2$.   Symbolically the work is:

$$-3 + 5 = [4B,7R] + [19B,14R] = [23B,21R] = [2B] = +2.$$

Example 2.   Find: $-3 - 4$.

Work.   We may regard the expression $-3 - 4$ as denoting the sum of -3 and -4: $(-3) + (-4)$. We may also regard it as asking for the subtraction of 4 from -3. Here we show the work related to the latter interpretation. Let -3 be represented by a set of structure [10B,13R], 4 by a set of structure [6B,2R]. Then:

$$-3 - 4 = [10B,13R] - [6B,2R] = [4B,11R] = [7R] = -7.$$

The "structure" of the positive integers, $+1$, $+2$, $+3$, . . . is exactly the same as the structure of the natural numbers 1, 2, 3, ... (The "structure" is given by the set of interrelations. For any given relation involving positive integers, such as $(+2) + (+3) = +5$, there is a like relation involving natural numbers, $2 + 3 = 5$, and vice versa.) Hence we ordinarily write "2" whether we are thinking of the number so denoted as a member of the system of integers or as a member of the system of natural numbers. Therefore we must exercise care when we use an expression like $2 - 5$. Relative to the system of integers, this expression is meaningful, and may be replaced by -3. Relative to the system of natural numbers, the expression is an absurdity. (A person with only two cookies cannot eat five of them. But a golfer may win two and lose five holes, becoming "three down").

§8. ZERO

It is frequently convenient to refer to the system of numbers:

$$0, 1, 2, 3, 4, 5, . . . \qquad .$$

We will call this the system of the **whole numbers.**

Many writers use the term "whole number" as a synonym for the term "integer." Also, zero is often included as one of the natural numbers. Our own choice of terminology will enable us to avoid certain awkward phraseologies, like "nonnegative integer" and "except when ___ is zero."

We met zero in §7 of Chapter 2 as *the number of the empty set*. In §7 of this chapter we encountered it in different guize—as an integer, the number of a *null* set. Under either interpretation the common zero properties are easily established:

$$\text{For any number } x: \qquad x + 0 = x \qquad \text{and} \qquad 0 \cdot x = 0.$$

Let E denote the empty set. Let X denote a set whose number is $x = n(X)$. For the union of X and E, we have $X + E = X$. For the set product, we have $XE = E$, since no couples can be formed.

How is zero as a whole number different from zero as an integer? The empty set is void of elements; the null set has a "balance" of elements. There can be no such thing as a corporation whose dollar value is zero in the *empty* set sense. A person with such status could only be a tramp in tattered rags and with gaping pockets. On the other hand, a corporation valued at zero in the *null* set sense may be an immense going concern, employing thousands of workers and operating costly equipment, but with a balance sheet reading: Assets $93,000,000; liabilities, $93,000,000. A person in a similar position may support a family, own a car, and live in a comfortable house, in spite of his debts.

Many people never outgrow the *empty* set conception of zero. In the early grades they learn that zero means "nothing" and are ever after unwilling or unable to broaden their point of view. It is an important duty of the elementary school teacher to ensure that her pupils do not acquire such fixed and narrow ideas during the educational process— rather to instill in her pupils a sense of the relative nature of their early conceptions, an anticipation that these will grow and evolve.

For most students it is the conception of the *continuous number scale* which stands at the end of the road. This, the system of the "real numbers," is the most inclusive system treated in precollege mathematics (with the exception that the high school student may briefly meet the "complex number system" in which the expression $\sqrt{-1}$ has meaning).

In our technologically minded world we measure everything that we possibly can. It is thus the system of the real numbers that we use most. In much of this usage, zero is just like any other number—a scale mark that cannot be associated with the empty set or with a null set, a number with properties quite unlike those suggested by the word "nothing." The temperature that the American householder reads as 0° on his outdoor thermometer (Fahrenheit scale) would be measured as $-18°$ by the European on his Centigrade scale, but labeled 255° by a physicist using an Absolute scale.

The identification of zero with "nothing" is a particularly unfortunate blunder. Even in the simplest case, when zero is regarded as but the label of the empty set, its properties are not fully similar to those suggested by the word "nothing." The pupil who takes 0×5 to mean that "nothing is multiplied times five" is likely to conclude that $0 \times 5 = 5$, for the "5" is bound to remain unchanged if nothing is done to it! Later on, in algebraic work, this same pupil will compute the "value" of the function $y = 1/x$ for $x = 0$ by confidently writing the monstrosity $1/0 = 1$.

§9. CARDINAL AND ORDINAL NUMBERS

As Max White waits in line at a ticket office, he may observe that he is *sixth* in line. In the pantry, a jar of preserves may be placed on the *third* shelf from the bottom. These are *ordinal* usages of number. A *cardinal number* tells the "size" of a set. An *ordinal number* designates a position in a linear (line) arrangement.

In §1 of Chapter 2 we referred to *matching* and *counting* as cardinal and ordinal conceptions, respectively. In application, however, these two processes are linked—we often find the sizes of sets by counting their elements. We count: 1, 2, 3, ... During this procedure the named numbers are apparently to be regarded as ordinals. Upon finding the count, however, we identify the last ordinal named as the number of the counted set, a cardinal.

Because we switch back and forth so speedily and frequently between the two conceptions, it is convenient to use the same symbols for the cardinals and ordinals, also to use the term "natural number" for both cardinals and ordinals.

The housewife's note to the milkman, "3 quarts homogenized," employs the number 3 as a cardinal. The "3" in the upper right-hand corner of a newspaper page denotes an ordinal. The suffix "th" is frequently attached to the ordinal numerals (from "4th" on). They are then written "1st, 2nd, 3rd, 4th, . . . ," and read as "first, second, third, fourth, . . . " in place of "one, two, three, four, ..."

3 as a CARDINAL   **3 as an ORDINAL**

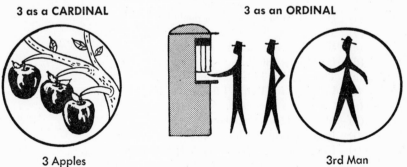

3 Apples   3rd Man

Fig. 22   Cardinal and Ordinal

We chose to develop the theory of the natural numbers on the basis of their cardinal interpretation. The fundamental notion was then that of *set*. For the ordinals, the basic notion is that of *progression* or *sequence*. The theory of the ordinals can be developed from the idea of "matching sequences." The finite cardinals and ordinals turn out to be structurally alike, enabling us to pass from one system to the other automatically and trivially. Curiously enough, the situation is grossly different with the *transfinite* ordinals and cardinals. In the domain of the infinite, these two kinds of numbers act quite unalike, so that different names must be assigned to them and separate groups of operational rules for adding, subtracting, etc., worked out for them.

PROBLEM SET 6 (§7–§9)

1. In the notation of §7, let $+2$ be represented by a set of type [6B,4R] and $+3$ by one of type [10B,7R]. Verify that $(+2) + (+3) = +5$.

2. As in Problem 1, verify that $(-4) + (+3) = -1$, using sets of type [2B,6R] and [20B,17R].

3. Verify $(+5) - (+3) = +2$, using [8B,3R] and [5B,2R].

4. Verify $(+5) - (-3) = +8$, using [12B,7R] and [2B,5R].

5. Verify $(+6) + 0 = +6$, using [6B] and [2B,2R].

6.* Form the "product" of the sets of type [3B,1R] and [2B,5R] by writing 28 couples of elements, each containing an element from each set. Show that if like-colored couples are called B's and unlike R's, then the set of couples will represent -6, in accordance with the usual rule $(+2) \times (-3) = -6$.

7. As a person deposits and withdraws, his bank balance gives his net position. Considered as a number of cents, is the value of this balance properly thought of as a natural number or as an integer? Explain fully.

8. Same as Problem 7 for a golfer's 18-hole score.

9. Is the following explanation (a) correct, (b) wise to use? "$0 + 5 = 5$ because $0 + 5$ means that nothing is added to five, that is, nothing is done to five, leaving it unchanged."   *Answers:* (a) No; (b) No. (See §8.)

10. In each case, is the number cited used in the cardinal or in the ordinal sense or in neither?

    (a)   He has 10 marbles in his pocket.
    (b)   The golfers did not play out on Hole No. 9.
    (c)   His address is 721 Westmount Place.
    (d)   He weighs 180 lb.
    (e)   This sheet is 140-count muslin.
    (f)   Look out for Public Enemy No. 1!
    (g)   Give me a 3¢ stamp.
    (h)   Math. 432 is a popular course.
    (i)   Page 37 is ink-stained.
    (j)   In cadence, count: 1, 2, 3, 4; 1, 2, 3, 4.

4

Addition and
Subtraction

§1. ADDITION: FIRST NOTIONS

We have now developed the logical basis of the addition operation and have established the basic laws (commutative, etc.) governing the operation. The next task is that of working out practical techniques for performing the operation efficiently upon given numerals. From the "why" we proceed to the "how."

An obvious way of adding is by direct counting—a favorite scheme with young children and a necessary preliminary to their later learning. To add 14 to 23, for example, we may count 1, 2, . . . , 23 and then 1, 2, . . . , 14, marking a stroke with each count. A count of the whole group of tally strokes then gives the result, 37:

$$\text{IIIIIIIIIIIIIIIIIIIIIIII} \qquad \text{IIIIIIIIIIIIII}$$

The Egyptian, Greek, and Roman numerals may be regarded as abbreviated ways of keeping the tallies. In Roman numerals, 23 and 14 appear as

$$\text{XXIII} \qquad\qquad \text{XIIII.}$$

Pushing these together gives the result:

$$\text{XXXIIIIIII} = \text{XXXVII.}$$

Addition with Roman numerals is thus a sort of improved counting process.

With our own Hindu-Arabic numerals, the process is carried out on a more "sophisticated" level, as required by the position-value feature of our system.

Our children first learn how to add one digit to another. They establish "addition facts," like $3 + 4 = 7$, by direct counting. Eventually, they learn an entire 10 by 10, 100-entry, addition table:

	0	1	2	3	4	5
0	0	1	2	3	4	
1	1	2	3	4	5	
2	2	3	4	5	6	

It might seem that nearly half the memorization effort could be saved (table reduced to 55 entries) by applying the commutative principle $2 + 1 = 1 + 2$, etc., and eliminating entries below the main diagonal from upper left to lower right corner. But a child so taught would be handicapped. Having the answer to $2 + 1$, say, on the "tip of his tongue," when confronted by $1 + 2$ he would have to mentally reverse the order of the 1, 2 before producing the answer. (A person familiar with "touch typing" can readily and dramatically prove to himself the difference between learning a response in one direction and in reverse. Shown a letter, the typist's response is immediate—a certain finger bangs down a certain key. But if someone places the typist's finger on a key and asks that the letter be named, the response will likely be quite slow.)

There is some difference of opinion as to whether young children should be taught the "zero" addition facts, like $0 + 3 = 0$. In summing a column of digits, a child may be directed just to skip whenever he comes to a zero, so that he need not think explicitly of adding zero. But this evasion must perforce be temporary. Eventually the pupil must learn that $0 + N = N$ for every number N.

Knowing how to add digits, we are ready to add a pair of numerals like 23 and 14. Even as the Hindus, we may *name* the places and proceed as follows:

$$
\begin{array}{rl}
23 & = 2 \text{ Tens} + 3 \text{ Units} \\
+ \quad 14 & = 1 \text{ Ten } + 4 \text{ Units} \\
\hline
(37) & = 3 \text{ Tens} + 7 \text{ Units}
\end{array}
$$

Simplification—an exchange replacing 10 Units by 1 Ten, etc.—will often be necessary:

$$
\begin{array}{rl}
27 & = 2 \text{ Tens} + 7 \text{ Units} \\
+ \quad 36 & = 3 \text{ Tens} + 6 \text{ Units} \\
\hline
& 5 \text{ Tens} + 13 \text{ Units} \\
(63) & = 6 \text{ Tens} + 3 \text{ Units}
\end{array}
$$

A child quickly learns to perform the exchange or "carry" process in rote fashion while summing the columns in right-to-left order. It is so easy to learn to do the task mechanically and without insight that the teacher must take much care to ensure that her pupils fully understand the meaning of what is done. It is of special importance that a child's early mathematical work should be fully "meaningful" to him. If it is not—if he merely learns the appropriate motions to go through to get the "right answer"—then he is likely to be handicapped and frustrated in all his future mathematical efforts, and the domain of mathematics may become for him an area of senseless fumblings, "school" stuff unrelated to the realities of life.

The addition procedures above may be effectively illustrated by using sets of matchsticks to represent the numerals. We sort 27 sticks into 2 bundles of ten and 7 individual sticks; 36 sticks give 3 bundles of ten and 6 loose sticks. When the sets are combined, there are 5 bundles of ten and 13 loose sticks. Ten of the latter may be grouped and a rubber band put around them to make a new bundle of ten, which is "carried" over to be added to the other 5.

A somewhat more abstract type of illustration makes use of dimes and pennies, 27 being represented by 2 dimes and 7 pennies, etc. Abacus illustrations are still more abstract and hence usually of less value in the early learning stages. However, the vertical wire form of line abacus shown in Fig. 5 of Chapter 1 may be effectively employed, provided the wires extend high enough to accommodate 18 beads, so that digital sums may be shown directly without midway exchanges.

§2. ADDITION: GENERAL

Addition procedures involve: (1) the separate summing of the digits representing units, tens, hundreds, etc., (2) the rearrangement of the results in standard numeral form.

To carry out (1), a pupil must know how to add a digit to any number. Assuming that he knows how to add a digit to a digit, how may he mentally add a digit to a two-digit number? Consider the case: 25 + 3. He mentally adds the digit 3 to the units digit 5 of the 25, and stays in the twenties: "twenty-(five plus three) = twenty-eight." Consider 25 + 7. Adding the 7 to the 5 gives him twelve, which is 2 over ten, so he advances to the thirties. These examples are typical of the two principal cases. (Textbooks on arithmetic refer to the twenties as one "decade," the thirties as another, and so on. In what circumstances would the sum of a digit and a number in a certain decade be a number in the same decade? In the next decade?)

Let us see what addition looks like without rearrangement. Consider the sum of the four numbers 27631, 5917, 232, 14826. Abbreviate "Units" by "U," "Tens" by "T," etc. Then:

T Th	Th	H	T	U
2	7	6	3	1
	5	9	1	7
		2	3	2
1	4	8	2	6
3	16	25	9	16

Note that the order of summing the columns is irrelevant—right to left, left to right, or higgledy-piggledy. But exchanging or carrying always takes place from right to left. The surplus 10 in the Units column, for example, must eventually be carried as 1 Ten to the Tens column. The most efficient total rearranging procedure is also one that goes along from right to left, because adjusted columns will then receive no further carries that might make readjustment necessary. The successive steps of adjustment are:

T Th	Th	H	T	U
3	16	25	9	16
3	16	25	10	6
3	16	26	0	6
3	18	6	0	6
4	8	6	0	6

With our common adding scheme, the adjustments are effected along with the summing. As each column is summed, the units of the sum are written and the tens carried immediately, to be added in with the digits of the next column to the left. It would seem that no speedier scheme could be possible.

$$
\begin{array}{ccccc}
2 & 7 & 6 & 3 & 1 \\
  & 5 & 9 & 1 & 7 \\
  &   & 2 & 3 & 2 \\
1 & 4 & 8 & 2 & 6 \\
\end{array}
$$

Unwritten Carries $\longrightarrow$ (1) (2) (1) (1)

$$
\begin{array}{ccccc}
4 & 8 & 6 & 0 & 6 \\
\end{array}
$$

Despite the efficiency of our right-to-left interlinked sum-carry process, the right-to-left order is an unfortunate choice from one important aspect. Not only does it deal with the digits of the numerals in the reverse order to that in which we write them, but it focuses first attention upon the *least important* end of the numeral. An error made in adding units is trivial in comparison with one made in adding thousands.

It may be interesting and enlightening to the student to experiment with left-to-right procedures. They all involve extra writing, or mental estimations of carries which will affect a column sum that is to be put down:

```
  2 7 6 3 1        2 7 6 3 1        2 7 6 3 1
    5 9 1 7          5 9 1 7          5 9 1 7
      2 3 2            2 3 2            2 3 2
  1 4 8 2 6        1 4 8 2 6        1 4 8 2 6
  ─────────        ─────────        ─────────
  3 2 5 9          3 6 5 9 6        3 6 5 9 6
  1 6   1 6        1 2   1          1 2   1
  ─────────        ─────────        ─────────────────────────
  4 8 5   6        4 8 5 0 6        4 8 6 0 6  (1 mental carry)
      1 0                1
  ─────────        ─────────            WORK DIRECTION
  4 8 6 0 6        4 8 6 0 6        ──────────────────────→
                                        Left to Right
```

The Hindus added from left to right. As carries turned up to change column sums already written, they adjusted by erasing and rewriting. This was easy for them, since they wrote on a "dust" board (red flour on a white background was common), and an erasure was but a smoothing of the "dust." Hence their work took this form at successive stages:

```
27631       27631       27631       27631       27631
 5917        5917        5917        5917        5917
  232         232         232         232         232
14826       14826       14826       14826       14826
─────       ─────       ─────       ─────       ─────
    3          46         485        4859       48606
```

(What actually showed on their tiny slates was less than displayed above. They may have summed the Ten Thousands digits first, erasing as they worked, ending with the numeral 3 alone on the slate; next the Thousands digits; and so on.)

When Europeans took over the Hindu arithmetic, they *crossed out* instead of erasing, this being the easier thing to do when the writing medium is ink on parchment or paper. Then the steps of the work looked like this:

27631	27631	27631	27631	27631
5917	5917	5917	5917	5917
232	232	232	232	232
14826	14826	14826	14826	14826
3	3̸6	3̸6̸5	3̸6̸59	3̸6̸5̸9̸6
	4	48	48	4860

The Europeans called this process a **scratch method**. Naturally there were also scratch methods for the other arithmetic processes. During the sixteenth century these methods declined in popularity. To print the "scratched" digits, extra type was needed. This led to the printing of some examples without scratches. This made the examples hard for the reader to follow. The upshot was, the methods were changed.

PROBLEM SET 1 (§1–§2)

1. Perform the following additions by expressing each number as a sum of units, tens, etc., combining and simplifying (23 = 2 Tens + 3 Units, etc.):

(a)   27   (b)   66   (c)   78   (d)   85
     + 31   + 28   + 25   + 79

(e)   376   (f)   487   (g)   729   (h)   9206
     + 52   + 215   + 271   + 5728

2. Demonstrate the additions in Problem 1 by using pennies, dimes, dollars and ten-dollar bills to represent units, tens, hundreds and thousands, respectively. ("Play money" bills will do, made by writing $1 or $10 on slips of paper.)

3. Use matchsticks or toothpicks, making bundles of ten with the aid of rubber bands (or use squares of paper and paper clips, etc.), to demonstrate these additions:

(a)   13   (b)   18   (c)   28   (d)   27
     + 24   + 36   + 32   + 38

4. Can you tell without adding that the following additions will all give the same result?

2736	727	323
924	2324	716
6317	6513	2927
+ 523	+ 936	+ 6534

5. Carry out the addition at the left in Problem 4 by the separate column scheme of §2, with columns headed "Th, H, T, U." Show the successive steps of adjusting the answer to the usual numeral form.

6. Carry out the addition at the left in Problem 4 by a left-to-right procedure (no erasing or scratching).

7. Add by the scratch method:

(a)	231	(b)	3718	(c)	2693	(d)	43207
	328		292		371		18928
	67		6		56920		21329
	+ 1089		+ 9237		+ 4768		+ 64718

§3. SUBTRACTION

Somehow subtraction never became wholly standardized. Several different methods are currently taught in United States schools. A teacher in the middle grades is likely to find that some pupils who received their earlier schooling elsewhere are accustomed to using a different scheme from that common in her locality.

Four methods are in use:

    1.   Take-Away Borrow
    2.   Take-Away Carry
    3.   Add Borrow
    4.   Add Carry

The names of the methods are also not standard. The "Add Carry" scheme may be called "Additive Equal-Additions" or "Austrian Method." The "Take-Away Carry" scheme may be called "Take-Away Equal-Additions" or "Take-Away Repay," etc.

With a **Take-Away** method, there is direct subtraction of digits. The subtraction of 23 from 57 proceeds as follows:

(*2*) (*1*)		*Steps*	(*Said to Oneself*)
5 7	(*1*)	$7 - 3 = 4$	"3 from 7 gives 4"
− 2 3	(*2*)	$5 - 2 = \overline{3}$	"2 from 5 gives $\overline{3}$"
3 4			

With an **Add** method, the question is asked, "What must be added to the lower digit to produce the upper?"

(*2*) (*1*)		*Steps*	(*Said to Oneself*)
5 7	(*1*)	$3 + \underline{4} = 7$	"3 plus what is 7? 4"
− 2 3	(*2*)	$2 + \overline{3} = 5$	"2 plus what is 5? $\overline{3}$"
3 4			

With a **Borrow** method, there is borrowing where necessary from digits of the *upper* number. With a **Carry** method, there is carrying where necessary to digits of the *lower* number.

With these principles in mind, the student may easily grasp the way each of the four methods work. They are described below for the subtraction of 4768 from 9825.

1. *Take-Away Borrow*

(1) $15 - 8 = \bar{7}$

(2) $11 - 6 = \bar{5}$

(3) $7 - 7 = \bar{0}$

(4) $9 - 4 = \bar{5}$

2. *Take-Away Carry*

(1) $15 - 8 = \bar{7}$

(2) $12 - 7 = \bar{5}$

(3) $8 - 8 = \bar{0}$

(4) $9 - 4 = \bar{5}$

3. *Add Borrow*

(1) $8 + 7 = 15$

(2) $6 + \bar{5} = 11$

(3) $7 + \bar{0} = 7$

(4) $4 + \bar{5} = 9$

4. *Add Carry*

(1) $8 + 7 = 15$

(2) $7 + \bar{5} = 12$

(3) $8 + \bar{0} = 8$

(4) $4 + \bar{5} = 9$

(4)	(3)	(2)	(1)
9	8	2	5
− 4	7	6	8
5	0	5	7

Which method is best? A variety of experiments have been made pitting one method against another. Generally speaking, the results have been inconclusive—as might have been anticipated at the outset. The manipulative procedures are similar with all four methods, so that a child could be expected to become skilled in using any one of them about as readily as in using any other. The crucial test might therefore be: Which method is most easily explained by the teacher and clearly understood by the pupil? This kind of criterion calls more for subjective agreement on the part of experts or of "master teachers" than for elaborate experimentation by graduate students in education. There being little such agreement, perhaps there is no point in disputing the relative merits of the methods, except as follows: By choosing a method and arguing for it, a teacher will be stimulated toward devising effective ways of teaching it.

There is little point here in presenting a systematic treatment of the "logic" or "meaning" underlying each method. As the student actually teaches a method, he will discover for himself various ways of helping his students see the "why" of the process. As in the case of the addition process, matchstick illustrations are useful.

Consider the example of subtracting 28 from 64 according to the Take-Away Borrow scheme. Let 64 be represented by 6 bundles of ten and 4 loose matchsticks. The "borrow" is illustrated by slipping the rubber band off one bundle, so that there are 5 bundles and 14 loose sticks. Now 8 loose sticks and 2 bundles may be "taken away."

When the Add-Carry scheme is to be illustrated, the teacher may begin with 2 bundles and 8 loose sticks (28). Adding 6 sticks gives 14 loose ones. The "carry" is illustrated by grouping 10 of these to make a new bundle. To the three bundles now present, 3 more must be added to end up with 6 bundles and 4 loose sticks. Another way is to lay out bundles and sticks to represent both 64 and 28, then to add a new bundle to each group. The new bundle going to the 64 group, however, is immediately converted into ten loose sticks, so that the problem becomes: What must be added to 3 bundles and 8 sticks to get 6 bundles and 14 sticks?

Dimes and pennies may be used in place of bundles and loose sticks. A rod or line abacus may be used, especially if 18 or more beads or count-

ers are available for each line or rod. Efficient subtraction on a standard
rod abacus (9 or 10 beads per rod) may be performed as a "take-away"
procedure. In the case of 64 − 28, put 64 on the abacus. Since 8 units
beads cannot be taken from the 4 that show in registering position, *add* 2
and take away 1 tens bead (10 − 8 = 2). Taking away 2 more tens beads
then finishes the work.

PROBLEM SET 2 (§3)

*In Problems 1–12, carry out the subtractions by each of the four methods explained
in §3. As in the text examples, list each step, keying the number of the step to indices
(1), (2), . . . written above each digit column in the subtraction setup.*

1.	67	2.	62	3.	964	4.	273
	− 42		− 48		− 512		− 82

5.	372	6.	253	7.	681	8.	4192
	− 169		− 57		− 298		− 2818

9.	3046	10.	5123	11.	60918	12.	21231
	− 2618		− 4166		− 27374		− 18749

13. Demonstrate the following subtractions according to a Take-Away
Borrow procedure, using matchsticks and bundles of ten sticks held by rubber
bands:

(a)	48	(b)	32	(c)	43	(d)	51
	− 12		− 8		− 35		− 18

14. Same as Problem 13, but by Take-Away Carry.
15. Same as Problem 13, but by Add Borrow.
16. Same as Problem 13, but by Add Carry.
17. Use pennies and dimes in place of matchsticks to demonstrate the subtractions of Problem 13.
18. Use pennies and dimes, Problem 14.
19. Use pennies and dimes, Problem 15.
20. Use pennies and dimes, Problem 16.
21. Carry out the following subtractions on a line abacus (4 lines labeled 1,
10, 100, 1000, ruled on a sheet of paper):

(a)	392	(b)	475	(c)	500	(d)	6327
	− 158		− 369		− 138		− 2785

§4. SIGNED DIGITS

Our numeral scheme is *additive*, the value of a numeral being the sum
of the values associated with the digits by virtue of their position in the
numeral.

As with Roman numerals, suppose we introduce a *subtractive* conception. To indicate that a digit value is to be subtracted, we will place a bar (minus sign) over the digit. Thus:

$$2\bar{3} = 20 - 3 = 17; \qquad 5\bar{3}\bar{6}2 = 5000 - 300 - 60 + 2 = 4642.$$

We will refer to this conception as one of using **signed digits.**

In 1726 J. Colson advocated a "negativo-affirmative arithmetick" based on the use of signed digits. The scheme is fully described in Chapter 22 of *Biomathematics*, by Cedric Smith, Hafner, New York, 1954. The aim of the presentation of this and of other *curiosa* is to broaden the student's outlook and to stimulate his mathematical imagination. If he intends to teach arithmetic, he should early realize that the subject is not cut and dried, not fixed immutably in its current form, that it is a fertile field for research of a sort or even just for playful toying.

A numeral written with signed digits may speedily be converted into standard numeral form by proceeding from left to right and converting only two-digit sections at a time (except when a zero digit is followed by a negative digit). Thus if the sequence $2\bar{3}$ appears anywhere in a numeral it may be replaced by 17. *Example:*

$4\ \bar{3}\ 7\ \bar{2}\ \bar{8}\ 0\ \bar{4}$	*Reasons*	
$= 3\ 7\ 7\ \bar{2}\ \bar{8}\ 0\ \bar{4}$	$4\ \bar{3} = \ \ 40 - 3 = \ \ 37$	
$= 3\ 7\ 6\ 8\ \bar{8}\ 0\ \bar{4}$	$7\ \bar{2} = \ \ 70 - 2 = \ \ 68$	
$= 3\ 7\ 6\ 7\ 2\ 0\ \bar{4}$	$8\ \bar{8} = \ \ 80 - 8 = \ \ 72$	
$= 3\ 7\ 6\ 7\ 1\ 9\ 6$	$2\ 0\ \bar{4} = 200 - 4 = 196$	

With a little practice the converted result can be written at once.

Several plus and minus numbers (representing amounts taken in and paid out, for example) may be written in a single column and added in one operation if signed digits are used. To carry out the work, the student must have some facility in the handling of negative numbers. The signed digit idea will be referred to later in several connections. Here we use it as the basis of a novel scheme of subtraction.

To subtract a number from another, proceed in either left-to-right or right-to-left order. When a lower digit is less than an upper, take it away. When the upper is less, *take that from the lower instead*, but put a bar over the answer digit to show that it is negative. Thus:

$$\begin{array}{r} 7\ 4\ 6\ 5\ 8\ 0 \\ -\ 4\ 8\ 9\ 1\ 3\ 7 \\ \hline 3\ \bar{4}\ \bar{3}\ 4\ 5\ \bar{7} = 257443. \end{array}$$

§5. COMPLEMENTS

A *complementary* method of subtraction was taught in many United States schools in the nineteenth century. Such methods have been known at least since medieval times. They arose because of the ease with which a number may be subtracted from the power of ten next greater than the number. Call this result the **complement** of the number.

The complement of 297 is 703, because $1000 - 297 = 703$. The complement of 32 is 68, because $100 - 32 = 68$. That of 3 is 7, since $10 - 3 = 7$.

If 1 is subtracted from any power of ten, the result is "all nines": $10,000 - 1 = 9999$; $100 - 1 = 99$, etc. Hence to find a number's complement, proceed from left to right along its digits, taking each from 9 and writing down the result. But take the last (units) digit from 10, so as to restore the missing 1:

$$
\begin{array}{r} 100,000 \\ -\ \ 57,218 \\ \hline 42,782 \end{array}
\ = \
\begin{array}{r} 9\ 9\ 9\ 9\ 10 \\ -\ 5\ 7\ 2\ 1\ \ 8 \\ \hline 4\ 2\ 7\ 8\ \ 2 \end{array}
\quad \text{because} \quad
\begin{array}{r} 99,999 \\ +\ \ \ \ \ \ \ 1 \\ \hline 100,000 \end{array}
$$

Using complements speeds number work in many special instances. Anyone who does much computing or mental arithmetic learns to recognize the possibilities as they turn up. No formal drill or rule memorizing is needed. Most people when asked to subtract 38 from 104 "in their heads" will do it by thinking: "38 from 100 is 62, and 4 is 66." (Some will insert an intermediate step of complementary type: "38 from 40 is 2, and 60 is 62 . . . .")

A complementary type of method is ordinarily used by clerks in returning change to customers. In this usage, complements are taken with respect to the next higher monetary denomination instead of the next higher power of ten. When a dollar bill is tendered for a 23¢ purchase, the clerk usually returns two pennies, then a quarter and a half-dollar, saying "23, and 2 makes 25, and 25 makes 50, and 50 makes one (100)."

To subtract 4768 from 9825, one may write the complement of 4768, add this to 9825, then deduct the appropriate power of ten (10,000). It is especially convenient just to write the signed digit $\bar{1}$ in front of the complement of 4768, as this will automatically provide for the deduction:

$$
\begin{array}{r} 9\ 8\ 2\ 5 \\ -\ 4\ 7\ 6\ 8 \\ \hline \end{array}
\ = \
\begin{array}{r} 9\ 8\ 2\ 5 \\ +\ \bar{1}\ 5\ 2\ 3\ 2 \\ \hline 5\ 0\ 5\ 7 \end{array}
$$

A digital process making use of complements is easily contrived. The following is a **Complement Carry** scheme. The work is from right to left. When possible, take away. When not, add the complement and carry 1 to the next place:

Steps

(6)	(5)	(4)	(3)	(2)	(1)		
7	4	6	5	8	0	(1)	$10 - 7 = 3$ $3 + 0 = 3$
−4	8	9	1	3	7	(2)	$8 - 4 = \bar{4}$
2	5	7	4	4	3	(3)	$5 - 1 = \bar{4}$
						(4)	$10 - 9 = 1$ $1 + 6 = 7$
						(5)	$10 - 9 = 1$ $1 + 4 = \bar{5}$
						(6)	$7 - 5 = \bar{2}$

It is left to the student to work out a "Complement Borrow" scheme, and to observe that it is precisely this scheme by which he may most efficiently subtract on the simple rod abacus with nine or ten beads per rod.

PROBLEM SET 3 (§4–§5)

1. Convert the following "signed digit" numerals to ordinary numerals:

   (a) $4\bar{3}$ (b) $7\bar{8}$ (c) $4\bar{3}2$ (d) $4\bar{3}26$
   (e) $5\bar{2}4$ (f) $30\bar{2}$ (g) $4\bar{2}3\bar{8}$ (h) $5\bar{4}3\bar{2}$
   (i) $7\bar{2}3480\bar{4}$ (k) $63\bar{4}2\bar{7}8\bar{3}$ *Answer:* (e) $5\bar{2}4 = 48\bar{4} = 476$

2. Subtract by the signed digit method:

   (a) $\begin{array}{r} 62 \\ -\ 48 \end{array}$ (b) $\begin{array}{r} 273 \\ -\ 82 \end{array}$ (c) $\begin{array}{r} 372 \\ -\ 169 \end{array}$ (d) $\begin{array}{r} 253 \\ -\ 57 \end{array}$

   (e) $\begin{array}{r} 681 \\ -\ 298 \end{array}$ (f) $\begin{array}{r} 4192 \\ -\ 2818 \end{array}$ (g) $\begin{array}{r} 60918 \\ -\ 27374 \end{array}$ (h) $\begin{array}{r} 21231 \\ -\ 18749 \end{array}$

3.* At the right, it is shown how a column of positive and negative numbers can be added directly by using signed digits. Try this out on the problems below:

(3)	(2)	(1)		*Steps*
2	1	8		
−	6	7	(1)	$-3 + 5 + 2 - 7 + 8 = 5$
	5	2	(2)	$-4 + 0 + 5 - 6 + 1 = -4$
1	0	5	(3)	$1 + 2 = 3$
−	4	3		
3	$\bar{4}$	5	= 265	

   (a) $\begin{array}{r} 507 \\ -\ 23 \\ 37 \\ -158 \\ 29 \end{array}$ (b) $\begin{array}{r} 21 \\ -\ 368 \\ 2013 \\ -\ 187 \\ -\ 96 \end{array}$ (c) $\begin{array}{r} 320 \\ -166 \\ -\ 19 \\ 285 \\ 36 \end{array}$ (d) $\begin{array}{r} 2631 \\ 507 \\ -1182 \\ 19 \\ -\ 72 \end{array}$

4. Write the complements of the following numbers:

   (a) 3   (b) 26   (c) 98   (d) 999
   (e) 20   (f) 723   (g) 2006   (h) 3276

5.   Subtract, by adding the complement:

(a)   8   (b)   64   (c)   125   *Answer:* (d)
       − 3   − 26   − 98   20342
                                                             + $\overline{1}$277
(d)   20342   (e)   8761   (f)   11823   2$\overline{1}$619
       − 723   − 2006   − 3276   = 19619

6. Carry out the subtractions in Problem 2 by the Complement Carry method. List the steps, as shown in the text example (§5).

7.* (This problem is only for students who have had considerable work with logarithms.) How may the signed digit notion be used to facilitate the handling of logarithms with negative characteristics? How is the complementary notion used in connection with cologarithms?

5

Multiplication
and Division

§1. MULTIPLYING BY DOUBLING

The Egyptians used a multiplication process which we will call **doubling and summing.**

It is easy to express any number as a sum of powers of 2. Keep in mind the way these powers ascend:

$$1, 2, 4, 8, 16, 32, 64, \ldots \quad .$$

Consider the number 27. Run along the sequence above to find the largest power of 2 which is less than 27. This is *16*. Taking 16 from 27 leaves 11. (Note that this remainder, 11, *must* be less than the power of 2 taken off, 16. Otherwise a higher power of 2 could have been subtracted.) The largest power of 2 less than 11 is *8*, and this is deducted, leaving 3. When *2* is taken from this, *1* remains. Hence.

$$27 = 16 + 8 + 2 + 1.$$

To multiply a number by 27, therefore, one may multiply it by 1, 2, 8, 16 and then sum the results. But these multiplications may be done by successive *doublings*.

Example 1.   Find 27 × 31 by doubling and summing.

Work.	*Step* 1		*Step* 2	
	27	* 1	31	31
	− 16 *	* 2	62	62
	11	4	124	
	− 8 *	* 8	248	248
	3	* 16	496	496
	− 2 *			837 (*Answer*)
	1 *			

This kind of multiplication process continued in use century by century, not disappearing until the Hindu-Arabic arithmetic quite routed the older ways. The doubling was easily performed with any type of abacus as well as with Egyptian or Roman numerals: It amounted merely to matching each numeral or abacus counter with one of the same value.

Textbooks on the history of arithmetic refer to the above method by the term "duplation." They call the variation next described, "duplation and mediation."

In medieval Europe the process usually took a form which we will call **doubling and halving.**

Example 2. Find 27 × 31 by doubling and halving.

Work.

Halve on this side				*Double on this side*
Discard remainders.	* 27	31	31	
Star (*) each odd	* 13	62	62	Add where the stars
number.	6	124		are.
	* 3	248	248	
	* 1	496	496	
			837	

This method is based upon the principle that if one factor of a product is halved while the other is doubled, the result is unchanged. In the above work, for example, 6 × 124 = 3 × 248. It would be true that 27 × 31 = 1 × 496 = 496 were it not that there are losses along the way. Because 27 is an odd number, in proceeding from 27 × 31 to 13 × 62, a 31 term is lost. A 62 term is lost in passing from 13 × 62 to 6 × 124. The rule of starring the odd numbers (on the left) and adding where the stars are (on the right) restores the lost parts of the product.

Russian peasants were still using the doubling and halving scheme at the time of World War I.

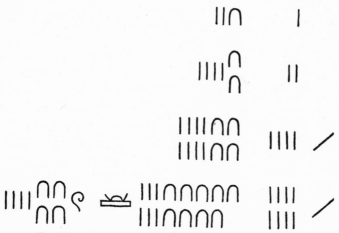

Fig. 23 An Egyptian Multiplication: 12 × 12 = 144

Can you decipher the above? It is a hieroglyphic rendition of work from Problem No. 32 of the Rhind papyrus (Peet edition), as cited on page 18 of Science Awakening, by B. L. Van Der Waerden, Noordhoff, Holland, 1954. The "sealed scroll" hieroglyph on the bottom line is an answer indicator.

PROBLEM SET 1 (§1)

In Problems 1–15, perform each multiplication
  (a) *By "Doubling and Summing,"*
  (b) *By "Doubling and Halving."*

1. 4×13	**2.** 5×13	**3.** 6×13	**4.** 7×13
5. 8×13	**6.** 9×13	**7.** 10×13	**8.** 12×27
9. 15×35	**10.** 21×34	**11.** 36×52	**12.** 75×216
13. 192×373	**14.** 219×405	**15.** 648×2341	

16. Explain in detail why the Doubling and Halving method works correctly
in each following case:

  (a) 8×42 (b) 9×42 (c) 10×42 (d) 13×42

§2. SCRATCH METHOD

Indian and European *scratch* methods of multiplying came in various
arrangements. We show here successive stages in the multiplication of
2417 by 362. The order of work is always from left to right. In the first
stage each digit of 2417 is multiplied by 3, and the result continuously
cumulated:

In the above, the units place is over the 2 of the 362, so that in actuality
2417 has been multiplied by 300, with the result 725100. Next comes the
multiplication by 60. To get the partial products in their correct place-
value positions, the 2417 is written one place further to the right.

Another shift of the 2417, and we are ready to multiply by 2.

The final answer is read over the top of the completed work: 874,954.

Although this scratch multiplication process appears formidable at first glance, it is really not difficult and is reasonably rapid. The reader will recall that the European scratches correspond to Hindu *erasures*. When a Hindu finished the multiplication exercise above, the *only* figures showing on his dust board were the answer digits 874954. He *had* to keep a cumulative result in order to accommodate the work on his tiny board.

PROBLEM SET 2 (§2)

Perform each multiplication by the scratch method.

1.	23 × 31	4.	67 × 528	7.	412 × 3526
2.	42 × 37	5.	231 × 824	8.	235 × 3708
3.	43 × 302	6.	322 × 794	9.	5218 × 32764

§3. GRATING METHOD

In sharp contrast to the scratch method, with its cumulative progress toward the product, stands the **grating** method, in which the digital products are separately set down, then added to give the answer. The method received its name because the computation was done in a framework resembling a window grating, *gelosia* in Italian (French, *jalousie*).

The "grating" is a rectangle ruled into cells by evenly spaced vertical and horizontal lines. A set of diagonals is drawn dividing the cells in twain. The number to be multiplied is written across the top and the multiplier down the right side, as shown below for the example 362 × 2417. Each digital product is written in a cell, with the units in the lower portion and the tens, if any, in the upper. Addition takes place along diagonal strips from right to left, just as though the strips were vertical columns.

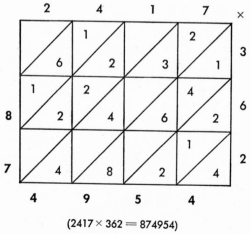

(2417 × 362 = 874954)

The grating method is quick and easy once the grating is drawn. But for this last handicap, it might have become our present process.

Besides those which we have described, a variety of other multiplication methods have been used in Europe and in other parts of the world. Our modern process first appeared in print in an Italian text dated 1470. Its general adoption was not rapid, as may be judged by the fact that an American text published in 1710 treated multiplication by a scratch method.

§4. MULTIPLICATION: ANALYSIS

Why do the grating and scratch methods of multiplication work? Using our knowledge of numeral structure, we can break down a multiplication into its smallest "atoms": the products of the digit values. Consider 23 × 456. Write 23 in the form $2T + 3U$, where T stands for "Tens," U for "Units." Applying the commutative, associative, and distributive laws as needed, we find:

$$
\begin{aligned}
23 \times 456 &= (2T + 3U) \times 456 \\
&= 2T \times 456 \quad + \quad 3U \times 456 \\
&= 2T \times (4H + 5T + 6U) \quad + \quad 3U \times (4H + 5T + 6U) \\
&= (2 \times 4)(T \times H) + (2 \times 5)(T \times T) + (2 \times 6)(T \times U) \\
&\quad + (3 \times 4)(U \times H) + (3 \times 5)(U \times T) + (3 \times 6)(U \times U)
\end{aligned}
$$

Evidently a product can be found by summing all the possible digital products (digit of one number times digit of the other), provided each of these is given an appropriate place value. It is left to the student to show how the geometry of the grating framework ensures the correct placement. (The analysis will be simpler if the cells are not split by diagonals. This modification just makes the final adding simpler, and is easily justified by a separate argument.)

Performing a multiplication according to some systematic scheme reduces the possibility of error, especially the error of omitting some digital product or placing it wrongly, and may avoid readjustments required by carries. However, it may be worth while for a student to try out a few "disorderly multiplications," as this will help him remember what is essential, and what is not, to multiplication procedures.

In the following "disorderly multiplication" of 23 × 456, the digital product 2 × 5 was put down first, its position determined by noting that the 2 and the 5 are both in T (Tens) position, so that their product will be in $T \times T = H$ (Hundreds) position:

$23 \times 456 = 10488$

TTh	Th	H	T	U
		10		
				18
			15	
			12	
		12		
	8			
	8	22	27	18
1	0	4	8	8

Left labels (read against the rows above):

2×5
3×6
3×5
2×6
3×4
2×4

PROBLEM SET 3 (§3–§4)

Perform each multiplication by the grating method.

1. 23×31
2. 42×37
3. 43×302

4. 67×528
5. 231×824
6. 322×794

7. 412×3526
8. 235×3708
9. 5218×32764

10. Analyze the following multiplications as was done at the beginning of §4, decomposing each product into digital products to which are assigned appropriate place values. (In (b), begin by replacing 43 by $4T + 3U$, etc.)

     (a) 8×324 (b) 43×87 (c) 24×563

11. Carry out a "disorderly multiplication" in these cases:

     (a) 43×87 (b) 24×563

12. Carry out a grating multiplication of 563 by 24 without drawing the diagonals through the cells. Explain how, by the geometry of the cell array, the digital products receive their proper place values (when added along diagonal directions).

13. Using the example of Problem 12, 24×563, but now putting in the diagonals, explain how this modification simplifies the work and still produces a correct result.

14. Explain why the scratch method works, in the cases (a), (b), (c) of Problem 10.

15.* Prepare a brief report on "Napier's Bones," a computational device based on the grating scheme.

§5. MODERN MULTIPLICATION

All multiplication procedures with Hindu-Arabic numerals involve the multiplication of the digits of one number by those of the other. So the child's primary task is that of learning a *multiplication table*. Ideally, this learning is not a matter of rote memory, but a lengthy cumulative process during which every multiplication "fact," like 3 × 4 = 12, is engraved upon the child's mind by his own initiative following many "discoveries" or verifications of the "fact" by counting or adding (3 × 4 = 4 + 4 + 4) as well as applications of the "fact" in a variety of situations.

The next step is that of learning how to multiply a number by a digit. Let us use 4 × 372 as an illustration. According to the distributive and associative laws,

$$4 \times 372 = 4 \times (3 \text{ Hundreds} + 7 \text{ Tens} + 2 \text{ Units})$$
$$= (4 \times 3) \text{ Hundreds} + (4 \times 7) \text{ Tens} + (4 \times 2) \text{ Units}$$

Thus to multiply a number by 4, it is only necessary to multiply its units, tens, hundreds, etc., separately by 4, and sum. There are many ways in which this may be made obvious on a concrete level. With a two-digit example, like 3 × 24, if 24 is represented by 2 bundles of ten and 4 loose matchsticks, it is plain that the tripling of the bundles and loose sticks separately results in the tripling of the whole group.

The basic idea of multiplying by one digit is therefore as follows:

4 × 372

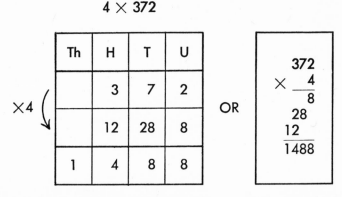

With the above exhibit as a basis, various ways of arranging a single-digit multiplication may be devised. Selecting a left-to-right direction of work leads to a scratch method. Writing down the digital products as shown, then simplifying by carries in a right-to-left direction of work, produces a grating method. If the digital products are not written until the carries are mentally added to them, then the scheme becomes our common one:

(4) (3) (2) (1)	Steps
3 7 2	(1) 4 × 2 = 8. Set 8
× 4	(2) 4 × 7 = 28. Set 8, carry ②
1 4 8 8	(3) 4 × 3 = 12. And ② gives 14.
	Set 4, carry ①
	(4) And ①. Set 1.

Once multiplication by a digit is mastered, the step to general multiplication is easy. For with our present-day method of multiplying, general multiplication is simply a summing of *partial products* found by single-digit multiplication. To keep place values straight, we shift these partial products so that their units digits line up (vertically) with the digit of the multiplier to which they belong:

```
      2 4 1 7                2 4 1 7              2 4 1 7
        3 6 2                  3 6 2                  3 6 2
      4 8 3 4      OR      1 4 5 0 2      OR      7 2 5 1
  1 4 5 0 2                  4 8 3 4          1 4 5 0 2
  7 2 5 1                7 2 5 1                  4 8 3 4
  8 7 4 9 5 4            8 7 4 9 5 4          8 7 4 9 5 4
```

Our common method, shown at the left above, possesses the virtue that all work directions, including the direction of "shift" of the partial products, are from right to left. With the method at the right, the digits of the multiplier are used in the left-to-right order, giving an arrangement useful in some special ways, as in connection with "abridged" multiplication schemes occasionally taught in upper grade or in high school courses (§12, Chapter 12). The middle arrangement is simply disorderly.

It is easy to explain any of these arrangements by filling in zeros and taking into account the numeral structure of the multiplier, as follows:

```
        2 4 1 7
    ×   3 6 2
        4 8 3 4 =     2 × 2 4 1 7
    1 4 5 0 2 0 =    6 0 × 2 4 1 7
    7 2 5 1 0 0 = 3 0 0 × 2 4 1 7
    8 7 4 9 5 4 = 3 6 2 × 2 4 1 7
```

To multiply 2417 by 362 on an abacus, use the partial-product scheme set forth above, modified as follows:

$$2 \times 2\,4\,1\,7 = 2 \times \quad 2\,4\,1\,7$$
$$6\,0 \times 2\,4\,1\,7 = 6 \times \quad 2\,4\,1\,7\,0$$
$$3\,0\,0 \times 2\,4\,1\,7 = 3 \times 2\,4\,1\,7\,0\,0$$

$$\overline{3\,6\,2 \times 2\,4\,1\,7}$$

Add

$$\left.\begin{array}{r} 2\ 4\ 1\ 7 \\ 2\ 4\ 1\ 7 \end{array}\right\} 2$$

The right-hand products are found by repeated additions. That is, 2 4 1 7 is put on the abacus twice, 2 4 1 7 0 six times, and 2 4 1 7 0 0 three times, the addition being cumulative. The work scheme to the right is thus a guide for the abacus operation. Electric calculating machines of the type used in business offices multiply according to this abacus scheme.

$$\left.\begin{array}{r} 2\ 4\ 1\ 7\ 0 \\ 2\ 4\ 1\ 7\ 0 \\ 2\ 4\ 1\ 7\ 0 \\ 2\ 4\ 1\ 7\ 0 \\ 2\ 4\ 1\ 7\ 0 \\ 2\ 4\ 1\ 7\ 0 \end{array}\right\} 6$$

$$\left.\begin{array}{r} 2\ 4\ 1\ 7\ 0\ 0 \\ 2\ 4\ 1\ 7\ 0\ 0 \\ 2\ 4\ 1\ 7\ 0\ 0 \end{array}\right\} 3$$

$$\overline{8\ 7\ 4\ 9\ 5\ 4}$$

PROBLEM SET 4 (§5)

1. Use matchsticks and bundles to demonstrate these multiplications:

    (a) 2×24 (b) 3×24 (c) 4×13 (d) 5×14

2. Use pennies, dimes, and "play money" one and ten dollar bills (or use slips of paper with 1, 10, 100, 1000 written on them) to demonstrate these multiplications:

    (a) 2×368 (b) 3×572 (c) 7×486 (d) 3×1628

3. In each case of Problem 2, multiply according to the U, T, H, Th column scheme shown in §5, then convert to ordinary numeral form by both a left-to-right and a right-to-left procedure.

4. In each case of Problem 2, multiply according to our usual procedure and list the steps of the work, as shown in §5.

5. In multiplying by a several-digit multiplier, why do we place the units digit of each partial product below the corresponding multiplier digit?

6. Multiply in the usual way, then multiply again, this time using the digits of the multiplier in left-to-right order:

    (a) 26×304 (b) 203×451 (c) 427×5136

7. "Explain" the multiplications in Problem 6 by filling out the partial products with zeros, etc., as shown in the text.

8. Set up abacus work schemes for each multiplication in Problem 6. Carry out the work on a line abacus.

§6. DIVISION

How many times does 3 "go into" 19? We may take away 3's one at a time and count the number of times, as shown at the right. This number, 6, is called the **quotient**. With the six 3's taken away, what is left of the 19 is 1, and this is called the **remainder**. By our work we have shown that

$$19 \quad = \quad 3 \times 6 \quad + \quad 1.$$

In words:

Dividend = Divisor $\times$ Quotient + Remainder.

Take
Away   19

$$6 \left\{\begin{array}{r} 3\quad 16 \\ 3\quad 13 \\ 3\quad 10 \\ 3\quad 7 \\ 3\quad 4 \\ 3\quad 1 \end{array}\right.$$

This will be referred to as the **basic division relation.**

The remainder may be zero, in which case the division is said to "come out even." It is always less than the divisor, simply because we keep taking away the divisor as long as possible:

$$0 \leqq \text{Remainder} < \text{Divisor}.$$

In practice the result of a division is often stated in quotient or fractional form:

$$\frac{19}{3} = 6 + \frac{1}{3} = 6\frac{1}{3}.$$

In words:

$$\frac{\text{Dividend}}{\text{Divisor}} = \text{Quotient} + \frac{\text{Remainder}}{\text{Divisor}}.$$

How many times does 3 go into 1900? It would be absurd to take away 3's one at a time. Why not ten at a time, or a hundred, or a thousand, . . . ? Write down some of these multiples of 3:

$$3, 30, 300, 3000, \ldots \quad .$$

Since 3000 exceeds 1900, a thousand 3's at once is too big a lump. But 300 is under, and we proceed to deduct 300's as long as we can, as shown in the work scheme at the right. With six 300's, or six hundred 3's, taken away, we can next take away 3's ten at a time, finally one at a time. In all, the number of 3's taken away is $600 + 30 + 3 = 633$. Hence the basic division relation reads:

$$1900 \quad = \quad 3 \times 633 \quad + \quad 1.$$

This *continued subtraction* method of division is an entirely feasible general process, simpler and more efficient than many division schemes used in medieval times. The subtractions are readily made on an abacus, the count of their number being kept on unused rods. This is the method used with electric calculating machines; on all but the cheapest machines the whole process is automatic.

If a bright grade-school pupil were taught this method of division, he would soon of his own accord begin to shorten the procedure. Why should he take away 300's one by one when it is apparent that six of them can be removed at one fell swoop?

At first his work might take the form shown at the left below. It should not be difficult to guide him toward the rearrangement of the work as shown in the middle, then toward the form at the right, which is the one in common use.

	Take	
	Away	1900
	300	1600
	300	1300
6	300	1000
	300	700
	300	400
	300	100
	30	70
3	30	40
	30	10
	3	7
3	3	4
	3	1

Quotient: 633
Remainder: 1

$$
\begin{array}{rr}
1900 \div 3 & \\
\hline
& 1900 \\
6 \quad -\ 1800 & \\
\hline
& 100 \\
3 \quad -\ \ 90 & \\
\hline
& 10 \\
3 \quad -\ \ \ 9 & \\
\hline
& 1
\end{array}
\qquad
\begin{array}{r}
633 \\
\hline
3\,)\overline{1900} \\
1800 \\
\hline
100 \\
90 \\
\hline
10 \\
9 \\
\hline
1
\end{array}
\qquad
\begin{array}{r}
633 \\
\hline
3\,)\overline{1900} \\
18 \\
\hline
10 \\
9 \\
\hline
10 \\
9 \\
\hline
1
\end{array}
$$

Our common arrangement is superior on several counts. Not only is unnecessary writing eliminated, but *place values of quotient digits are taken care of automatically.* In the case of 1900 ÷ 3, for example, the pupil's thinking need not be in terms of 3 into 1900, but only of 3 into 19, and next of 3 into 10 instead of 3 into 100.

The analysis applies as well when the divisor has two or more digits. Consider the division of 7707 by 24:

$$
\begin{array}{rr}
7707 \div 24 & \\
\hline
& 7707 \\
300 \times 24 = & 7200 \\
\hline
& 507 \\
20 \times 24 = & 480 \\
\hline
& 27 \\
1 \times 24 = & 24 \\
\hline
& 3
\end{array}
\qquad
\begin{array}{r}
321 \\
\hline
24\,)\overline{7707} \\
7200 \\
\hline
507 \\
480 \\
\hline
27 \\
24 \\
\hline
3
\end{array}
\qquad
\begin{array}{r}
321 \\
\hline
24\,)\overline{7707} \\
72 \\
\hline
50 \\
48 \\
\hline
27 \\
24 \\
\hline
3
\end{array}
$$

BASIC DIVISION RELATION: $7704 \ = \ 24 \times 321 \ + \ 3.$

In carrying out the work, one complication enters. To see that 3 goes into 19 six times is easy—it is a matter of mentally scanning the multiples of 3: ... $5 \times 3 = 15$, $6 \times 3 = 18$, $7 \times 3 = 21$, ... But who can rattle off the multiples of 24?

The pupil can avoid this difficulty by listing the digit multiples of the divisor (found by cumulative addition) before he begins the division. First he wishes to know how many times 24 goes into 77:

$$
\begin{array}{r}
? \\
\hline
24\,)\overline{7707}
\end{array}
$$

Multiples of 24	
1	24
2	48
3	72
4	96
5	120
6	144
7	168
8	192
9	216

Reading down the list of multiples he sees that 72 is less and 96 greater than 77, so that "24 goes 3 times." He writes:

$$
\begin{array}{r}
3 \\
\hline
24\,)\overline{7707} \\
72 \\
\hline
50
\end{array}
$$

Reading down the list again, he spots 48 as the greatest multiple less than the partial remainder of 50. So 2 is his next quotient digit.

Yet the tabulation of multiples is a cumbersome "crutch" which most pupils will hasten to discard even for nothing better than sheer guessing and the frequent correcting that will then be necessary. In the next section we will take up rules that help pupils make good guesses, or estimates, of their "trial quotient digits."

PROBLEM SET 5 (§6)

1. Perform the following divisions "physically," i.e., in the case of 19 ÷ 3, lay out 19 pennies or other objects, then remove 3 at a time, counting the number of removals to get the quotient and calling the final number left the remainder. Write the basic division relation for each case.

  (a) 19 ÷ 3   (b) 24 ÷ 4   (c) 32 ÷ 5   (d) 41 ÷ 7   (e) 30 ÷ 11
  Partial Answers: (b)   24 = 4 × 6 + 0, (d)   41 = 7 × 5 + 6

2. For each division in Problem 1, show the "continued subtraction form as displayed for 19 ÷ 3 at the beginning of §6.

3. For each division in Problem 1, use the continued subtraction form obtained in Problem 2 as an abacus work scheme, and carry out the work on a line abacus.

4. Perform these divisions as continued subtractions. Show the basic division relations found in each case.

  (a)   300 ÷ 13   (b)   736 ÷ 32   (c)   5681 ÷   13
  (d)   14864 ÷ 64   (e)   9774 ÷ 362   (f)   9900 ÷ 362

5. Carry out the divisions in Problem 4 in the usual way. Fill in zeros and show that the work is essentially the same as with the continued subtraction scheme.

6. Carry out the divisions in Problem 4 on a line abacus.

§7. ESTIMATING QUOTIENT DIGITS

The **one-step rule** is the most popular technique for estimating quotient digits.

Consider the division of 7707 by 24. We look just at the *first digit* of the divisor, 2, and ask how many times 2 goes into 7 (first digit of the dividend). The answer is 3, and this is set down as a *trial quotient digit,* as shown at the right. Next, instead of 24 into 50, we consider 2 into 5. The resulting "trial" digit, 2, is again correct, and we continue.

$$\begin{array}{r} 3 \\ \hline 24)\overline{7707} \\ 72 \\ \hline 50 \end{array}$$

In general, the quotient digit problem is one of finding how many times a given divisor goes into a temporary dividend which is *less than ten times the divisor.* In applying the one-step rule, we discard all the divisor digits after the first. We must discard just as many digits from the temporary dividend, leaving at most a two-digit number. The three possibilities, two, one, or no digits, are met in the example at the right. Our first problem is 76 into 79, and we consider 7 into 7 instead, obtaining 1. This is correct. Next we have 76 into 34. Here no rule need be used, for the quotient digit is obviously zero. Finally, we have 76 into 349, and we consider 7 into 34 instead, finding 4, which is correct.

$$
\begin{array}{r}
104 \\
76\overline{)7949} \\
76 \\
\hline
349 \\
304 \\
\hline
45
\end{array}
$$

The one-step rule gives the correct quotient digit nearly 65% of the time. Fortunately the error is one-sided. A trial digit given by the rule, if not correct, must be *too large*—and in most cases need only be reduced by 1. Here is an especially bad example: $800 \div 29$. If 29 into 80 is replaced by 2 into 8, we obtain 4. Not only this, but even 3 is too large. At the next stage, in place of 29 into 220, we consider 2 into 22. Finding 11, we automatically choose the largest possible digit, 9, as the one to be tried. Again, not only this, but even 8 is too large.

$$
\begin{array}{r}
27 \\
29\overline{)800} \\
58 \\
\hline
220 \\
203 \\
\hline
17
\end{array}
$$

Why cannot a trial digit be too small? Let us examine the situation in a numerical case, say with 24 as a divisor. Let the temporary dividend be 87. Instead of considering 24 into 87 we consider 2 into 8. This is equivalent to considering 20 into 80. But this last is equivalent to considering 20 into 87, since we can vary the units digit of the temporary dividend at will without affecting the number of times that a multiple of ten will go into it. But in dividing 87 by 20, we are dividing by a smaller number than 24, and so must obtain either the same or a larger digit quotient.

Because the one-step rule is imperfect, several modifications have been suggested. The "two-step" rule is like the one-step, except that it calls for using the digit next higher than the first digit of the divisor whenever the second digit is over 5. In dividing by 36, for example, 4 would be used throughout in place of 3.

The two-step rule works like a charm in the "bad" case of $800 \div 29$ above. But it too is imperfect. It furnishes the correct quotient digit nearly 80% of the time. When it fails, moreover, it may give either too small or too large a trial digit, depending upon whether it is the first divisor digit or the next higher one which is being used. The two-step rule is thus a potentially greater source of confusion than the one-step. Some writers have suggested a variation of the two-step rule in which the digit next higher than the first divisor digit is used only when the second divisor digit is 9.

Example 1. Divide 7029 by 36, (a) using the one-step rule, (b) using the two-step rule.

Work. The corrected work is shown at the left below, and on the appropriate lines are listed the three stages at which trial digits are found. In this case, each rule fails at two of the three stages:

	Stages	ONE-STEP RULE		TWO-STEP RULE	
		Test	*Digit*	*Test*	*Digit*
195					
36)7029 (*1*)	36 into 70	3 into 7	2 (Wrong)	4 into 7	1 (Right)
36					
342 (*2*)	36 into 342	3 into 34	9 (Right)	4 into 34	8 (Wrong)
324					
189 (*3*)	36 into 189	3 into 18	6 (Wrong)	4 into 18	4 (Wrong)
180					
9					

Instead of introducing more complicated rules, it is feasible to teach only the simple one-step rule while encouraging the pupil to spot the times when the trial quotient digit will need to be reduced and so to avoid scratching out, erasure, or other marked corrections. Only a little mental arithmetic is needed. In the case of the example, 7029 ÷ 36, the trial digits can be tested mentally as follows:

		One-Step Rule	
	Stages	*Trial Digit*	*Mental Test*
(*1*)	36 into 70	2	2 times 30 is 60, leaving 10 to go (since 70 − 60 = 10). 2 times 6 is over 10. Reduce the digit to 1.
(*2*)	36 into 342	9	9 times 30 is 270, leaving 72 to go. 9 times 6 is under 72. O.K.
(*3*)	36 into 189	6	6 times 30 is 180, leaving 9 to go. 6 times 6 is over 9. Reduce the digit to 5. (5 times 30 is 150, leaving 39. 5 times 6 is under 39. O.K.)

No matter what trial digit rules may have been introduced to aid the pupil in his early work in division, the eventual aim should be that the rules are to be put aside. Mental practice of the sort detailed above should sharpen and improve a pupil's numerical judgment to the extent that he may finally rely wholly upon it.

In the astronomical treatise known as the *Almagest*, A.D. 140, Ptolemy computed with sexagesimal numerals, employing various arithmetic techniques much like our own. His method of testing trial division digits was the reverse of ours: he *divided* the trial digit into the *dividend*, then compared the result with the divisor. Applying this scheme to the example 7029 ÷ 36, we have:

		One-Step Rule	
	Stages	*Trial Digit*	*Ptolemy's Test*
(*1*)	36 into 70	2	2 into 70 gives 35, *under* 36. Reduce digit to 1.
(*2*)	36 into 342	9	9 into 342 gives 38, *over* 36. O.K.
(*3*)	36 into 189	6	6 into 189 gives 31, under 36. Reduce to 5. 5 into 189 gives 37. O.K.

Ptolemy's method is perhaps mechanically superior to our usual method. But if both methods are regarded as "crutches," our own may be preferable because it is more direct, hence more readily discarded.

§8. DIVISION MISCELLANY

In practical application, it is sometimes the "under," sometimes the "over," and sometimes the "nearest" result of a division which furnishes the appropriate answer.

If rolls cost 5¢ each, and a customer has only 33¢, then he can buy only 6. This is an "under" result, with remainder 3, associated with the *basic* division relation:

$$\begin{array}{r} 6 \\ 5\overline{)33} \\ 30 \\ \hline 3 \end{array} \qquad 33 \;=\; 5 \times 6 \;+\; 3$$

If rolls are 5 for 33¢, and a customer wishes only one, he must pay 7¢. This is an "over" result. The remainder is *negative; −2.* The division relation is:

$$\begin{array}{r} 7 \\ 5\overline{)33} \\ 35 \\ \hline -2 \end{array} \qquad 33 \;=\; 5 \times 7 \;-\; 2$$

When the "nearest" result is needed, either the "under" or the "over" result must be chosen, whichever one involves the remainder of least "size." (The "size" or *absolute value* of a number is its "distance from zero" on the number scale. Both $+3$ and -3 have the same absolute value, 3.) With $33 \div 5$, therefore, the "nearest" result is 7. This furnishes the appropriate answer to the problem: "If 33 lb. of flour are to be distributed equally among five families, about how many pounds will each get?"

The work involved in carrying out a division may occasionally be shortened by allowing negatives to enter. Suppose that in dividing 24 into 682, the computer sets down 3 as his first quotient digit. This is "wrong," in that $3 \times 24 = 72$, which exceeds 68. $3\overline{2} = 28$
But suppose that the subtraction is carried through any-
way, as shown at the right. (Note that in order to avoid
$$\begin{array}{r} 24\overline{)682} \\ 72 \\ -38 \\ -48 \\ \hline 10 \end{array}$$
the awkward form $\overline{4}2$, the digit 2 of 682 which is to be
brought down next, is taken into account during the subtraction: 720 is taken from 682.) The partial remainder,
-38, being negative, the next quotient digit is negative,
and is written in *signed digit* notation, $\overline{2}$ instead of -2. The final quotient, $3\overline{2}$, may be converted to standard numeral form, 28.

Until a few hundred years ago, division was considered a very difficult art, and its mastery was sought only by "specialists" who needed to become skilled in computation for professional or business purposes. (In still older eras, to be sure, only the priests were adept at mathematical skills.) Today, all who are literate learn to divide. Yet we may be thankful that we need not struggle to comprehend some of the involved and complicated division techniques that were employed in medieval times in Europe. Texts on the history of mathematics describe a variety of curious historical processes.

A scratch method of division was commonly used in Europe for several centuries preceding the seventeenth. Even some American texts, one of date 1719, show the method. It was often called the "galley" method because the arrangement suggested the form of a ship. After successfully navigating the treacherous course of a problem like 297603942163 ÷ 753218, a sixteenth-century pupil frequently spent the next half-hour in decorating his work, supplying as embellishments flags, masts, and so on, even as a schoolboy may today—but with a difference: the teachers in those times often required it!

These are the successive steps in the galley division of 7704 by 24 to get the quotient 321:

$$
\begin{array}{llll}
& 1 & \overset{.}{1}5 \\
7704 \quad (& 7704 \quad (3 & 7704 \quad (3 & 7704 \quad (3 \\
24 & 24 & 2\overset{.}{4} & 2\overset{.}{4}
\end{array}
$$

$$
\begin{array}{llll}
& & 1 & \overset{.}{1} \\
\overset{.}{1}5 & \overset{.}{1}5 & \overset{.}{1}\overset{.}{5} & \overset{.}{1}\overset{.}{5}2 \\
7704 \quad (3 & 7704 \quad (32 & 7704 \quad (32 & 77\overset{.}{0}4 \quad (32 \\
2\overset{.}{4}4 & 2\overset{.}{4}4 & 2\overset{.}{4}4 & 2\overset{.}{4}4 \\
2 & 2 & 2 & 2
\end{array}
$$

$$
\begin{array}{llll}
\overset{.}{1} & \overset{.}{1} & \overset{.}{1} & \overset{.}{1} \\
\overset{.}{1}\overset{.}{5}2 & \overset{.}{1}\overset{.}{5}2 & \overset{.}{1}\overset{.}{5}2 & \overset{.}{1}\overset{.}{5}2 \\
77\overset{.}{0}4 \quad (32 & 77\overset{.}{0}4 \quad (321 & 77\overset{.}{0}4 \quad (321 & 77\overset{.}{0}4 \quad (321 \\
2\overset{.}{4}\overset{.}{4}4 & 2\overset{.}{4}\overset{.}{4}4 & 2\overset{.}{4}\overset{.}{4}4 & 2\overset{.}{4}\overset{.}{4}4 \\
2\overset{.}{2} & 2\overset{.}{2} & 2\overset{.}{2} & 2\overset{.}{2}
\end{array}
$$

On the first row, 3 × 24(00) is deducted from 7704, leaving 504. This is done by first deducting 3 × 2(000), leaving 1704, then taking off 3 × 4(00) more, leaving 504. On the second row, 2 × 24(0) is deducted from 504, leaving 24. On the third row, 1 × 24 is deducted from 24, leaving a remainder of 0. Despite the unusual arrangement, the general scheme of the galley method is therefore much like our own.

PROBLEM SET 6 (§7–§8)

In Problems 1–6, carry out each division (a) using the one-step rule, (b) using the two-step rule. Show each stage of the work, etc., as in the Example of §7. Then do the divisions again (c) *using the one-step rule, aided by mental testing of the trial quotient digits.*

1.   300 ÷ 13   2.   736 ÷ 32   3.   5681 ÷ 13
4.   14864 ÷ 64   5.   9774 ÷ 362   6.   9900 ÷ 362

7. Using the case 820 ÷ 23 in illustration, discuss why a trial digit found by the one-step rule cannot be too small.

8. Using the case 820 ÷ 28 in illustration, discuss why a trial digit found by the two-step rule, in the case in which the first divisor digit is increased, cannot be too large.

9. In each case, find the quotient by "nearest" division, tell whether the result is "over" or "under," and write out the associated division relation:

(a)   25 ÷ 4   (b)   27 ÷ 4   (c)   40 ÷ 11
(d)   135 ÷ 20   (e)   62 ÷ 26   (f)   22 ÷ 4

10.* Do the divisions in Problems 1–6 using the one-step rule and applying Ptolemy's division method of testing the trial digits.

11–16.* Do the divisions in Problems 1–6 by the scratch method.

6

Twelves
and Twos

§1. NUMBER SCALES

A tribe living along the Belyando River in Australia counts like this:

1.	wogin	3.	booleroo wogin	$(= 2 + 1)$
2.	booleroo	4.	booleroo booleroo	$(= 2 + 2)$

Had a tribesman occasion to count beyond four, he might continue with *booleroo booleroo wogin, booleroo booleroo booleroo*. In the Torres Straits a tribe does count to six in just such a way, using *urapan* and *okasa* for "one" and "two"; this tribe calls anything larger than six, *ras*, which might be translated as "a lot of."

Since these numbering schemes involve counting by twos, they may be regarded as on a binary scale. They are scarcely worthy of being termed numeral "systems," being little more than devices of abbreviation (*booleroo* instead of *wogin wogin*) and not involving *powers* of a base. In the latter part of this chapter, we will study the structure and operation of a true *base two*, or *binary system*.

An Australian tribe called the *Kamilaroi* counts on a mixed binary-ternary scale:

1.	mal	4.	bular bular	$(= 2 + 2)$
2.	bular	5.	bular guliba	$(= 2 + 3)$
3.	guliba	6.	guliba guliba	$(= 3 + 3)$

The Luli of Paraguay have a mixed scheme:

1.	alapea	2.	tamop	3.	tamlip	4. lokep

5.	lokep moile alapea (*or* is alapea)	$(= 4 + 1$ or 1 hand)
6.	lokep moile tamep	$(= 4 + 2)$
7.	lokep moile tamlip	$(= 4 + 3)$
8.	lokep moile lokep	$(= 4 + 4)$
9.	lokep moile lokep alapea	$(= 4 + 4 + 1)$
10.	is yaoum	(both hands)

11.	is yaoum moile alapea	(hands + 1)
20.	is eln yaoum	(hands, feet)
30.	is eln yaoum moile is yaoum	(hands, feet, hands)

Here may be noted an initial preference for counting by fours. But once ten is reached, the scale of ten thereafter dominates.

A wide variety of number bases have been found in current use in obscure portions of the world. (See *The Number Concept*, by L. L. Conant, Macmillan, New York, 1896.) The scales come in twos, threes, fours, sixes, eights, tens—even in twenties and sixties, if some systems of older times are included (Mayan, Babylonian). All well-developed systems, however, have placed special emphasis on *ten*. Most, like our own, have been wholly based on ten.

Much has been written to tell how the evolutionary development of the human hand, with its opposed thumb, has spurred the cultural growth of man—how hand and brain have joined to create our human way of life. That our number scales mirror our hands is but one token of the profound respect we have for these, our basic tools, the fingers of our hands.

Insofar as our number scale is concerned, it may therefore be unfortunate that we have ten fingers rather than six or eight or twelve. A system based on any of these numbers would be superior to our tens, or decimal, system. A preference for bases other than ten may be discerned among our scales of weights and measures.

There are *twelve* inches in a foot, and we commonly use *two*, *four*, *eight*, or *sixteen* divisions of the inch. Quantities are often purchased by the *dozen* or by the *gross*. The ordinary pound has *sixteen* ounces. Liquid volume measures go by *twos*; cup (half-pint), pint, quart, half-gallon, gallon.

The arithmetic of everyday life, used by the housewife, the baker, the carpenter, etc., would be substantially simpler if our number scale and our measurement scales agreed. Various reformists have urged the legislation of such agreement, usually arguing that the United States should adopt the *metric* system of measure. Some groups would have us change the number system instead, basing it on the twelve or *duodecimal* scale.

§2. COUNTING BY TWELVES

It is excellent training for a future teacher to practice simple arithmetical computation in different number scales. The work may help him spot gaps in his understanding and application of the common arithmetical processes. Further, it may give him useful insight into the kinds of difficulties that will later trouble his own pupils as they too learn to use a system unfamiliar to *them*. What is more, it is *fun* to deal with strange arithmetics—to add 7 and 9 and get 14, to divide 40 by 8 and get 6.

The building blocks used in forming our decimal numerals are the ten digits: 0, 1, 2, 3, 4, 5, 6, 7, 8, 9. In counting, we begin with 1 and name the digits in order up to the last, 9. We *construct* a symbol for the next number, writing "10" and interpreting this to mean "1 Ten plus 0 Units." Continuing, we write "11" for "1 Ten plus 1 Unit," etc.

In the **duodecimal** or **dozen** system, there are *twelve digits*. It is convenient to use our usual names for these: zero, one, two, . . . , nine, ten, eleven. But we need two extra digit symbols. Rather than to devise new typographical forms that might be hard to remember, we choose T for *ten* and E for *eleven*, so that the twelve duodecimal digits become:

$$0, 1, 2, 3, 4, 5, 6, 7, 8, 9, T, E.$$

We now name the next number *dozen*, and write it as "10" (read "one – oh" and *not* "ten"), meaning "1 Dozen plus 0 Units." Similarly, "11" (read "one – one") means "1 Dozen plus 1 Unit." We continue counting systematically:

$$12 = 1 \text{ Dozen} + 2 \text{ Units} = \text{Tens Number } 14$$
$$13 = 1 \text{ Dozen} + 3 \text{ Units} = \text{Tens Number } 15$$
$$\cdot \quad \cdot \quad \cdot \quad \cdot \quad \cdot$$
$$19 = 1 \text{ Dozen} + 9 \text{ Units} = \text{Tens Number } 21$$
$$1T = 1 \text{ Dozen} + T \text{ Units} = \text{Tens Number } 22$$
$$1E = 1 \text{ Dozen} + E \text{ Units} = \text{Tens Number } 23$$
$$20 = 2 \text{ Dozen} + 0 \text{ Units} - \text{Tens Number } 24$$
$$\cdot \quad \cdot \quad \cdot \quad \cdot \quad \cdot$$
$$99 = 9 \text{ Dozen} + 9 \text{ Units} = \text{Tens Number } 117$$
$$9T = 9 \text{ Dozen} + T \text{ Units} = \text{Tens Number } 118$$
$$9E = 9 \text{ Dozen} + E \text{ Units} = \text{Tens Number } 119$$
$$T0 = T \text{ Dozen} + 0 \text{ Units} = \text{Tens Number } 120$$
$$\cdot \quad \cdot \quad \cdot \quad \cdot \quad \cdot$$
$$EE = E \text{ Dozen} + E \text{ Units} = \text{Tens Number } 143$$
$$100 = \qquad 1 \text{ Gross} \qquad = \text{Tens Number } 144$$
$$\cdot \quad \cdot \quad \cdot \quad \cdot \quad \cdot$$
$$EEE = E \text{ Gross} + E \text{ Dozen} + E \text{ Units} = \text{Tens Number } 1727$$
$$1000 = \quad 1 \text{ Great Gross} \quad = \text{Tens Number } 1728$$

It is vital to realize just what these equalities signify—that a twelves system user, for example, in writing "*1E*" is referring to the *same natural number* as is the tens system user who writes "23." If the two of them are both counting simultaneously along a line of people, the "twelves" counter will be saying "*One – E*" at the same time the "tens" counter is saying "*Twenty – Three*," and both of them will be pointing at the same person in the line.

§3. CONVERSION BETWEEN SCALES

It is easy to find the tens number that corresponds to a given dozen-system number. Each digit in the dozens number has a value by virtue of its position in the number. Thus according to the dozen system:

$$3T07E \quad = \quad 3 \times 10000 \quad + \quad T \times 1000 \quad + \quad 0 \times 100$$
$$+ \quad 7 \times 10 \quad + \quad E \times 1$$

To convert to tens, just re-express these values in the tens system, and sum:

Twelves			Tens		
$E \times 1$	=	$11 \times$	1	=	11
7×10	=	$7 \times$	12	=	84
0×10^2	=	$0 \times$	144	=	0
$T \times 10^3$	=	$10 \times$	1728	=	17280
3×10^4	=	$3 \times$	20736	=	62208
					79583

∴   Twelves No. 3T07E = Tens No. 79583.

A tens number may be converted to a twelves number by a similar procedure, but the re-expression of values is more difficult (10 replaced by T, 100 by 84, etc.), and the subsequent work has to be carried out within the dozen system. Hence the following division scheme is preferable.

A small tens number may be converted to a twelves number by grouping it into dozens and units. How many dozens are there in 41? This is a simple division problem. There are three dozen, and five units left over:

$$
\begin{array}{r}
3 \\
12\overline{)41} \\
36 \\
\hline
5
\end{array}
\qquad \therefore \quad 41 \quad = \quad 3 \times 12 \quad + \quad 5.
$$

∴   Tens No. 41 = Twelves No. 35.

Consider the tens number 524. Division by 12 shows:

$$524 \quad = \quad 43 \times 12 \quad + \quad 8.$$

We must separate out groups of twelve 12's from the 43. Dividing 43 by 12 shows:

$$43 \quad = \quad 3 \times 12 \quad + \quad 7.$$

Hence:

$$524 \quad = \quad 3 \times 144 \quad + \quad 7 \times 12 \quad + \quad 8.$$

$$\therefore \quad \text{Tens No. } 524 = \text{Twelves No. } 378.$$

The work may be conveniently arranged in successive division form as follows:

```
12)524
  12)43    8 │ Read the answer up
    12)3    7 │ along this column
      0     3 │ of remainders
```

The given tens number is divided by 12, the quotient being written below and the remainder at its right. The operation is repeated upon that quotient, and the work goes on until a zero quotient is reached. The column of remainders, *read upward*, gives the corresponding twelves number. Note how in the example at the right the original 11 and 10 remainders had to be rewritten as the twelves system digits E and T.

```
12)79583
  12)6631    E
    12)552    7
      12)46    0
        12)3    T
          0     3
```

Answer: 3T07E

PROBLEM SET 1 (§1–§3)

1. Cite some examples of measurement scales involving groups of twenties.

2. Sets of measuring spoons used by housewives follow what scale?

3. The *Ngarrimowro* (Australia) count on a binary scale, their number names for one and two being *warrangen* and *platir*. How do they say "three" and "four"? Check your answer on page 110 of Conant's *The Number Concept*.

4. What scale is associated with the sequence of time units, *second, minute, hour?* With the sequence of angle units, *second, minute, degree?*

5. What scale is associated with our sequence of (large) number names, *thousand, million, billion, trillion, quadrillion,* etc.? With the sequence used by the British, *million, billion, trillion,* etc.?

6. What scale is used by radio engineers in the sequence, *cycle, kilocycle, megacycle?* Also, *microwatt, milliwatt, watt, kilowatt?*

7. Mentally convert the tens number 40 to a twelves number. *Hint:* 36 is 3 dozen, so 40 is 3 dozen plus 4. *Answer:* 34

8. Same as Problem 7 for the tens numbers 29, 33, 34, 35, 36, 100, 120, 132, 144, 154, 300. *Last Answer:* 210

9. Check your answers in Problem 8 by the division method of the text.

10. Convert the following twelves numbers to tens numbers: 57, 6T, 2E6, T0E. *Answers:* 67, 82, 426, 1451

11. Convert the following twelves numbers to tens numbers: 7T016, T000, TTT, 375E. *Last Answer:* 6263

12. Convert the following tens numbers to twelves numbers: 1953, 20000, 5754, 1000000.   *Last Two Answers:* 33E6, 402854

13.* Construct a table of multiples of T in the twelve system (1 × T = T; 2 × T = T + T = 10 + 8 = 18; 3 × T = 2 × T + T = 18 + T = 20 + 6 = 26; . . . ; E × T = 92). Using this table, convert the twelves numbers 57 and 6T to tens numbers by the division method. (*Hint:* Divide each by T.)

§4. DUODECIMAL ARITHMETIC

Digits may easily be added mentally. Consider 7 + 9. Either of the following methods may be used:

METHOD A	METHOD B
Add in Tens System and convert:	Group into Dozens and Units:
7 + 9 = Tens No. 16	7 + 9 = (7 + 5) + 4
= 1 Dozen + 4 = 14	= 1 Dozen + 4 = 14

Knowing how to add digits, we may add dozens numbers of any size by our common adding procedure:

(*5*) (*4*) (*3*) (*2*) (*1*)		*Steps*	
7 E T 3 2	(*1*)	3 + 2 = 5.	Set 5.
+ 5 1 9 3	(*2*)	9 + 3 = 1 Dozen = 10.	Set 0, carry ①.
8 5 0 0 5	(*3*)	① + 1 + T = 1 Dozen = 10.	Set 0, carry ①.
	(*4*)	① + 5 + E = 1 Dozen + 5 = 15.	Set 5, carry ①.
	(*5*)	① + 7 = 8.	Set 8

We may subtract by any common procedure. The Take-Away Borrow method is used in the following example:

(*3*) (*2*) (*1*)		*Steps*	
2 3 6	(*1*)	16 − 9 = (1 Dozen − 9) + 6 = 3 + 6 = 9.	
− T 9	(*2*)	12 − T = (1 Dozen − T) + 2 = 2 + 2 = 4.	
1 4 9	(*3*)	1 − 0 =	1.

For efficient multiplication and division, a multiplication table is needed. This is supplied here. However, the student would do well to make his own, to ensure that he understands its construction. Successive addition may be used. To list the multiples of 8, for example, add 8 to 8 to get 2 × 8 = 14. Add 8 to this to get 3 × 8 = 20, etc., up to E × 8 = 74.

In the illustrative examples that follow, the corresponding tens-system problems are also shown. In problem assignments, the student may be asked to check his work by "converting to tens numbers," as this will give him practice in converting and in comparing the tens and twelves expressions, and will also serve to bolster his confidence in the correctness of the work.

MULTIPLICATION TABLE: BASE TWELVE

	1	2	3	4	5	6	7	8	9	T	E	
1	1	2	3	4	5	6	7	8	9	T	E	1
2		4	6	8	T	10	12	14	16	18	1T	2
3			9	10	13	16	19	20	23	26	29	3
4				14	18	20	24	28	30	34	38	4
5					21	26	2E	34	39	42	47	5
6						30	36	40	46	50	56	6
7							41	48	53	5T	65	7
8								54	60	68	74	8
9									69	76	83	9
T										84	92	T
E											T1	E
	1	2	3	4	5	6	7	8	9	T	E	

Example 1. 23×78.

Work.

$$
\begin{array}{r}
78 \\
\times\,23 \\
\hline
1E0 \\
134 \\
\hline
1530
\end{array}
\qquad\qquad
\begin{array}{r}
\textit{Tens Numbers} \\
92 \\
\times\,27 \\
\hline
644 \\
184 \\
\hline
2484
\end{array}
$$

To get 3×78: According to the multiplication table, $3 \times 8 = 20$. Put down 0 and carry ②. Again, $3 \times 7 = 19$. Add the carried ②, getting 1E, which is put down. The other partial product, $2 \times 78 = 134$ (in actual value, 1340), is found in the same way, and the two values are added.

Example 2. $290E5 \div 57$.

Work.

$$
\begin{array}{r}
5E1 \\
57\overline{)290E5} \\
23E \\
\hline
51E \\
515 \\
\hline
65 \\
57 \\
\hline
T
\end{array}
\qquad\qquad
\begin{array}{r}
\textit{Tens Numbers} \\
853 \\
67\overline{)57161} \\
536 \\
\hline
356 \\
335 \\
\hline
211 \\
201 \\
\hline
10
\end{array}
$$

To estimate how many times 57 will go into 290, apply the one-step rule, testing 5 into 29. According to the multiplication table, $6 \times 5 = 26$, and $7 \times 5 = 2E$. So 6 is taken as a trial quotient digit. But $6 \times 57 = 296$, which is more than 290. The correct digit is 5. Subtracting $5 \times 57 = 23E$ from 290 gives 51, and the E is brought down. The work continues, in the pattern of our usual division procedure.

A duodecimal abacus is easily made, in either rod or line form. The rod abacus bears eleven or twelve beads on each rod (just as the usual simple abacus bears nine or ten). The line abacus is our former one, unchanged: a sheet ruled with several lines marked with the values 1, 10, 100, etc. (i.e., one, dozen, gross, etc.). The new rule for the line abacus is: A dozen counters on a line are equivalent to a single counter on the line above.

Illustration

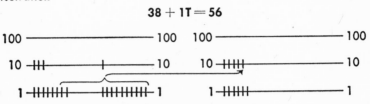

$$38 + 1T = 56$$

*§5. DUODECIMAL FRACTIONS

When the numbers involved in an arithmetical problem have many divisors (factors), the work is likely to go nicely, with "cancellations" and other handy simplifications. Expressions containing numbers like 6, 8, 12 reduce more easily than if the numbers are like 7, 11, 13.

It is especially advantageous for the number system itself to have a base with many divisors. Besides 1 and itself, twelve has four divisors: 2, 3, 4, 6. Ten has only two: 2, 5. Arithmetic in the dozen system is therefore generally easier than in the tens system. In particular, it is much easier to handle the simple fractions that so frequently turn up in the day-by-day use of arithmetic (in kitchen, store, shop, office, and easy-chair) when the base-twelve system is used.

"Thirds" are especially nasty to deal with in the tens system. A third of a dollar does not come out even, being 33 cents, to the nearest cent. But a third of a dozens-system "dollar" would be exactly 40¢, since $3 \times 40 = 100$. A half-dollar and a quarter-dollar would be 60¢ and 30¢, respectively. Here are duodecimal equivalents for some common fractions:

$.1 = \frac{1}{10}$	$.4 = \frac{1}{3}$	$.16 = \frac{1}{8}$
$.2 = \frac{1}{6}$	$.6 = \frac{1}{2}$	$.09 = \frac{1}{14}$
$.3 = \frac{1}{4}$	$.8 = \frac{2}{3}$	$.046 = \frac{1}{28}$

The rightmost column shows the equivalents corresponding to the usual ruler graduation into eighths, sixteenths, and thirty-secondths. The corresponding decimals are: $\frac{1}{8} = .125$, $\frac{1}{16} = .0625$, $\frac{1}{32} = .03125$.

PROBLEM SET 2 (§4–§5)

In Problems 1–22, every number is written as a base-twelve numeral. Carry out the indicated computations. For practice in conversion, check your work as follows: Convert the given numbers to base ten and do the indicated computation. Convert this base-ten result to base twelve and compare with your former answer.

1.	4E + T5	5.	70T − T5
2.	305 + 70T	6.	214 − T5
3.	1072 + 19ET8	7.	19ET8 − 70T
4.	19ET8 + 7ET04	8.	7ET04 − 19ET8
9.	4E × T5	16.	4E ÷ 5
10.	4E × 214	17.	T5 ÷ 5
11.	T5 × 19ET8	18.	214 ÷ 4E
12.	214 × 70T	19.	1072 ÷ 214
13.	214 × 19ET8	20.	19ET8 ÷ 4E
14.	70T × 19ET8	21.	19ET8 ÷ T5
15.	70T × 7ET04	22.	19ET8 ÷ 214

23. As directed, carry out the computations in Problems 1–22 on a twelve-system line abacus.

24.* Write the duodecimals .1, .2, .3, .4, .5, .6, .7, .8, .9, .T, .E as twelve-system fractions in lowest terms.   *Last Two Answers:* 5/6; E/10

25.* As in Problem 24 for .01, .02, .03, .04, .05, .06, .07, .08, .09, .0T, .0E.
        Last Two Answers: 5/60; E/100

26.* Convert the twelve-system fractions 1/8, 1/14, 1/28, 1/54, 1/T8 (each half the preceding) to duodecimal form by long division.   *Last Answer:* .0116

§6. THE BINARY SYSTEM (BASE TWO)

The one disadvantage of the dozen system with respect to the tens system is that two extra digits are needed. Instead of a 10 by 10 addition table with $10 \times 10 = 100$ entries, or "addition facts," a 12 by 12 table with 144 entries must be learned.

On the small side of ten, 6 and 8 are good candidates for bases. The resulting *hexal* and *octal* number systems are both superior to the decimal system. How small a base may be used? There can be no "base one" system, for this would have the single digit 0, from which no positive number could be constructed. The *base two* or *binary* system is thus the extreme possibility.

The only digits in the binary system are 0 and 1, so that the basic tables become nearly trivial:

Addition

	0	1
0	0	1
1	1	10

Multiplication

	0	1
0	0	0
1	0	1

In other words, for binary arithmetic a pupil need learn, besides the usual zero properties, only the two "facts"

$$1 + 1 = 10 \quad \text{and} \quad 1 \times 1 = 1$$

So ultrasimple is the binary system that even *counting* in it is apt at first to be confusing. For no sooner is the *first* digit, 0, passed then the *last* digit, 1, is met, whereupon a change of form to two places, 10, is at once in order. The number following 1111 is 10000, just as in the tens system 9999 is followed by 10000.

The first sixteen binary numbers are:

1.	1	5.	101	9.	1001	13.	1101
2.	10	6.	110	10.	1010	14.	1110
3.	11	7.	111	11.	1011	15.	1111
4.	100	8.	1000	12.	1100	16.	10000

The rules for converting from base two to base ten, and vice versa, are like the ones used with base twelve. Binary place values are *powers of two;* 1, 2, 4, 8, ... At the left below is shown the conversion of the binary numeral 1011001 into the equivalent tens numeral 89. At the right is shown the reverse conversion, from 89 to 1011001, accomplished through successive division by 2.

1	$\times$	1	=	1	2)89		
0	$\times$	2			2)44	1	
0	$\times$	4			2)22	0	
1	$\times$	8	=	8	2)11	0	
1	$\times$	16	=	16	2)5	1	
0	$\times$	32			2)2	1	
1	$\times$	64	=	64	2)1	0	
				89	0	1	

A binary rod abacus needs only one bead per rod, but needs quite a few rods. For the line abacus, the rule is: A pair of counters on a line is equivalent to a single counter on the line above.

Adding a column of binary numbers is a bit tricky, because column sums are likely to be three-digit numbers:

(8)	(7)	(6)	(5)	(4)	(3)	(2)	(1)
		1	0	1	1	0	1
		1	1	0	1	1	
		1	0	1	1	0	
	1	0	0	1	1	1	
		1	1	1	0		
1	0	0	1	0	0	1	1

Steps

(1)   1 plus 1 gives 10, plus 1 gives 11. Set 1; carry ①.

(2)   ① plus 1 gives 10, plus 1 gives 11, plus 1 gives 100, plus 1 gives 101. Set 1; carry ⑩.

(3)   ⑩ plus 1 gives 11, plus 1 gives 100, plus 1 gives 101, plus 1 gives 110. Set 0; carry ⑪.

Etc.

(The corresponding tens problem is: 45 + 27 + 22 + 39 + 14 = 147.)

In *dividing* binary numbers, there is no need to estimate trial quotient digits: The divisor either "goes" or it doesn't, *period*. For the example at the right, the corresponding tens problem is 656 ÷ 26 (quotient 25, remainder 6).

```
              11001
      ───────────────
11010)1010010000
       11010
      ───────
        11110
        11010
       ───────
       100000
        11010
        ───────
          110
```

The distinguished mathematician and philosopher Gottfried Wilhelm Leibniz (1646–1716) seriously urged that we discard the decimal system in favor of the binary. Were we to do this, children would romp through arithmetic in the early grades, and long division would no longer be a "bogie" for them. But new troubles would come to plague them later. It is tedious to read and to write lengthy binary numbers, and it is easy to mix up the 0's and 1's. In commerce and industry, large numbers are constantly handled: sums of money, production figures, etc. Suppose that in making the change-over, we were to take for our binary "dollar" the amount which we now call 64¢. In that case, the sum now written $155,963.49 would appear on the books as

$$\$111,011,011,111,101,100.111101$$

We should have to build new wings on our asylums to house schizophrenic bookkeepers.

Leibniz was intrigued by his own mystical interpretation of the binary system. He glimpsed in it the "image of Creation": the Universe symbolically fashioned from the Void (0) by the Supreme Being (1 = Unity). This metaphysical enchantment lured him to advocate the binary system despite its practical shortcomings.

PROBLEM SET 3 (§6)

1. Convert these binary numbers to base ten:

(a)	101	(e)	10011001
(b)	1001	(f)	1100101001
(c)	1111	(g)	1111111111
(d)	10100	(h)	10000000000

Answers: (f) 809, (g) 1023, (h) 1024

2. A small tens number can readily be converted mentally to base two, by the procedure used with the Egyptian doubling and summing method to express a number as a sum of powers of 2. Thus 21 = 16 + 4 + 1. Hence its binary representation is 10101. Try this scheme with the tens numbers 6, 10, 13, 18, 19, 35, 50.

3. Use the division process to find the base-two numbers corresponding to the following tens numbers:

(a)	19	(e)	100	(h)	572
(b)	35	(f)	1000	(i)	573
(c)	50	(g)	10000	(j)	574
(d)	61				

Answer: (j)   1000111110

In Problems 4–17, every number is written as a binary numeral. Carry out the indicated computations. Check as directed.

4.
```
     101
    1000
    1010
 +  1101
```

5.
```
     1010
     1101
    10110
 + 101000
```

6.
```
     1101
   101100
  1001011
+ 1101000
```

7.
```
   1101
 - 1010
```

8.
```
   10100
 -  1101
```

9.
```
  1101000
 -1000001
```

10. 101×1101
11. 1011×1101
12. 1101×101010
13. 1101×1101000

14. $1010 \div 101$
15. $1101 \div 101$
16. $101000 \div 1011$
17. $1000001 \div 101$

18. As directed, carry out the computations in Problems 4–17 on a base-two line abacus.

19.* Just as a base-ten fraction has a decimal form ($\frac{1}{4} = .25$, for example), so a binary fraction has a "duocimal" form. Corresponding to the base-ten fractions $\frac{1}{4}$, $\frac{1}{2}$, $\frac{3}{4}$ are the binary fractions $\frac{1}{100}$, $\frac{1}{10}$, $\frac{11}{100}$, with duocimal forms .01, .1, .11, respectively. What duocimal forms correspond to the tens-system fractions $\frac{1}{8}$, $\frac{2}{8}$, $\frac{3}{8}$, $\frac{4}{8}$, $\frac{5}{8}$, $\frac{6}{8}$, $\frac{7}{8}$?   *Last Answer:* .111

§7. APPLICATIONS OF BINARY NUMBERS

The applications of binary numbers are many and varied. They are used in statistical investigations and in problems involving probabilities. They facilitate the analysis and explanation of the strategy and play of various simple games and puzzles. They are sometimes used in proving theorems of pure mathematics. They are put to more plebian use by the giant electronic "brains" of today, which compute in terms of them, and which speed calculations to solve in hours scientific and industrial problems that once took years.

Many important events and decisions in everyday life and in social, industrial, or scientific work depend upon successive dual choices of alternatives: "yes" or "no," "on" or "off," "present" or "absent," etc. The two choices may be symbolized by 0 and 1, respectively. A succession of choices then generates a binary number. Thus the coin-tossing sequence *head, head, tail, tail, tail, head, tail* could be coded as 1100010. A transformation of this sort may greatly simplify the analysis of a problem.

Example 1. How many subsets has a set of five objects?

Work. Let the objects be thought of as numbered 1, 2, 3, 4, 5, and associated with the five boxes so labeled below:

Any particular subset can now be coded as follows: If the subset contains Object No. 1, write 1 in Box No. 1; if the subset does not contain Object No. 1, write 0 in Box No. 1. Likewise, write 1 or 0 in Box No. 2 according as Object No. 2 is or is not an element of the subset. Continue. The resulting sequence of 1's and 0's is a binary number, like 10110 or 00101 (= 101). The various subsets, empty set included, are thus matched with the binary numbers from 0 to 11111, inclusive. Add 1 at each end: 1 to 100000. Hence the number of subsets is 100000. In tens-system notation this is $2^5 = 32$.

A monetary system is based upon some smallest or unit coin (penny) and certain other coins or "denominations" that are multiples of the unit (nickel, quarter, ten-dollar bill, etc.). With an efficiently arranged system, a person should not have to carry many coins in order to take care of his everyday transactions. There must be neither too few nor too many denominations.

The most efficient scheme is the binary, with coins of value 1, 2, 4, 8, 16, 32, 64, etc. With it, any given amount can be put together using no more than one coin of each denomination. Suppose that an amount of 89¢ is needed. The binary number that corresponds to 89 is 1011001. Hence

$$89 = 1 + 8 + 16 + 64,$$

so that the four coins having these values make up the required sum. (In a true decimal system, with denominations 1, 10, 100, etc., $8 + 9 = 17$ coins would be needed.)

United States coinage follows the binary pattern as best it can, being hampered by the decimal restriction that 10 and 100 (one dollar) must be among the denominations. Each denomination has nearly twice the value of the one before:

$$1, - , 5, 10, 25, 50, 100.$$

The gap is reserved for our nonexistent two-cent piece.

True binary "coins" can be constructed by placing the amounts 1¢, 2¢, 4¢, 8¢, 16¢, 32¢, 64¢, $1.28, $2.56 into nine envelopes. With these nine envelopes, a person can guarantee to furnish any amount from 1¢ to $5.00, say (actually to $5.11). Thus if 89¢ is called for (1011001), the four envelopes of values 1¢, 8¢, 16¢, 64¢ may be given. The demonstration can be made a fairly effective "magic" act if given a good build-up.

"Age cards" were once popular, and are still seen. These are four cards bearing numbers as follows:

NUMBER REPRESENTATIONS ACCORDING TO DIFFERENT BASES

In each row of this table are shown different representations for the same number. On the average, the numbers of digits required to represent the same whole number in two different systems compare as the logarithms of the bases of the systems. Since the common logarithms of 10 and 2 are 1 and .30..., respectively, it takes about 3⅓ times as many digits to represent numbers dyadically instead of decimally.

DECIMAL *Ten*	BINARY OR DYADIC *Two*	TERNARY *Three*	HEXAL *Six*	OCTAL *Eight*	DUODECIMAL *Twelve*
1	1	1	1	1	1
2	10	2	2	2	2
3	11	10	3	3	3
4	100	11	4	4	4
5	101	12	5	5	5
6	110	20	10	6	6
7	111	21	11	7	7
8	1000	22	12	10	8
9	1001	100	13	11	9
10	1010	101	14	12	T
11	1011	102	15	13	E
12	1100	110	20	14	10
13	1101	111	21	15	11
14	1110	112	22	16	12
15	1111	120	23	17	13
16	10000	121	24	20	14
17	10001	122	25	21	15
18	10010	200	30	22	16
19	10011	201	31	23	17
20	10100	202	32	24	18
100	1100100	10201	244	144	84
1000	1111101000	1101001	4344	1750	6E4
10000	10011100010000	111201101	114144	23420	5954

	DECIMAL	BINARY OR DYADIC	TERNARY	HEXAL	OCTAL	DUODECIMAL
½	.5	.1	.111111...	.3	.4	.6
⅓	.333333...	.010101...	.1	.2	.252525...	.4
¼	.25	.01	.020202...	.13	.2	.3
⅙	.166666...	.001010...	.011111...	.1	.125252...	.2
⅛	.125	.001	.010101...	.043	.1	.16
1/12	.083333...	.000101...	.002020...	.03	.052525...	.1
1/16	.0625	.0001	.001200...	.0213	.04	.09
1/32	.03125	.00001	.000211...	.01043	.02	.046

Card A		Card B		Card C		Card D	
8	12	4	12	2	10	1	9
9	13	5	13	3	11	3	11
10	14	6	14	6	14	5	13
11	15	7	15	7	15	7	15

A child is shown the cards and asked which ones have his age on them. Suppose he answers: A, C, D. When the numbers in the upper left-hand corners of these cards are added, his age is found: $8 + 2 + 1 = 11$. It is left to the student to figure out the "why" of the cards. (*Hint:* Write down the first fifteen binary numbers. Regard the list as a "code.")

An inspector of weights and measures carries a set of standard weights. These are on the binary pattern: 1 oz., 2 oz., 4 oz., 8 oz., 16 oz., etc. Let us imagine using them with a "seesaw" type of balance, consisting of a bar supported on a knife-edge at its middle and bearing a pan at each end. With a 13-oz. object in a pan, what weights must be placed in the other pan in order to balance? The binary number corresponding to 13 is 1101, so that $13 = 1 + 4 + 8$. (*Answer:* 1 oz., 4 oz., 8 oz.)

On a *ternary* (base-three) scale, the standard weights would be 1, 3, 9, 27, etc., ounces. *Two* of each would be required. Suppose, for example, we wish to balance 46 oz. The corresponding ternary number may be found by successive division by 3. It is 1201. This means that

$$46 \;=\; 1 \times 27 \;+\; 2 \times 9$$
$$+\; 0 \times 3 \;+\; 1 \times 1.$$

```
3)46
3)15   1
3) 5   0
3) 1   2
   0   1
```

So one 1-oz., two 9-oz. and one 27-oz. weights must be used.

If the weights may be placed *in either pan*, only one each of the standard ternary weights will be needed. Let us rewrite the ternary number 1021 in terms of the "signed" digits $\bar{1}$, 0, 1 (where $\bar{1} = -1$). This can be done by replacing the digit 2 by $1\bar{1}$ (since $1\bar{1}$ means $3 - 1 = 2$):

$$1201 = 2\bar{1}01 = 1\bar{1}\bar{1}01.$$

Hence we may balance a 46-oz. object by placing weights of 9 and 27 oz. in the pan with the object, and weights of 1 and 81 oz. in the other pan.

PROBLEM SET 4 (§7)

1. List the $2^3 = 8$ subsets of the set whose elements are the letters a, b, c.

2. Your Christmas-card list ends with a group of ten people, and you are undecided whether to send cards to any, or to some certain ones of them, or to all. In how many ways could you make up your mind?   *Answer:* 1024

3. Which do you suppose is the larger number, that of the atoms in the known universe or that of the number of subsets of the set of hairs on your head?

4. If we used a ternary (base-three) monetary system, so that we had coins of denominations 1¢, 3¢, 9¢, etc., how many coins would be needed to make up the sum of 77¢? Solve by converting 77 to a base-three number, by division.

5. Can you work out a mental scheme for converting a small number, like 77, to base three, i.e., expressing it as a sum of multiples (0, 1, 2) of powers of 3?

6. The Slobbovian coin of smallest value is the "scent." Other coins have these values: 4 scents = 1 neck; 4 necks = 1 dyme; 4 dymes = 1 qwat; 4 qwats = 1 haf; 4 hafs = 1 doll. What coins are needed (minimum number) to pay for an item costing 3597 scents?

7. Make up a set of five "age cards" covering the range 1 to 31.

8. What combination of standard weights (base two: 1 oz., 2 oz., 4 oz., etc.) is needed to balance an item weighing 361 oz.?

9. What combination of base-three scale weights (2 each: 1 oz., 3 oz., 9 oz., etc.) is needed to balance an item weighing 139 oz.? 524 oz.?

10. If weights may be put in both pans, what combination of base-three scale weights (*one* each: 1 oz., 3 oz., 9 oz., etc.) is needed to balance an item weighing 139 oz.? 524 oz.?

11.* Discuss the efficiency of the British monetary system. The values are:

1 Sixpence	=	6 Pennies
1 Shilling	=	12 Pennies
1 Florin	=	2 Shillings
1 Half-crown	=	2 Shillings and sixpence
1 Crown	=	5 Shillings
1 Ten Bob note	=	10 Shillings
1 Pound (£1)	=	20 Shillings

(In June, 1956, a British pound was worth about $2.80 in United States currency.)

12.* *Nim* is a clever game played with piles of coins, matches, etc. Its theory is best explained in terms of binary numerals, and is set forth in several popular mathematics books and texts, such as *Elementary Concepts of Mathematics*, by Burton W. Jones, Macmillan, New York, 1947. As a minor project, learn the theory of the game and explain it to the class.

13.* Write a report on the giant calculating machines of today and on their future impact on our society. Among others, these references may prove helpful: *Giant Brains*, by Edmund C. Berkeley, Wiley, New York, 1949; *The Human Use of Human Beings*, by Norbert Wiener, Houghton Mifflin, Boston, 1950.

7

Number
Structure

§1. PRIME AND COMPOSITE NUMBERS

The last three chapters have treated ways of performing number operations in terms of our Hindu-Arabic numerals, base ten or otherwise. Now we return to the *natural numbers* themselves (1, 2, 3, 4, . . . , or I, II, III, IV, . . . , etc.). We will examine their structural properties, and will derive some relations involving them which are basic to arithmetic.

The number 1 is singled out and called the **unit.** Every other natural number is divisible by itself and by 1. Some are divisible by no other number. These are called **primes.** The rest are called **composite.** The first few primes are:

$$2, 3, 5, 7, 11, 13, 17, 19, 23, 29, 31, 37, \ldots \quad .$$

We will learn later that any composite number can be expressed as a product of primes, also that there is essentially only one way in which this factoring can be done. *Example:* $6 = 2 \times 3$.

Since every natural number other than the unit is either a prime or a product of primes, *the primes are the keys to the natural numbers:* That which we find out about the primes, we may apply toward learning things about all the natural numbers. By this approach, we will be able to justify various common arithmetic processes, especially those having to do with fractions.

§2. FINDING PRIMES

"How can I tell if a number is prime?" If a *formula* for telling primes is expected, the questioner will be disappointed. Such a "formula," known as *Wilson's Theorem*, does exist, but its value is theoretical rather than practical, and there is no reason to believe that a truly practical formula can be found.

113

WILSON'S THEOREM. *The number **N** is prime if and only if the number $(N - 1)!$ + 1 is divisible by **N**. Examples:* For $N = 7$, $(N - 1)! = 6! = 1 \times 2 \times 3 \times 4 \times 5 \times 6 = 720$, and 721 is divisible by 7. For $N = 6$, $(N - 1)! + 1 = 121$, not divisible by 6. The expression $(N - 1)! + 1$ rapidly becomes too large to be dealt with conveniently. For $N = 97$, the number $96! + 1$ has 150 digits.

Finding primes is essentially a matter of testing divisors in turn: 2, 3, 4, 5, 6, 7, ... Composite divisors, however, need not be tried, for they themselves have smaller divisors which will already have been eliminated in the trials. For example, a number that is not divisible by 2 cannot be divisible by 6. (A number divisible by 6 has the form $6n = (2 \times 3)n = 2 \times (3n) = 2m$, and hence is also divisible by 2.)

Is 37 prime? We try to divide it by 2, and this cannot be done. We try 3, which fails. Since 4 is a multiple of 2, we need not try it. We try 5, then 7, then 11, ... Need we keep on?

As a matter of fact, we could have ended the trials before 7. For $7 \times 7 = 49$, which exceeds 37. Hence if 7 or some higher number were to divide evenly into 37, the quotient would be less than 7 and would *itself* be a factor of 37. Our earlier trials, through 6, have rejected this possibility. *Conclusion:* 37 is prime.

When the considerations above are made more general, the following rule results: To find if the number N is prime, test the primes in turn (2, 3, 5, 7, 11, . . .) for divisibility into N, but do not test beyond $\sqrt{N}$ (i.e., beyond the largest natural number whose square is less than or equal to N).

Example 1. Is 97 prime?

Work. Yes. For 97 is not divisible by 2, 3, 5, or 7. This is far enough, since $10^2 = 100 > 97$, while 8 and 9 are composite. Note that if 11 is tried, the quotient will be 8 (and remainder 9); that the quotient turns out to be less than the divisor is an automatic *stop* signal.

Example 2. Is 1943 prime?

Work. Mentally noting that $50^2 = 2500 > 1943$, we have the comforting knowledge that we need not test past 50. (We could actually narrow the bound to 43.) We test successively: 2, 3, 5, 7, 11, 13, 17, 19, 23, 29. Lo! 29 is a divisor. (The prime factorization is: $1943 = 29 \times 67$.)

COMMENT. Some of the small books of mathematical tables designed for school and ready reference use contain tables listing the prime factors of all numbers up to 1000 or more.

A practical device for listing all primes less than some given number was designed about 230 B.C. After its Greek inventor, it is called *Eratosthenes' Sieve*.

To set up the Sieve, list the natural numbers up to some last one, say 100. Cross out the unit 1. Now go through the list striking out all the multiples of 2 (except 2 itself): 4, 6, 8, ... Next, strike out all multiples of 3 still on the list (except 3 itself): (6), 9, (12), 15, ... The next number still on the list is 5. Strike out all its multiples. Next, those of 7. This is far enough, since 8, 9, 10 are no longer on the list and $11^2 = 121 > 100$. The 25 numbers which remain are the primes under 100.

*§3. HOW MANY ARE THE PRIMES?

If a person did not know the answer, he might reasonably conjecture that really *big* numbers must necessarily be divisible by some smaller ones—that the primes come to an end. This possibility occurred to Euclid. He ruled it out by proving that **there is no greatest prime.**

With some care and concentration, we can follow this remarkable proof. Let us suppose that there *is* a largest prime. Call it P. Form the product of the natural numbers from 1 to P, inclusive: $1 \times 2 \times 3 \times \cdots \times P$. This product is usually denoted by $P!$, read "P factorial." Now add 1 to this product, and call the new number N:

$$N = P! + 1 = (1 \times 2 \times 3 \times \cdots \times P) + 1.$$

Since this new number N exceeds the largest prime P, it must be composite, hence divisible by some number other than 1 and itself. Let X be the smallest such number. If X were composite, some divisor of it would also divide into N, contradicting our provision that X is the smallest divisor of N (other than 1). Therefore X is prime. Since P is the largest prime, X is among the numbers $1, 2, 3, \ldots, P$. Consequently, X divides evenly into $P! = 1 \times 2 \times 3 \times \cdots \times P$. But then X *cannot divide into N,* a remainder of 1 being left when the division is attempted.

Our original supposition that there is a largest prime has led us to an impossible conclusion, a contradiction. We are forced to admit that the supposition is itself impossible—and we conclude that there is no largest prime. This means that the primes are scattered along the whole infinite sequence of the natural numbers and are themselves infinite in number.

The primes do indeed gradually thin out as the natural numbers mount in size. There are 25 primes under 100, a rate of 25%. There are 50,847,478 primes under 1,000,000,000, a rate of 5%.

PROBLEM SET 1 (§1–§3)

1. Test each number to find if it is prime or composite:

(a)	71	(g)	127	(m)	269	(s)	403	(y)	827
(b)	83	(h)	133	(n)	299	(t)	437	(z)	943
(c)	87	(i)	151	(o)	301	(u)	439	(A)	1003
(d)	91	(j)	187	(p)	307	(v)	611	(B)	1007
(e)	101	(k)	233	(q)	323	(w)	613		
(f)	103	(l)	253	(r)	347	(x)	817		

2. Construct the Sieve of Eratosthenes for the numbers from 1 to 100 as explained at the end of §2. List the 25 primes found.

3. Prove that if a number is divisible by 8, then it is divisible by 2.

4.* Prove that the smallest number other than 1 which divides into some other number must be prime.

5.* "Fermat numbers" are those of form $2^{2^t} + 1$. For $t = 0, 1, 2, 3, 4$, these are primes. Verify this up to $t = 3$.

6.* Apply Wilson's Theorem to the numbers $N = 4, 5, 11$.

§4. TWO MOTIVATIONS FOR NUMBER STUDY

Perhaps the Greeks stood so much in respect and awe of numbers as individuals and as members of special groups that they were unable to conceive of them in a "classless society," that is to say, as in practical arithmetic, where particular numbers are not more important nor significant than others. The Greeks expended much energy toward the discovery and exploitation of special and novel properties of numbers. We may discern these polar motivations that spurred their studies:

I. (RATIONAL). An intellectual drive of the sort that has always stimulated "pure" research in every field, a powerful and compulsive urge which is nevertheless kept under control by rigorous logical discipline.

II. (INTUITIVE). A spiritual, aesthetic, or mystical zeal, marked by impatience with and distrust of rationalism, a conviction that inner meanings and ultimate truths may be intuitively sensed, grasped by miraculous insights.

Nearly every subject of broad importance is still approached in both these ways today, though seldom by the same person. In older times, a Kepler might partition his activity between astronomy and astrology. Nowadays, astronomy is a serious subject, astrology either a recreational diversion or a fraud—no one can be professionally involved in both. There are spheres of activity in which the intuitive is the serious side, the rational the frivolous. In the arts—in painting, for example—either approach may be serious and important.

Under the rational approach, the study of the structure of the natural numbers and of the special relationships found within this structure has become the field of pure mathematics called "Number Theory." Specialists in this field have claimed it to be the most abstruse and difficult of the many branches of mathematics—"the most brilliant gem in the diadem of the Queen of the Sciences."

Under the intuitive approach, the same study has degenerated in various ways. We may lump these under the heading "Numerology." In some esoteric and mystical religions we still find forms of number worship. The Rosicrucians are steeped in mystic number lore. There are also the less imaginative "numerologists" who ply their absurd trade in many urban areas.

Euclid devoted a chapter of his "Elements" to *perfect* numbers. A perfect number is defined to be one which is the sum of its own divisors, where 1 is counted as a divisor but the number itself is not. The smallest perfect number is 6 ($=1 + 2 + 3$). The first five are: 6, 28, 496, 8128, 33550336.

Euclid proved that whenever the natural number n is such that $2^{n+1} - 1$ is a prime number, then multiplying this prime by 2^n produces a perfect number. Euclid conjectured that all perfect numbers could be obtained by this process. But this problem presented such difficulty that twenty centuries rolled by until Euler proved the conjecture for *even* perfects. Whether or not there is an *odd* perfect number is not known to this day.

Should the ambitious student be tempted to try to find an odd perfect number by experiment, let him take heed as follows: He should begin with numbers larger than two million and consider only those with five or more distinct prime factors . . . ! The "to be or not to be" entity, the odd perfect number, must satisfy these criteria, among others.

Euclid's contribution belongs to the great body of serious mathematics. His was surely a rational motivation. Yet the study of perfect numbers may well have been *initiated* as a result of the intuitive type of motivation. Under the latter approach, the study assumed a wholly "non-Euclidean" (and nonmathematical) aspect, as the following quotations reveal.

St. Augustine wrote: "Six is a number perfect in itself, and not because God created all things in six days; rather the inverse is true; God created all things in six days because this number is perfect, and it would remain perfect even if the work of the six days did not exist."

The Jewish philosopher Philo Judaeas wrote " . . . such great sanctity is there in the number seven, that it has a pre-eminent rank beyond all the numbers in the first decade. . . . it displays a great and comprehensive power, contributing to the improvement of all terrestial things and affecting even the periodical changes of the moon. And in what manner it does this, we must consider. The number seven when compounded of numbers beginning with the unit, makes eight-and-twenty, a perfect number, ..." (For a fuller quotation, see page 27 of *Number Theory and Its History*, by Oystein Ore, McGraw-Hill, New York, 1948.)

A modern mathematician, inspecting the very *definition* of the "perfect" numbers, would regard the definition as a wholly arbitrary construction, which has proved felicitous in that it has led to some interesting problems. No virtue resides in any definition as such, but virtue may accumulate as a definition is constantly used in a fruitful way.

The Greeks called a pair of numbers *amicable* if the divisors of each added up to the other. Check this for the pair 220, 284. From Greek times through the medieval period, much was written about these numbers and their divine or mystic relation to human friendship. Yet no second pair was found until the year 1636, when the famous mathematician Fermat constructed the pair 17296, 18416. Amateurs as well as professional mathematicians have since dabbled with this notion, finding some 390 pairs. But having led to no problems of special interest or importance, the notion has dwindled to the status of a mathematical "curiosity."

§5. NUMBER LORE

In the Pythagorean lexicon, *even* numbers were feminine or earthly in their nature, *odd* numbers masculine or celestial. The number *One* was not included in this scheme, being regarded as the source of all numbers.

Each of the first few dozen numbers partook of special divine or mystical significance. *Five* and *Six* referred to *marriage*, being the sum and product, respectively, of 2 and 3, the first female and male numbers. *Four*, as a product of equals, 2 × 2, or as a "balance" of equals, 2 + 2, connoted *justice*.

We ourselves speak of "foursquare justice." Of phrases like this in use today, some are relics of the far past, others recent acquisitions based on associations as irrational as those cited above. The difference is that we regard these phrases merely as colorful aspects of our language, whereas our predecessors took them seriously. When we shed our dignity to swear at the auto motor which declines to start on a frigid morning, few of us expect that our *words* will persuade the motor to do its duty—we know them to be for our own benefit. But older peoples, including the writers of the Christian Bible, thought that power resided in the words or symbols themselves. "In the Beginning was the Word."

The Egyptian *hieratic* was an "alphabetic" type of numeral scheme, in which numbers were represented by the letters of the alphabet, in order. The Greeks also used such a scheme, augmenting their alphabet with one archaic and two Phoenician symbols:

α	β	γ	δ	ε	ς	ζ	η	θ
1	2	3	4	5	6	7	8	9

ι	κ	λ	μ	ν	ξ	ο	π	ϙ
10	20	30	40	50	60	70	80	90

ρ	σ	τ	υ	φ	χ	ψ	ω	ϡ
100	200	300	400	500	600	700	800	900

A Greek accustomed to using this scheme would naturally often think of the corresponding number when he used a word. The Greek word for *amen* is αμην, and from the table we find the corresponding number to be $1 + 40 + 8 + 50 = 99$. In many old editions of the Bible, the number 99 appears as a substitute for the word *amen*.

From the simple association of word and number, the Greeks and their successors proceeded further. They projected the occult personality of the number through the word onto the object named by the word. In *Number, the Language of Science* (Macmillan, New York, 1933, page 39), Dantzig refers to an instance in which a poet took "revenge" upon an enemy named Thamagoras by showing this name to have the same number as the word λοιμοσ (loimos), a sort of pestilence.

The Hebrews also represented numbers alphabetically. Interpreting words according to their numbers became for them a popular occupation. The subject was known as *gematria*. Many evidences of its use are found in the Bible and in other of their writings, even unto the present day.

Gematria was a popular weapon on the theological battlegrounds of the late Middle Ages. The number of the Beast of the Revelation being 666, the sanguine scholars of the day took lusty enjoyment in affixing this symbol onto all and sundry who displeased them. Peter Bungus, Catholic theologian, succeeded in showing that a form of the name of Martin Luther gave 666 as its numerical equivalent. Not to be outdone, the Lutheran Michael Stifel retaliated as follows. The name of the Pope at that time, written in Latin capitals, was LEO DECIMVS X. The letters of this title which correspond to Roman numerals are LDCIMVX. Take away the M to remove the "mystery" (Latin: *mysterium*), and there remains the Roman number D C L X V I = 666. In this medieval "logic," Pope = Antichrist.

Many a stage and screen star chooses the name that he or she will go by according to the "number" of the name (with $a = 1, b = 2, \ldots, z = 26$), a number which he is told will suit his personality type and career aims. Set beside its vigorous ancestor gematria, however, modern *numerology* makes a feeble showing. The average scientist has no patience with stupidities like numerology, palmistry, phrenology, and astrology, but he usually feels that it is not worth while to take time and energy from his work to combat such relatively innocuous frauds. They gradually wither and die.

PROBLEM SET 2 (§4–§5)

1. Show that the following numbers are "perfect":
   (a)   28   (b)   496
2. For what small values of n is $2^n(2^{n+1} - 1)$ "perfect"?
3.* Prove that no power of 2 can be "perfect."
4. Show that the numbers 220 and 284 form an "amicable pair."

5.   In 1866, an Italian schoolboy, Nicolo Paganini, published the amicable pair 1184, 1210. Can you verify his result? *Hint:* $1184 = 2^5 \times 37$; $1210 = 2 \times 5 \times 11^2$.

§6.   GREATEST COMMON DIVISOR (GCD)

The *basic division relation* is a principal tool used in the investigation of the basic properties of natural numbers. We recall its form:

$$\text{Dividend} = \text{Divisor} \times \text{Quotient} + \text{Remainder}$$
$$\text{(Remainder} < \text{Divisor)}$$

The **greatest common divisor** (GCD) of a pair of natural numbers is just what the name suggests. It is the largest natural number that divides both numbers of the given pair. Thus 4 is the GCD of the pair 8, 20. We express this fact by writing

$$\text{GCD } (8{,}20) = 4.$$

When both numbers of the pair are prime, the GCD will be 1. But the GCD may be 1 in other cases, as for the pair 8, 15. In such a case, the numbers of the pair are said to be *prime to each other;* 8 is prime to 15, and vice versa.

The *direct* way to find a GCD would be to list the divisors of each number (the number itself included), and to pick out the largest divisor appearing on both lists:

Divisors of 8: 1, 2, 4, 8
Divisors of 20: 1, 2, 4, 5, 10, 20
∴   GCD (8,20) = 4

The most usual way to find a GCD is to construct it out of the common factors of both numbers. This method will be taken up later, after we have established the needed factoring principles.

Euclid developed a technique for finding the GCD that was based on the division relation. His process, called the *Euclidean Rule*, is applied as follows:

We will find the GCD of 84 and 270. Divide the *smaller*, 84, into the *larger*, 270. The *remainder* is 18. As will soon be shown, the original GCD is equal to the GCD of this remainder, 18, and the smaller given number, 84:

$$\text{GCD } (84{,}270) = \text{GCD } (18{,}84).$$

Remainder $(270 \div 84)$

This procedure is *repeated*. Since each remainder is less than the one before, a zero remainder must eventually be obtained. But we stop one step earlier, when it is apparent that the next division will come out even:

GCD (84,270) = GCD (18,84) = GCD (12,18) = GCD (6,12) = 6.

When the division comes out even, as with 6 into 12, then the smaller number (6) is obviously a divisor both of itself and of the larger number (12), and so must be the GCD. Hence the final step: GCD (6,12) = 6.

To see the "why" of the process, consider the basic division relation resulting from the division of 84 into 270:

$$270 \quad = \quad \underline{84 \times 3} \quad + \quad \underline{18}.$$

Any divisor of both 84 and 270 must also divide 18. For otherwise, upon dividing both sides of the above equation by that divisor of 84 and 270, we would get the impossible form:

Integer = Integer + Fraction.

Therefore, the GCD of 84 and 270 is a *divisor* of 18 and 84. If it is not the *greatest* such divisor, then we will have

GCD (84,270) < GCD (18,84).

But this is impossible. For it may be seen from the same division relation previously written that GCD (18,84), being a divisor of 18 and 84, is also a divisor of 270, so that GCD (18,84) is a *divisor* of 84 and 270, and hence cannot exceed GCD (84,270).

The conclusion is:

GCD (84,270) = GCD (18,84).

It is apparent that this numerical illustration furnishes the complete pattern for a general proof justifying the Euclidean Rule. (It would only be necessary to repeat the steps of the argument using letters in place of the specific numbers 84 and 270.)

Examples

1. GCD (6,15) = GCD (3,6) = 3.
2. GCD (391,544) = GCD (153,391)
    = GCD (85,153)
    = GCD (68,85)
    = GCD (17,68) = 17.
3. GCD (8,15) = GCD (7,8) = GCD (1,7) = 1.

The GCD is found most quickly by using "nearest" division, with remainder of least absolute size, instead of our usual "under" division with positive remainder. Consider GCD (18,84). In reducing this earlier, we divided 18 into 84, with quotient 4 and remainder 12. "Nearest" division produces the quotient 5 and remainder -6. Neglect the minus sign, and write

$$\text{GCD }(18,84) = \text{GCD }(6,18) = 6.$$

Similarly,

$$\text{GCD }(391,544) = \text{GCD }(153,391)$$
$$= \text{GCD }(68,153) = \text{GCD }(17,68) = 17.$$

$$\text{GCD }(8,15) = \text{GCD }(1,8) = 1.$$

The argument by which the Euclidean Rule was justified for ordinary division is equally valid with respect to nearest division, since the proof depends only upon the *form* of the division relation, the size of the remainder (or its sign) being irrelevant.

One obvious application of the GCD is to the reduction of fractions. Because GCD $(391,544) = 17$, we know that

$$\frac{391}{544} = \frac{17 \times 23}{17 \times 32} = \frac{23}{32}.$$

Is this answer in lowest terms? To put the question another way: Are 23 and 32 prime to each other? Yes. For if they shared a divisor larger than 1, the product of that divisor with 17 would obviously be a common divisor of 391 and 544, contrary to our determination of 17 as the greatest such divisor. (In general, if a and b are two natural numbers with GCD $(a,b) = g$, then $a' = a/g$ and $b' = b/g$ are prime to each other.)

The GCD of three or more numbers is found by finding the GCD of the first two, next of that GCD and the third number, etc. To find GCD $(48,72,108,150)$, for example, we have successively:

$$\begin{aligned}
\text{GCD }(48,72) &= 24 \\
\text{GCD }(24,108) &= 12 \\
\text{GCD }(12,150) &= 6 \qquad (Answer)
\end{aligned}$$

§7.   LEAST COMMON MULTIPLE (LCM)

The **least common multiple** (LCM) of a pair of natural numbers is the smallest natural number that is divisible by both numbers of the pair. Thus the LCM of 8 and 12 is 24, written

$$\text{LCM }(8,12) = 24.$$

The LCM of a pair of natural numbers may be found by dividing the product of the numbers by their GCD. In practice, this operation is best performed by dividing the GCD into *one* of the numbers of the given pair, then multiplying this quotient by the other number.

The proof of this rule is postponed to §8. Note, however, the following: If g denotes the GCD of the two numbers a and b, then we have $a = ga'$, $b = gb'$. Hence the product ab contains the factor g *twice*, whereas it is needed only *once*, to go with either a' or b' to produce a multiple of a or b: $ga'b' = b'a = $ multiple of $a = a'b = $ multiple of b. Hence the extra factor g ($= $ GCD of a,b) may be divided out.

Example 1.   Find LCM $(8,12)$.

Work.   GCD $(8,12) = $ GCD $(4,8) = 4$.

$$\text{LCM } (8,12) = \frac{8 \times 12}{4} = 2 \times 12 = 24.$$

Example 2.   Find LCM $(84,270)$.

Work.   From §6, GCD $(84,270) = 6$.

$$\text{LCM } (84,270) = \frac{84 \times 270}{6} = 14 \times 270 = 3780.$$

Example 3.   Find LCM $(36,56,60)$.

Work Outline.   The LCM of three or more numbers may be found by the same "successive" type of procedure as shown for the GCD at the end of §6:

GCD $(36,56)\ =\ 4$.   ∴   LCM $(36,56)\ =\ 504$.
GCD $(60,504) = 12$.   ∴   LCM $(60,504) = 2520\ (Answer)$.

PROBLEM SET 3 (§6–§7)

1.   Find the GCD of each pair of numbers by listing all the divisors of each number of the pair and picking out the GCD:

(a) $(4,6)$ (b) $(8,12)$ (c) $(6,18)$ (d) $(30,42)$

2.   In which cases are the numbers of the pair prime to each other?

(a) $(1,12)$ (b) $(4,9)$ (c) $(50,63)$ (d) $(20,35)$

3.   Using the relation $84 = 60 + 24$, give an argument to show that any divisor of 60 and 84 must also be a divisor of 24.
4.   Continue on with the argument begun in Problem 3, as in §6, to show that GCD $(60,84) = $ GCD $(24,60)$.
5.   Complete the task begun in Problems 3 and 4 above by *proving* that GCD $(24,60) = $ GCD $(12,24) = 12$.
6.*   Prove that if GCD $(a,b) = g$, then $a' = a/g$ and $b' = b/g$ are prime to each other.

In Problems 7–18, find the GCD for each pair of numbers by the Euclidean Rule. (Use "under" or "nearest" division as directed by the instructor.)

7.	(9,16)	11.	(42,90)	15.	(806,1116)
8.	(22,46)	12.	(74,111)	16.	(1936,3630)
9.	(30,42)	13.	(260,611)	17.	(1728,5400)
10.	(35,66)	14.	(264,1512)	18.	(6912,20160)

19–30. For the pairs of numbers in Problems 7–18, find the LCM's by the method of §7.   *Answer to Problem 26:* 16632

31.   Find the GCD and LCM for each number triple:

(a)   (12,18,42)   (b)   (36,48,60)   (c)   (180,288,432)

§8. PRIME-PRODUCT THEOREM

The GCD of a pair of numbers can always be written as a difference between some two multiples of the numbers.

This can be shown in any particular case by writing down the division relations obtained at each stage of applying the Euclidean Rule, then "solving" for the GCD in terms of the original numbers by proceeding backwards from last to first relation, in turn.

Thus in finding GCD (18,84) = 6, the steps were:

$$\text{GCD } (18,84) = \text{GCD } (12,18) = \text{GCD } (6,12).$$

The corresponding division relations are

$$84 = 18 \times 4 + 12,$$
$$18 = 12 \times 1 + 6 \quad (\text{GCD} = 6).$$

"Solve" these for the remainders 6, 12 and write them in reverse order:

$$6 = 1 \times 18 - 1 \times 12,$$
$$12 = 1 \times 84 - 4 \times 18.$$

The first equation expresses the GCD = 6 in terms of 12 and 18. Eliminate the smaller, 12, by replacing it by the expression given for it in the second equation:

$$6 = 1 \times 18 - 1 \times (1 \times 84 - 4 \times 18) = 5 \times 18 - 1 \times 84.$$

Thus the GCD of 18 and 84 has been expressed as a multiple of 18 minus a multiple of 84.

Using "nearest" division, with $84 = 18 \times 5 - 6$, the above result could have been obtained in one step. However, the use of positive remainders shows the general pattern of the work (and of the suggested proof) more clearly. The result is not unique. Combining $14 \times 18 - 3 \times 84 = 0$ with $5 \times 18 - 1 \times 84 = 6$ gives $19 \times 18 - 4 \times 84 = 6$, etc.

One consequence of the above result is the rule:

Any common divisor of a pair of numbers is also a divisor of their GCD.

For a common divisor of two numbers will divide into any multiple of either number, hence also into any difference of such multiples (by the distributive law).

Another consequence is the following theorem.

PRIME-PRODUCT THEOREM.   *If a prime divides a product of two natural numbers, then it must divide at least one of them.*

This theorem is much used in simple arithmetic, generally without the computer being aware that he is using it. To find out if 242×331 is divisible by 3 or not, for example, we need but test 3 into 242 and 3 into 331, without multiplying out. The *prime* is very necessary to the hypothesis. Thus 4 divides the product 2×6. Yet 4 divides neither 2 nor 6. The proof given below is standard. An unusual proof is given on page 25 of *Biomathematics*, by Cedric Smith, Hafner, New York, 1954.

Proof.   Let M and N denote any two natural numbers. Let P denote a prime number that divides the product MN. Let us suppose that P does not divide M. We propose to show that P must then divide N.

Since P is prime, its only divisors are 1 and P. But we are supposing that P is not a divisor of M. Hence GCD $(P,M) = 1$. This may be expressed as a difference between some multiples of P and M:

$$1 = aP - bM.$$

(The a and b are some unknown whole numbers. We may have the order wrong, the proper relation then being $1 = aM - bP$. But the argument is the same in either case.) Multiply each term of the equation by N:

$$N = aPN - bMN.$$

Now observe that P divides both terms on the right side of this equation, because, first, P is a factor in aPN, and second, by the theorem's hypothesis, P divides the factor MN of bMN. According to the distributive law, therefore, P is a factor of the right side of the equation. Hence P divides N.

A more general form of the prime-product theorem, proved by an argument quite like that above, is: If a number that divides a product is prime to one factor of the product, then it divides the other factor. We may use this to prove the rule:

Any common multiple of a pair of numbers is a multiple of their LCM.

Proof.   Suppose that M is a common multiple of the numbers a and b. Denote $g =$ GCD (a,b). Then $a = ga'$ and $b = gb'$, where a' and b' are prime to each other. Using the fact that M is a multiple of a, write

$$M = ha = hga',$$

where h is some natural number. Since M is also a multiple of b, and $b = gb'$, we know that

$$hga' \text{ is divisible by } gb',$$

hence that

$$ha' \text{ is divisible by } b'.$$

Since b' is prime to a', we find from the generalized prime-product theorem:

$$h \text{ is divisible by } b'.$$

Write $h = kb'$, where k is some natural number, and substitute into the previously written expression for M:

$$M = hga' = kb'ga' = k(ga'b') = k\left(\frac{ab}{g}\right).$$

In §7, we noted that $ga'b'$ is a common multiple of a and b, and we have just now found that *every common multiple* of a and b is a multiple of $ga'b'$. Therefore $ga'b'$ is the *least* common multiple of a and b. Not only have we proved that any common multiple of a pair of numbers is a multiple of their LCM, but we have also established the formula cited in §7:

$$\text{LCM} = \frac{\text{Product}}{\text{GCD}}.$$

§9. THE FUNDAMENTAL THEOREM OF ARITHMETIC

FUNDAMENTAL THEOREM OF ARITHMETIC. *Every composite number can be expressed uniquely as a product of primes.*

This theorem assures us that there is essentially only one way of completely factoring a given number. The prime factors, to be sure, may be written in different orders: $12 = 2 \times 2 \times 3 = 2 \times 3 \times 2$, etc. However, it is not the order, but the number of times each prime appears, that is essential: two 2's and one 3 in the case of 12.

There is nothing really obvious about this theorem. The student is surely long accustomed to using it, and familiarity may have bred contempt. Let the student ask himself: "When I factor a number, how can I be sure that there are not other ways of factoring it which are entirely different from the particular one which my work has produced?"

Is it *obvious*, for example, that the following equalities are impossible —just because all the factors are prime?

$$13 \times 37 = 19 \times 29,$$
$$23 \times 47 = \ \ 7 \times 11 \times 13.$$

Analyzing the first of these numerical cases will give us a clue to the method of proving the fundamental theorem. If it is true that

$$13 \times 37 = 19 \times 29,$$

then the product 19×29 must be divisible by the prime 13. According to the prime-product theorem, therefore either 19 or 29 must be divisible by 13. Yet these numbers are all primes, and we know that one prime cannot divide into a different prime. The possibility that $13 \times 37 = 19 \times 29$ is ruled out.

The above is essentially the pattern of the second part of the proof of the theorem. The first part consists of showing that every composite number can be factored in *some* way as a product of primes. The argument just involves a close look at the usual way in which we factor numbers. We try 2, and if it goes, then we try 2 again on the quotient, and again . . . . When 2 stops dividing in, we try 3, and keep trying so long as 3 goes; then 5 . . . , 7 . . . , 11 . . . —but we need not try primes larger than the number itself (or even larger than its square root), so that the process will surely end, the final quotient being 1. The various prime divisors used are the required factors. The process is applied to the number 126 at the right, with the result

$$2)\overline{126}$$
$$3)\overline{63}$$
$$3)\overline{21}$$
$$7)\overline{7}$$
$$1$$

$$126 = 2 \times 3 \times 3 \times 7.$$

The second part of the proof now consists of showing that the prime factorization obtained as above is *unique*. Suppose that some two different prime factorizations are equal. We may arrange the factors in each systematically, 2's first, if any, then 3's, then 5's, and so on. We will have a setup like this, where the letters P, Q, P', Q', and the various blanks in the parentheses, denote primes:

$$P \times Q \times (\ \ ) \times (\ \ ) \times \cdots = P' \times Q' \times (\ \ ) \times (\ \ ) \times \cdots.$$

According to a simple extension of the prime-product theorem, since the prime P divides the number denoted on the left and thus also the same number denoted differently on the right, P must divide into some one of the factors P', Q', $(\ \ )$, $(\ \ )$, ... Hence P must equal that factor. Since these factors are arranged so that they never become smaller in left-to-right order, P cannot be smaller than P'. On the other hand, by the same argument in reverse (P' must divide one of P, Q, $(\ \ )$, $(\ \ )$, . . .), P' cannot be smaller than P.   Hence

$$P = P'.$$

Upon dividing through by P, we have

$$Q \times (\ \ ) \times (\ \ ) \cdots = Q' \times (\ \ ) \times (\ \ ) \times \cdots.$$

Repeating the argument, we find

$$Q = Q'.$$

Next we may divide through by Q, and so on. Every factor on the left is shown in turn to equal the corresponding factor on the right, and vice versa. The "two" factorizations are one and the same.

§10. USING FACTORS

Practical arithmetic leans heavily upon factoring procedures to effect numerical simplifications. Needed GCD's and LCM's may be found without factoring, by the Euclidean Rule. But where the numbers involved are small, as they usually are in practical operations with fractions, then it is easier to form GCD's and LCM's from the prime factors of the numbers.

Example 1.   Find the GCD and LCM for the pair (84,270) by factoring.

Work.   Factor each number into prime factors by successive division (see right):

$$2)\overline{84} \qquad 2)\overline{270}$$
$$2)\overline{42} \qquad 3)\overline{135}$$
$$3)\overline{21} \qquad 3)\ \overline{45}$$
$$7 \qquad 3)\ \overline{15}$$
$$5$$

$$84 = 2 \times 2 \times 3 \times 7 \qquad (= 2^2 \times 3 \times 7),$$
$$270 = 2 \times 3 \times 3 \times 3 \times 5 \qquad (= 2 \times 3^3 \times 5).$$

There is one common factor equal to 2, another to 3. Hence

$$\text{GCD } (84,270) = 2 \times 3 = 6.$$

An economical way to construct a number divisible by both 84 and 270 is to write all the factors of 270 (the one with more factors), then to supply those factors of 84 which are missing, the *second* 2 and the 7:

$$\text{LCM } (84,270) = (2 \times 3 \times 3 \times 3 \times 5) \times (2 \times 7)$$
$$= 270 \times 14 = 3780.$$

NOTE.   The factoring method may be justified as follows. Let the numbers be a and b, with GCD $= g$, so that $a = ga'$ and $b = gb'$. Let d be the product of the common prime factors of a and b. Then d is obviously a common divisor of a and b. By §8, $g = kd$. Hence $a = kda'$ and $b = kdb'$. Hence if $d \neq g$, so that $k > 1$, there is some prime factor of k which is a common prime factor of a and b, and which was not included in forming d, a contradiction. It is left to the student to justify the LCM construction.

Example 2.   Find the GCD and LCM for (36,56,60) by factoring.

Work.   Factor by successive division:

$$2)\overline{36} \qquad 2)\overline{56} \qquad 2)\overline{60}$$
$$2)\overline{18} \qquad 2)\overline{28} \qquad 2)\overline{30}$$
$$3)\ \overline{9} \qquad 2)\overline{14} \qquad 3)\overline{15}$$
$$3 \qquad 7 \qquad 5$$

$$36 = 2 \times 2 \times 3 \times 3 \qquad (= 2^2 \times 3^2),$$
$$56 = 2 \times 2 \times 2 \times 7 \qquad (= 2^3 \times 7),$$
$$60 = 2 \times 2 \times 3 \times 5 \qquad (= 2^2 \times 3 \times 5).$$

As in Example 1, construct the GCD and LCM by inspection:

$$\text{GCD } (36,56,60) = 2 \times 2 = 4,$$

$$\text{LCM } (36,56,60) = (2 \times 2 \times 3 \times 3) \times (2 \times 7) \times (5) = 2520.$$

PROBLEM SET 4 (§8–§10)

1. In each case, express the GCD of the pair of numbers as a difference between multiples of the numbers.

    (a) (18,30)   (b) (35,66)   (c) (63,168)   (d) (264,1512)

              Answer: (d)   24 = 23×264 − 4×1512

2. Using the relation obtained in (1d), $24 = 23 \times 264 - 4 \times 1512$, show that every common divisor of 264 and 1512 is a divisor of 24.

3. (a) Is 142×705 divisible by 7?

   (b) Is 200×333 divisible by 6?

   (c) Is 200×301 divisible by 6?

Hint: A number is divisible by 6 only if it is divisible by both 2 and 3.

4. To help yourself to understand the argument for the Prime-Product Theorem, trace through it for the numerical case $M = 4, N = 6, P = 3$.

5. Taking $a = 18, b = 30$ (hence $g = 6$), trace through the argument in §8 for the theorem: "Any common multiple of a pair of numbers is a multiple of their LCM."

6. Show by the method of §9 (without multiplying out) that the equation $23 \times 19 = 11 \times 37$ is an impossibility.

7. In the proof of the fundamental theorem in §9, the following appears. Amplify the statement, filling in any missing details and justifying its assertions more fully:

"According to a simple extension of the prime-product theorem, since the prime P divides the number denoted on the left and thus also the same number denoted differently on the right, P must divide into some one of the factors $P', Q', (\ ), (\ ), \ldots$ Hence P must equal that factor. Since these factors are arranged so that they never become smaller in left-to-right order, P cannot be smaller than P'. On the other hand, by the same argument in reverse (P' must divide one of $P, Q, (\ ), (\ ), \ldots$), P' cannot be smaller than P. Hence $P = P'$."

In Problems 8–25, find GCD's and LCM's by factoring.

8. (30,42)	11. (74,111)	14. (1936,3630)
9. (35,66)	12. (264,1512)	15. (1728,5400)
10. (42,90)	13. (806,1116)	16. (6912,20160)
17. (2,4,6)	20. (36,48,60)	23. (4,6,8,10)
18. (6,10,15)	21. (180,288,432)	24. (24,54,60,72)
19. (12,18,42)	22. (1344,1536,2880)	25. (216,288,504,600)

§11.   DIVISIBILITY RULES

It is convenient to be able to tell whether a number is divisible by 2, 3, or certain other small numbers, without having to carry out the division.

For 2, 5, or 10, the rules are particularly simple. A number is divisible by 2, 5, or 10 if and only if its *units digits* is divisible by 2, 5, or 10, respectively. In other words:

1.   A number is divisible by 2 if its units digit is 0, 2, 4, 6, or 8.
2.   A number is divisible by 5 if its units digit is 0 or 5.
3.   A number is divisible by 10 if its units digit is 0.

The rules are derived by considering the *structure* of a base-ten numeral. Inspect this numerical illustration:

$$2436 = \boxed{2 \times 1000 \quad + \quad 4 \times 100 \quad + \quad 3 \times 10} + \boxed{6}$$

Units Digit

Since 10 is divisible by 2, 5, and 10, so are 100 and 1000. The long boxed-in portion of the numeral above is therefore automatically divisible by 2, 5, and 10—and this will be true with *every* number, not just with the number 2436 used in illustrating the structure. Hence if the units digit is divisible by 2, so is the number, and conversely. Similarly in the case of 5 and 10.

A number is divisible by 4 if and only if its last two digits (tens, units) form a number divisible by 4. For 100, hence 1000, etc., are divisible by 4, and any number can be split as shown in this illustration:

Two-Digit Number

$$2436 = \boxed{2 \times 1000 \quad + \quad 4 \times 100} + \boxed{3 \times 10 \quad + \quad 6}$$

A number is divisible by 3 [or 9] if and only if the *sum of its digits* is divisible by 3 [or 9].

The "why" of this rule depends upon the fact that every power of ten is one more than an "all nines" number:

$$10 = 9 + 1; \quad 100 = 99 + 1; \quad 1000 = 999 + 1; \quad \text{etc.}$$

Using 2436 as an illustration once more, we write it:

$$
\begin{aligned}
2436 &= 2 \times 1000 \;+\; 4 \times 100 \;+\; 3 \times 10 \;+\; 6 \\
&= 2 \times (999 + 1) \;+\; 4 \times (99 + 1) \;+\; 3 \times (9 + 1) \;+\; 6
\end{aligned}
$$

Sum of Digits

$$= \boxed{2 \times 999 \quad + \quad 4 \times 99 \quad + \quad 3 \times 9} + \boxed{2 + 4 + 3 + 6}$$

Since any "all nines" number is divisible by 3 and by 9, the first boxed-in portion of the numeral above is divisible by 3 and by 9—and again this will be so with *every* number. The remaining portion is just the sum of the digits of the numeral. The rules follow.

In the case of the number 2436, the sum of the digits is $2 + 4 + 3 + 6 = 15$. Since 15 is divisible by 3, so is 2436. Since 15 is not divisible by 9, neither is 2436. Incidentally, the digital sum may itself be tested for divisibility by summing *its* digits. Thus, for 15, we have $1 + 5 = 6$, divisible by 3, but not by 9. As a second illustration, take the number 88,769. Summing digits: $8 + 8 + 7 + 6 + 9 = 38$. Summing again: $3 + 8 = 11$. Summing again: $1 + 1 = 2$. Since this is divisible by neither 3 nor 9 ,the number 88,769 is itself divisible by neither 3 nor 9.

The powers of ten differ from multiples of 11 by -1 and $+1$ alternately:

$$10 = 11 - 1 \qquad 100 = 99 + 1$$
$$1000 = 1001 - 1 \qquad 10000 = 9999 + 1 \qquad \textbf{etc.}$$

Hence if the digits of a number are alternately added and subtracted, beginning with the units digit and proceeding from right to left, the resulting "alternating digit sum" may be tested for divisibility by 11. For 2436, we have: $6 - 3 + 4 - 2 = 5$. Hence 2436 is not divisible by 11.

§12. CASTING OUT NINES

It was once the practice in our schools to have pupils check numerical computations by "casting out the nines."

The *nines excess* of a number is the remainder obtained when the number is divided by 9. The nines excess of 5 is 5; of 9 is 0; of 12 is 3; of 43 is 7; of 100 is 1. Carrying out a division is actually unnecessary, because the *nines excess of a number is equal to the nines excess of the sum of its digits.* The number 4873 has a digital sum of $4 + 8 + 7 + 3 = 22$; this number 22 has a digital sum of $2 + 2 = 4$. Being less than 9, this last number is equal to its own nines excess. Hence the nines excess of 4873 is 4.

The proof of the above follows the pattern of the proof of the rule for divisibility by 9 given in §11. With 4873 as a numerical illustration, we have:

$$4873 = 4 \times 1000 + 8 \times 100 + 7 \times 10 + 3$$

$$\text{Sum of Digits}$$

$$= \boxed{4 \times 999 + 8 \times 99 + 7 \times 9} + \boxed{4 + 8 + 7 + 3}$$

$$= (\text{A multiple of } 9) + (4 + 8 + 7 + 3)$$

Hence when 9 is divided into 4873, it goes evenly into the multiple in the left parenthesis, so that the remainder must equal the remainder obtained from dividing 9 into the sum of the digits in the right parenthesis. This argument is obviously of general type, applicable to any number.

Let a given numerical computation involve only additions, subtractions, and multiplications. *If the computation is carried out with the nines excesses in place of the original numbers, the nines excess of this result will equal the nines excess of the result of the original computation.*

Proof. Suppose two numbers a and b are added. Let their nines excesses be denoted by E_a and E_b. Then by definition of "nines excess":

$$a = (\text{A multiple of } 9) + E_a,$$
$$b = (\text{A multiple of } 9) + E_b.$$

Since the sum of two multiples of 9 is again a multiple of 9, we find:

$$a + b = (\text{A multiple of } 9) + (E_a + E_b).$$

Hence $a + b$ and $E_a + E_b$ have the same nines excess. Similarly, $a - b$ and $E_a - E_b$ have the same nines excess. (In this case, $E_a - E_b$ may be negative. Thus if $a = 50$ and $b = 17$, $a - b = 33$, with excess 6, while $E_a - E_b = 5 - 8$ $= -3$. Add 9 to the -3 to bring it into the usual 0-to-8 nines-excess range: $-3 + 9 = 6$.)

If the numbers a and b are multiplied, we have:

$$\begin{aligned} ab &= (9m + E_a)(9n + E_b) \\ &= (9 \times 9mn) + 9nE_a + 9mE_b + E_aE_b \\ &= 9 \times (9mn + nE_a + mE_b) + E_aE_b \\ &= (\text{A multiple of } 9) + E_aE_b. \end{aligned}$$

(In the above, m and n denote whole numbers, the quotients obtained when 9 is divided into a and b, respectively.) Hence the nines excess of ab is equal to that of E_aE_b.

Any computation involving additions, subtractions, and multiplications may be made in steps each involving the performance of one operation on two numbers. The results shown above for two numbers can therefore be extended to apply to a computation involving several numbers and operations.

Checking by "casting out the nines" consists of repeating calculations with nines excesses in place of original numbers.

CHECKING AN ADDITION		CHECKING A SUBTRACTION	
	Excesses		*Excesses*
2436	6	2407	4
218	2	− 982	1
+ 1602	0	~~1525~~ Wrong!	3
4256 ✓	8	1425 ✓	

In onetime school use, a special framework was used for the multiplication check:

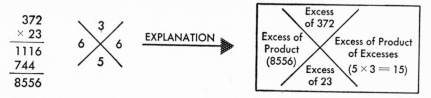

In case a multiplication does not check as a whole, the trouble can be localized by checking the computation of each partial product by excesses.

A *division* may be checked by forming the corresponding basic division relation, and checking that:

$$
\begin{array}{r}
28 \\
26)\overline{732} \\
52 \\
\hline
212 \\
208 \\
\hline
4
\end{array}
$$

Relation: $26 \times 28 \; + \; 4 \; = \; 732$

Excesses: $8 \times 1 \; + \; 4 \; = \; 12 \longrightarrow 3 \; \checkmark$

"Casting out the nines" fails to catch one very common numerical error, the transposition of two digits. If an answer ought to be 2936 and is accidentally set down as 2396, the false answer will pass the nines check because the sum of the digits, hence the nines excess, is unchanged. *Casting out elevens* will catch a transposition error.

The elevens check takes the same form as the nines check. The rule for finding the elevens excess of a number (remainder upon division by eleven) is to form the "alternating sum" of the digits: Add the units digit, subtract the tens digit, add the hundreds digit, subtract the thousands digit, etc. (See §11 regarding divisibility by 11.) For the number 180739, for example, we find: $9 - 3 + 7 - 0 + 8 - 1 = 20$. For 20, we find: $0 - 2 = -2$. Adding 11 gives 9. Hence the elevens excess of 180739 is 9. The double check, by both nines and elevens, is sometimes used in connection with large-scale machine computation.

Although these checking schemes have a limited sphere of usefulness, they cannot be trusted too far. It is not correct to suppose that the success of a check by casting out nines means that the odds are 8 to 1 in favor of the answer being right. Suppose that someone writes down a number x between 1 and 1,000,000,000, making an entirely random choice. If a friend now guesses a number y at random in the same range, there is a true chance of about 1 in 9 that x and y will have the same nines excess. But this is by no means the chance that y is "right," that is, that $y = x$. In other words, a check by casting out nines can hardly help—and may mislead—a student who is so poor that he hardly ever gets a right answer.

PROBLEM SET 5 (§11–§12)

1. Test for divisibility by 2, 5, and 4:

(a)	23	(f)	132	(k)	1296	(p)	80806
(b)	30	(g)	477	(l)	5291	(q)	222222
(c)	42	(h)	561	(m)	20700	(r)	353343
(d)	60	(i)	700	(n)	47232	(s)	591926
(e)	72	(j)	855	(o)	60006	(t)	938190

2. Test the numbers in Problem 1 for divisibility by 3.

3. Test the numbers in Problem 1 for divisibility by 9.

4. Test the numbers in Problem 1 for divisibility by 11.

5. Show that a number is divisible by 6 if and only if it is divisible by both 2 and 3.   What numbers of Problem 1 are divisible by 6?

6. Show that a number is divisible by 12 if and only if it is divisible by both 3 and 4.   What numbers of Problem 1 are divisible by 12?

7.* Verify that $37 \times 27 = 999$ and $37 \times 27027 = 999,999$. Then show that a number is divisible by 37 if the sum of the numbers formed by successive triples of digits, from right to left, is divisible by 37. (Thus for 435,823 we find $823 + 435 = 1258$, and for 1258 we find $258 + 1 = 259 = 7 \times 37$. Hence 435,823 is divisible by 37.) Test (l) (q), (r), (s), (t) of Problem 1 for divisibility by 37.

8.* Derive a rule for divisibility by 8.

9.* Derive a rule for divisibility by 99.

In Problems 10–21, carry out the indicated computations, then check by casting out nines.

10.	2307	11.	10786	12.	9999
	563		2341		999
	+ 4128		+ 30064		+ 9090

13.	232	14.	540	15.	10000
	− 76		− 205		− 9999

16. 26×37 17. 42×762 18. 397×5042

19. $5000 \div 27$ 20. $69321 \div 89$ 21. $24 \times 34 \times 75$

22–33. Check the results in Problems 10–21 by casting out elevens.

34.* Agnes Zilch "calculated" 24×312 by thinking of her best friend's phone number and putting that down as the answer. What is the probability that her work will pass the "casting out nines" test? The "casting out elevens" test? *Both* tests?

8

Fractions

§1. AN ANCIENT BUGABOO

In older eras, eminent scholars quailed before fractions even as the school children of today.

Unit fractions—those with numerators equal to 1, such as ½, ⅓, ¼— were used almost exclusively for centuries, even after notations had been developed for representing general fractions.

Perhaps it was difficult for our forebears to conceive of operating with a *pair* of numbers as though the pair were a single number. Yet in avoiding this conceptual difficulty, they had to resort to computational techniques of forbidding complexity. In the famed mathematical compendium of the Egyptians, the *Rhind papyrus*, the ratio of 2 to 43 is expressed in the form

$$\frac{1}{42} + \frac{1}{86} + \frac{1}{129} + \frac{1}{301}.$$

The papyrus gives a list of such decompositions, from ⅖ to ²⁄₁₀₁. (These quotients are the *doubles* of unit fractions, and were needed in order to facilitate multiplication and division by mixed numbers according to the Egyptian doubling and summing scheme.)

The Greeks finally developed an adequate notation for general fractions, similar to our own. But their early mathematicians had found repugnant the notion of taking parts of a unit, *unity* being for them a true numerical "atom," even a Diety symbol. So before Archimedes' time, only *ratios* of integers were treated, and great stress was laid upon the idea of proportion. Greek merchants were less particular, using fractions without troubling themselves over philosophical or theological objections.

The Romans side-stepped fraction difficulties by creating submultiples (twelfths, twenty-fourths, etc.) of their common units of money, weights, and measures—even as today we use inches instead of twelfths of feet, ounces instead of sixteenths of pounds, cents instead of hundredths of dollars.

The use of unit fractions carried over into medieval times, leading to many awkwardnesses and computational errors. The ordinary mercantile calculations did not suffer since they were usually carried out on the abacus or counting table, with the Roman subunits playing whatever fractional roles were required.

In early Renaissance times, the use of general fractions became widespread. The rules we use today for adding, subtracting, multiplying, and reducing fractions were set down in more or less their present forms. The last of our modern rules to appear was that for dividing by a fraction: *invert, then multiply.* Surprisingly enough, this simple rule did not come into common use until the seventeenth century, although a Hindu writer had cited it a thousand years earlier.

NOTE ON EGYPTIAN FRACTIONS. The Egyptian techniques for handling fractions are explained in detail in pages 19–30 of Van Der Waerden's *Science Awakening.* Also, see pages 73–78 of Neugebauer's *The Exact Sciences in Antiquity.* Apparently the Egyptians put down a few obvious relations between simple unit fractions, then applied these to derive other relations. This is a true example of deductive technique, perhaps the closest approach made by the Egyptians to the conception of mathematical and scientific derivation or "proof."

Let us write $\bar{2}$ for $\frac{1}{2}$, $\bar{3}$ for $\frac{1}{3}$, etc., so that our unit fraction notation will be structurally similar to the Egyptians'. Also, $\bar{\bar{3}}$ for $\frac{2}{3}$. Note that multiplying the number written under the "wave" by an integer actually divides the fraction by that integer: $\bar{6}$ is *half* of $\bar{3}$, etc. The following relations are obvious:

$$
\begin{aligned}
(1) && \bar{2} + \bar{2} &= 1 & \left(\tfrac{1}{2} + \tfrac{1}{2} = 1\right) \\
(2) && \bar{3} + \bar{3} &= \bar{\bar{3}} & \left(\tfrac{1}{3} + \tfrac{1}{3} = \tfrac{2}{3}\right) \\
(3) && \bar{3} + \bar{3} + \bar{3} &= 1 & \left(\tfrac{1}{3} + \tfrac{1}{3} + \tfrac{1}{3} = 1\right)
\end{aligned}
$$

Halving relations (2) and (3) above gives

$$\bar{6} + \bar{6} = \bar{3} \qquad \text{and} \qquad \bar{6} + \bar{6} + \bar{6} = \bar{2}.$$

These combine, giving $\bar{3} + \bar{6} = \bar{2}$. If $\bar{6}$ is added to both sides of this last relation, we find

$$\bar{3} + \bar{6} + \bar{6} = \bar{2} + \bar{6}, \quad \text{or} \quad \bar{3} + \bar{3} = \bar{2} + \bar{6}, \quad \text{or} \quad \bar{\bar{3}} = \bar{2} + \bar{6}.$$

Halving this gives $\bar{3} = \bar{4} + \bar{12}$. This procedure of deriving new relations can be carried on indefinitely.

One method of finding fractional quotients was to build up the dividend in terms of successive halves of the divisor: $1, \bar{2}, \bar{4}, \bar{8}, \ldots$. To find $\frac{2}{7}$, for example, we proceed by halving:

$$
\begin{aligned}
1 \times 7 &= 7 & (&= 6 + 1) \\
\bar{2} \times 7 &= 3 + \bar{2} & (&= 2 + 1 + \bar{2}) \\
\bar{4} \times 7 &= 1 + \bar{2} + \bar{4}
\end{aligned}
$$

At this stage, we need to add $\bar{4}$ to $1 + \bar{2} + \bar{4}$ to get 2. But $\bar{4} = \bar{28} \times 7$. Hence $2 = (\bar{4} + \bar{28}) \times 7$, so that

$$2 \div 7 = \bar{4} + \bar{28}.$$

§2. COMPARING SETS

The *meaning* of a natural number may be described in various ways. The number 3 may be used ordinally, to designate a counted position: "3rd shelf from bottom." It may be used as an integer, to characterize a net outcome: "3 up" (golf). It may be used as a scale number, "3 ft. long," an interpretation we have not yet explored. It may be used in a cardinal sense, to tell the size of a set: "3 eggs." It is, in fact, only this last interpretation which we have fully exploited, to the extent that it has been our basic theme. The relationship of other interpretations to the set, or cardinal, conception is generally apparent, so that it would scarcely be worth while to develop them all in detail.

Fractions likewise have various interpretations. We may describe their meaning in terms of *ratio, partition, division*, or concretely through *length, area*, etc. The Greeks conceived of a fraction as picturing a ratio. In theory, the ratio approach is perhaps the simplest. But the idea of a ratio is more abstract than, say, the idea of partition. Hence we will not fix upon any one interpretation as basic to the development, but use several. Such a procedure is contrary to the mathematician's idea of how a subject ought to be treated, but is in accordance with historical patterns of development (also with "learning" patterns), whereby conceptions may evolve in several directions simultaneously.

We ordinarily compare the sizes of two sets (groups) in one of two ways, *absolute* or *relative*.

Suppose that John has 6 apples, while Bill has only 2. To make an *absolute* comparison between the sets, we *subtract* the number of one from the number of the other. We say, "John has *4 more* apples than Bill."

To make a *relative* comparison we divide one number by the other. We say, "John has *3 times as many* apples as Bill."

If we are limited to natural numbers, our relative comparisons will be restricted. Suppose that Ted has 3 apples, while Bill has 2. In natural numbers, we can only make "proportional" or "ratio" statements: "Ted's apples are to Bill's as 3 is to 2," or "Bill's apples are to Ted's as 2 is to 3."

We now introduce new numbers, called **fractions**, which permit us to make relative comparisons between any two sets. The notation is

$$a/b \qquad \text{or} \qquad \frac{a}{b} \qquad (\text{"}a \text{ over } b\text{"}),$$

where a and b are the numbers of the sets. The fraction is associated with the ratio of a to b, *numerator* to *denominator*.

In place of saying, "Bill's apples are to Ted's as 2 is to 3," we may say, "Bill has ⅔ (two-thirds) as many apples as Ted." Or we may say, "Ted has 3⁄2 (three-halves) as many apples as Bill."

Returning to John and Bill, with 6 and 2 apples, respectively, we note that the statement "John has 3 times as many apples as Bill" implies a multiplication. The number of the second set (John's) is obtained from the number of the first (Bill's) by multiplying by 3, the quotient of 6 by 2:

$$② \xrightarrow{\times 3} ⑥$$

We take the statement "Bill has ⅔ as many apples as Ted" as also implying a multiplication. *We regard ⅔ as the quotient of 2 by 3:*

$$\frac{2}{3} = 2 \div 3.$$

And we say that when 3 is multiplied by ⅔, the result is 2:

$$\frac{2}{3} \times 3 = 2.$$

$$③ \xrightarrow{\times \frac{2}{3}} ②$$

§3. MULTIPLYING FRACTIONS

The considerations of §2 may be extended to fractions in general:

A fraction equals the quotient of its numerator by its denominator:

$$\frac{a}{b} = a \div b$$

To multiply a natural number by a fraction, multiply by the numerator, then divide by the denominator (or: *divide by the denominator, then multiply by the numerator*):

$$\frac{a}{b} \times N = \frac{aN}{b} \quad \text{or} \quad \frac{a}{b} \times N = a \times \frac{N}{b}$$

If we seek to extend these properties to whole numbers (zero as well as the natural numbers), we find that the extension does not work out in the case of a zero denominator. The fraction candidate ⅝₀, for example, would have to mean $5 \div 0$, a number which when multiplied by 0 gives 5:

$$\frac{5}{0} \times 0 = 5 \quad \text{(?)}$$

Hence ⅝₀ cannot denote a whole number, for the product of a whole number by zero is zero. Further, if we try to define ⅝₀ as some new kind of fraction, we meet with trouble. For assuming the above relation, (⅝₀) $\times 0 = 5$, and supposing that the associative law is to be maintained, we find:

$$25 = 5 \times 5 = \left(\frac{5}{0} \times 0\right) \times 5 = \frac{5}{0} \times (0 \times 5) = \frac{5}{0} \times 0 = 5.$$

It is therefore impossible to define $5/0$ in any satisfactory way. We must rule out the conception of a fraction with a zero denominator, as well as the equivalent conception of dividing by zero. *The operation of dividing by zero is not permissible.*

A zero *numerator* is allowable. The number 0 can be obtained by multiplying 0 by 5. The inverse operation, dividing by 5, when applied to the result 0, therefore gives 0 again. So $0 \div 5 = 0$, and $0/5 = 0$.

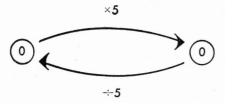

Also $2/3 \times 0 = 0 \times 2/3 = 0$, etc. For $2/3 \times 0 = 2 \times 0/3 = 2 \times 0 = 0$, while

$$0 \times \frac{2}{3} = \frac{0 \times 2}{3} = \frac{0}{3} = 0.$$

When the divisions come out even, dividing by two numbers in succession is equivalent to dividing by their product. Thus

$$(48 \div 2) \div 3 = 24 \div 3 = 8 = 48 \div 6.$$

Suppose that we assume this property to hold when the divisions do not come out even. Then we may define the product of two fractions upon the earlier pattern of a product of a fraction and a natural number:

$$\frac{a}{b} \times \frac{c}{d} = \left(a \times \frac{c}{d} \right) \div b = (ac \div d) \div b = ac \div bd = \frac{ac}{bd}.$$

The product of two fractions is a fraction whose numerator is the product of the numerators and whose denominator is the product of the denominators of the given fractions.

The commutative and associative laws of multiplication are easily seen to hold:

$$\frac{a}{b} \times \frac{c}{d} = \frac{ac}{bd} = \frac{ca}{db} = \frac{c}{d} \times \frac{a}{b}.$$

$$\left(\frac{a}{b} \times \frac{c}{d} \right) \times \frac{e}{f} = \frac{ac}{bd} \times \frac{e}{f} = \frac{(ac)e}{(bd)f} = \frac{a(ce)}{b(df)} = \frac{a}{b} \times \frac{ce}{df} = \frac{a}{b} \times \left(\frac{c}{d} \times \frac{e}{f} \right).$$

The quotient of two fractions may be defined in essentially the same way in which we defined the quotient of two natural numbers. Given the fractions f_1 and f_2, by $f_1 \div f_2$ is meant the number f such that $f \times f_2 = f_1$. So with $f_1 = a/b$ and $f_2 = c/d$, we have:

$$f \times \frac{c}{d} = \frac{a}{b}, \qquad \text{where } f = \frac{a}{b} \div \frac{c}{d}.$$

But to get a/b from c/d, we may multiply by d and divide by c to get 1, then multiply by a/b. Hence:

$$f = \frac{a}{b} \times \frac{d}{c}.$$

To divide by a fraction, invert and multiply.

In application the use of the word "of" following a fraction is a signal to multiply. "$\frac{2}{3}$ of 6" means "$\frac{2}{3} \times 6$." A person may be instructed to take two-thirds *of* a group of 6 apples, upon which he takes $\frac{2}{3} \times 6 = 4$ of them. A taxpayer complains that $\frac{2}{5}$ *of* his salary goes for taxes. If his salary is \$25,000, he is claiming that $\frac{2}{5} \times \$25,000 = \$10,000$ is paid out in taxes.

Problems involving successive multiplication by fractions may be treated as such, or may be handled by first multiplying the fractions. If a worker "takes home" $\frac{4}{5}$ of his gross pay, and his wife uses $\frac{3}{4}$ of this in her household budget, then the amount used by his wife is $\frac{3}{4} \times \frac{4}{5} = 12\frac{1}{20}$ ($= \frac{3}{5}$) of his gross pay. [For if the gross pay is P, we have $\frac{3}{4} \times (\frac{4}{5} \times P) = (\frac{3}{4} \times \frac{4}{5}) \times P$.]

Division applications occur now and then in everyday arithmetic. If a man walks $\frac{4}{5}$ of a mile in 16 min., then his speed in miles per hour is

$$\frac{4}{5} \div \frac{16}{60} = \frac{4}{5} \times \frac{60}{16} = \frac{4 \times 60}{5 \times 16} = 3.$$

If there are equal numbers of men, women, and children in a group, and there are 150 adults, then the whole group numbers $150 \div \frac{2}{3} = 150 \times \frac{3}{2} = 225$. (But this last problem would undoubtedly be worked in practice without using fractions explicitly—by dividing 150 by 2 to get the common number of the groups of men, women, children, then multiplying by 3 to get the total. The walking-rate problem can also be worked by considering that the walker traveled each $\frac{1}{5}$ mile in $\frac{4}{60}$ of an hour, hence 1 mile in $5 \times \frac{4}{60} = \frac{1}{3}$ of an hour, hence 3 miles in 1 hour.)

Yet the *invert, then multiply* rule is more frequently invoked than many teachers and educators realize. When the housewife cuts three grapefruit into *halves*, she knows at once that she will get *twice* three servings. In cases of this sort the division concept is applied, even though the problem is not explicitly formulated as one involving division by a fraction.

PROBLEM SET 1 (§1–§3)

1. Given that George has 8 pencils, while Ben has 2, compare the sets in two ways: (a) absolute, (b) relative.

2. Given sets A and B with a and b elements, respectively, B compares with A as b to a. We get b from a by multiplying:

$$\textcircled{a} \xrightarrow{\times \, b/a} \textcircled{b}$$

Show how this relationship works out in each of the following cases:

$a = n(A)$	2	3	3	6	4	8
$b = n(B)$	6	12	1	2	3	6

3. Express as single fractions or as whole numbers:

(a) $\dfrac{1}{3} \times 2$ (b) $\dfrac{2}{3} \times 6$ (c) $\dfrac{3}{4} \times 5$ (d) $\dfrac{3}{5} \times 15$

4. Show that if $\frac{3}{0}$ is regarded as a meaningful expression, with $\frac{3}{0} \times 0 = 3$, then it follows that $9 = 3$. (See §3.)

5. Show that $\frac{0}{3} = 0$.

6. Carry out the indicated operations:

(a) $\dfrac{2}{3} \times \dfrac{3}{8}$ (b) $\dfrac{1}{2} \times \dfrac{4}{3}$ (c) $\dfrac{2}{5} \times \dfrac{4}{3}$ *Answer:* (a) $\frac{6}{24}$

7. Carry out the indicated operations:

(a) $\dfrac{2}{3} \div \dfrac{5}{2}$ (b) $\dfrac{3}{5} \div \dfrac{3}{4}$ (c) $\dfrac{5}{1} \div \dfrac{1}{2}$

Answers: (b) $1\frac{2}{15}$, (c) 10

8. If plums are selling at 3 for 10¢, (a) how much will two dozen cost? (b) how many can be bought for 50¢? (Do these in terms of fractions.)

Answer: (b) $50 \div 1\frac{0}{3} = $ etc.

9. If a person pays an income tax of $\frac{1}{5}$ of his salary, and $\frac{3}{5}$ of this tax is used for defense expenditures, what fractional part of his salary goes toward defense?

10. What is a person's reading rate in words per minute if he reads 100 words in 8 sec.?

§4. REDUCING FRACTIONS

The two entries on each row of the table at the right give the numbers of elements in "set A" and "set B." On a relative basis, all pairs of sets compare alike. When A and B have 1 and 3 elements, respectively, then set B contains *3 times as many* elements as A, and the fraction associated with the comparison is $\frac{3}{1} = 3$. Likewise, when sets A and B have 4 and 12 elements, the set B contains 3 times as many elements as A, and the associated fraction is $\frac{12}{4} = 3$. *In these and in the other listed cases, the associated fraction is always the same number*, since the same relative comparison is obtained in all cases.

NUMBER IN SET	
Set A	*Set B*
1	3
2	6
3	9
4	12
5	15
6	18

The fractional symbols $\frac{3}{1}$, $\frac{6}{2}$, $\frac{9}{3}$, etc. are thus merely different ways of denoting the same number:

$$\frac{3}{1} = \frac{6}{2} = \frac{9}{3} = \frac{12}{4} = \cdots$$

This is also apparent, to be sure, from the fact that we have equated a fraction to a quotient, since $3 \div 1 = 3$, $6 \div 2 = 3$, etc.

The second tabular exhibit brings out the same facts with reference to a pair of sets with numbers in the ratio of 2 to 3. Set B has $\frac{2}{3}$ as many elements as set A. This associated fraction can be written in many ways:

$$\frac{2}{3} = \frac{4}{6} = \frac{6}{9} = \frac{8}{12} = \frac{10}{15} = \cdots .$$

| | NUMBER IN SET | |
Set A	Set B
3	2
6	4
9	6
12	8
15	10

The form $\frac{2}{3}$ is simplest, and the fraction so written is said to be **in lowest terms**. *Any fraction equal to $\frac{2}{3}$ can be obtained by multiplying both numerator and denominator by some natural number.* In symbols, every fraction equal to $\frac{2}{3}$ is of the form

$$\frac{2n}{3n},$$

where n denotes some natural number.

If numerator and denominator of a fraction share a common factor, this can be divided out of both numerator and denominator to produce a simpler form. Hence in the *lowest term form*, there is no common factor: *numerator and denominator are prime to each other.* Further, *any equal fraction can be obtained by multiplying both numerator and denominator by some natural number.*

What fractions, for example, are equal to $\frac{18}{24}$? We find GCD (18,24) = 6. Hence

$$\frac{18}{24} = \frac{18 \div 6}{24 \div 6} = \frac{3}{4},$$

the lowest term form. Multiplying above and below by 1, 2, 3, 4, . . . gives *all* the fractions equal to $\frac{18}{24}$:

$$\frac{3}{4} = \frac{6}{8} = \frac{9}{12} = \frac{12}{16} = \frac{15}{20} = \frac{18}{24} = \frac{21}{28} = \cdots .$$

We may compare the sizes of two fractions by dividing one into the other, but it is more direct to express them both with the same denominator, then to compare their numerators. According as one numerator is less than, equal to, or greater than the other, so are the fractions. Thus:

$$\frac{11}{24} > \frac{7}{24} \quad \text{and} \quad \frac{2}{9} < \frac{3}{9}.$$

Two or more fractions may be converted to forms having as their *common denominator* the LCM of the denominators of the given fractions.

(This LCM is occasionally called the "lowest common denominator.")
Suppose we wish to compare $\frac{3}{8}$ and $\frac{5}{12}$. We find:

$$\text{LCM }(8,12) = 24 \qquad \frac{3}{8} = \frac{9}{24} \qquad \frac{10}{24} > \frac{9}{24}$$
$$\frac{5}{12} = \frac{10}{24} \qquad \therefore \ \ \frac{5}{12} > \frac{3}{8}.$$

In multiplying or dividing fractions, we may reduce piecemeal or all
at once. The piecemeal scheme is usually easier. Using the fact that GCD
$(48,300) = 12$, we have:

$$\frac{6}{12} \times \frac{8}{15} = \frac{6 \times 8}{20 \times 15} = \frac{48}{300} = \frac{12 \times 4}{12 \times 25} = \frac{4}{25}.$$

However, we would normally proceed by dividing out, above and below,
any factor that we see to be common to a numerator and a denominator
term. As new numbers replace old, the latter are "scratched out" (as
in old-time scratch methods), a procedure now called "cancellation."

$$\frac{\cancel{6}}{\cancel{20}} \times \frac{\cancel{8}}{\cancel{15}} = \frac{1 \times 4}{5 \times 5} = \frac{4}{25}.$$

(Dividing 3 out of both 6 and 15, for example, is valid because were the
product written in the form $\frac{6 \times 8}{20 \times 15}$, the 3 would appear as a factor of
the entire numerator, also of the entire denominator.)

"Cancellation" is a physical, not a mathematical operation. Any procedure
involving a cancellation must therefore be justified in terms of whatever mathematical operation was performed—an *addition, subtraction, multiplication,* or
division. In the example cited above, three separate divisions by 3, 2, 2 were
made into both numerator and denominator:

$$\frac{6}{20} \times \frac{8}{15} = \frac{2}{20} \times \frac{8}{5} = \frac{1}{10} \times \frac{8}{5} = \frac{1}{5} \times \frac{4}{5} = \frac{4}{25}$$

The various rules and techniques for handling fractions which we have
discussed in the last few pages all stem from the multiplicity of ways that
exist of expressing a number in fractional form. It is of paramount importance that one should maintain in his mind the clear-cut distinction
between a *number* and the variable fractional forms by which it may be
designated: $\frac{1}{2}, \frac{2}{4}, \frac{3}{6}, \frac{4}{8}, \ldots$, for example. The forms may be regarded as different "names" for the same number. It is not just the scien-
tist and the engineer who must heed this lesson in the basic semantics
of symbolic usage. So must the housewife, as she indulges in painful

number juggling while trying to transform a recipe serving 6 into one serving 4.

Confusion between the number and the form is the common source of error in manipulating fractions. Even many college students cling to the delusion that fractions are "special" numbers characterized by a superior kind of invariance: "Whatever you do to them, you don't change the value." This blithe attitude records itself in ghastly muscle work like:

$$\frac{3}{4} = \frac{3-1}{4-1} = \frac{2}{3}; \qquad \frac{4}{5} + \frac{3}{4} = \frac{3}{5}; \qquad \frac{2\!\!\!/2}{3\!\!\!/2} = \frac{2}{3}.$$

It is difficult to shatter the delusion and restore the student to mathematical sanity by convincing him that a fraction as a number possesses no special property—that adding any number except 0 changes it, that multiplying by any number except 1 changes it, etc. Fractions have no special properties other than those which arise *notationally*, because of the variety of written fractional forms that can be used to denote the same fractional number.

PROBLEM SET 2 (§4)

In Problems 1–4, reduce each fraction to lowest terms. (Where common factors are apparent, divide them out. In other cases, find the GCD of numerator and denominator by the Euclidean Rule, and divide it out of numerator and denominator.)

1. (a) $\dfrac{12}{16}$ (b) $\dfrac{20}{25}$ (c) $\dfrac{6}{4}$ (d) $\dfrac{3}{111}$ (e) $\dfrac{32}{48}$

2. (a) $\dfrac{35}{60}$ (b) $\dfrac{200}{75}$ (c) $\dfrac{63}{84}$ (d) $\dfrac{60}{100}$ (e) $\dfrac{45}{72}$

3. (a) $\dfrac{127}{195}$ (b) $\dfrac{32}{200}$ (c) $\dfrac{105}{168}$ (d) $\dfrac{84}{270}$ (e) $\dfrac{120}{347}$

4. (a) $\dfrac{315}{445}$ (b) $\dfrac{264}{480}$ (c) $\dfrac{323}{437}$ (d) $\dfrac{391}{667}$ (e) $\dfrac{851}{1073}$

5. Is $\dfrac{6}{15} = \dfrac{74}{185}$?   *Answer:* Yes, for $\dfrac{6}{15} = \dfrac{2}{5} = \dfrac{2 \times 37}{5 \times 37} = \dfrac{74}{185}.$

6. Is $\dfrac{6}{15} = \dfrac{50}{124}$?   *Answer:* No, for $\dfrac{6}{15} = \dfrac{2}{5}$, and 124 is not a multiple of 5.

7. Is $\dfrac{9}{12} = \dfrac{35}{44}$?   *Answer:* No, for $\dfrac{9}{12} = \dfrac{3}{4} = \dfrac{3 \times 11}{4 \times 11} = \dfrac{33}{44} < \dfrac{35}{44}.$

8. (a) Is $\dfrac{70}{112} = \dfrac{45}{72}$?   (b) Is $\dfrac{6}{14} = \dfrac{11}{24}$?

9. (a) Is $\dfrac{216}{126} = \dfrac{284}{161}$?   (b) Is $\dfrac{33}{88} = \dfrac{2223}{5848}$?

10. (a) Is $\dfrac{17}{60} = \dfrac{8}{35}$?   (b) Is $\dfrac{13}{42} = \dfrac{17}{56}$?

11–16. In Problems 8–10, wherever the fractions are not equal, which is the larger?

17. Before multiplying out, simplify by "cancellation."

$$\text{(a)} \quad \frac{12}{35} \times \frac{21}{24} \qquad \text{(b)} \quad \frac{15}{32} \times \frac{56}{105} \qquad \text{(c)} \quad \frac{6}{10} \times \frac{4}{27} \times \frac{9}{15}$$

18. Are there any circumstances under which 1 can be added to both numerator and denominator of a fraction without changing its value? (*Hint:* Set $(a + 1)/(b + 1) = a/b$, and consider the implications.)

§5. ADDING FRACTIONS

A comparison of a part of a group with the whole is simpler to conceive and to talk about than is a comparison between just any two groups. In initially discussing the addition of fractions, we will use the part-whole conception, even though it temporarily restricts us to fractions of value under 1.

Consider a set of a dozen blocks. Several fractions can be represented concretely as subsets of this given *base set*. To represent ½, for example, we *partition* the given set into two mutually matching subsets—6 blocks in each. Either subset then *represents* ½. Since the representation is by 6 objects out of 12, we could characterize it more fully as *a representation of ½ in the form* $\frac{6}{12}$:

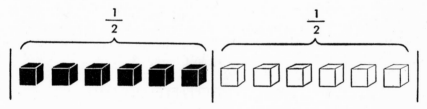

To represent ⅔, we partition the set of 12 into 3 mutually matching subsets, then take any 2 of them:

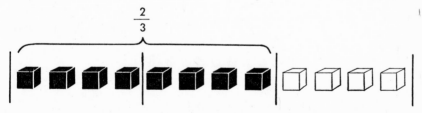

Since 8 blocks are chosen from 12, we may describe the above as *a representation of ⅔ in the form* $\frac{8}{12}$.

Other types of representation of ⅔ in the form $\frac{8}{12}$ can be obtained by beginning with other forms, $\frac{4}{6}$ or $\frac{8}{12}$. Beginning with $\frac{4}{6}$, for example, we may partition the set of 12 into 6 mutually matching subsets, then take any 4 of them:

Should we begin with the form $\frac{8}{12}$ itself, the "cells" of the partition will each contain only one block, and we may choose blocks from any 8 cells:

Should we wish to represent $\frac{2}{3}$ in the form $\frac{16}{24}$, our dozen blocks would be inadequate. We would have to use a new base set of 24 blocks (or some multiple of 24).

Let us now consider the addition of two fractions, $\frac{1}{3}$ and $\frac{1}{2}$, for example. Since $\frac{1}{3}$ can be represented by any 4 blocks and $\frac{1}{2}$ by any 6 blocks, the sum should apparently be represented by $4 + 6 = 10$ blocks. But 10 blocks out of 12 comprise a representation of $\frac{10}{12} = \frac{5}{6}$. Thus:

$$\frac{1}{3} + \frac{1}{2} = \frac{4}{12} + \frac{6}{12} = \frac{10}{12} = \frac{5}{6}.$$

What we have done above is to associate the *addition of two fractional numbers* with the *union of two sets that comprise their representatives*. In picturing this operation, we must choose disjoint sets, just as in the case of natural number addition discussed in Chapter 3.

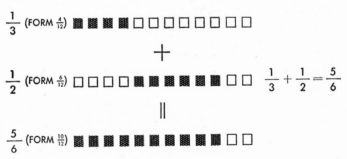

Consider the sum

$$\frac{1}{4} + \frac{3}{10}.$$

In order to picture this addition, we need a base set of blocks large enough for both $\frac{1}{4}$ and $\frac{3}{10}$ to be represented. A number of blocks equal to the product of denominators, $4 \times 10 = 40$, will do. The least choice, however, is given by the LCM: LCM (4,10) = 20. With 20 blocks we have:

$\dfrac{1}{4}$ (FORM $\tfrac{5}{20}$) ■ □ ■ □ □ ■ ■ □ □ □ ■ □ □ □ □ □ □ □ □ □

$+$

$\dfrac{3}{10}$ (FORM $\tfrac{6}{20}$) □ ■ □ □ □ □ □ ■ ■ □ □ □ □ ■ □ ■ ■ □ □ $\dfrac{1}{4} + \dfrac{3}{10} = \dfrac{11}{20}$

$\|$

$\dfrac{11}{20}$ (FORM $\tfrac{11}{20}$) ■ ■ ■ □ □ ■ ■ □ ■ ■ ■ ■ □ □ □ ■ □ ■ ■ □ □

On the basis of our discussion, we may frame a simple arithmetic rule for adding fractions: *Express both fractions in forms having the same denominator* (the LCM of the given denominators being the best choice). *Add the numerators of these forms. Place this result over the common denominator.* In symbols, the latter part of the rule reads

$$\frac{a}{n} + \frac{b}{n} = \frac{a + b}{n}.$$

Note that the above is a generalization of the *distributive law:*

$$\frac{a}{n} + \frac{b}{n} = \frac{1}{n} \times a + \frac{1}{n} \times b = \frac{1}{n} \times (a + b) = \frac{a + b}{n}.$$

The full distributive law for fractions reads $f(f_1 + f_2) = ff_1 + ff_2$, and may be established on the basis of the above definition of addition and our previous results. The commutative and associative laws of addition may also be proved easily.

The subtraction of one fraction from another can be pictured as a take-away procedure with the blocks, the rule being

$$\frac{a}{n} - \frac{b}{n} = \frac{a - b}{n}.$$

By allowing multiplication of the base set, we may represent fractions and sums exceeding 1. Consider the fraction $1\frac{1}{4}$. Let the base set be triplicated. This provides $3 \times 4 = 12$ blocks, of which we may select 11 as comprising the representation of $1\frac{1}{4}$:

BASE SET

   $\dfrac{11}{4}$

With the above arrangement, we could also picture an addition like

$$\frac{3}{4} + \frac{3}{2} = \frac{3}{4} + \frac{6}{4} = \frac{9}{4}.$$

A fraction whose numerator is less than its denominator is called *proper*. Others are called *improper*. These latter have values equal to or greater than 1. *Examples:* $4/4$. $13/9$, $2125/3$, etc. An improper fraction can be expressed as *a whole number plus a proper fraction* by using the basic division relation:

$$\frac{207}{5} = \frac{5 \times 41 + 2}{5} = \frac{5 \times 41}{5} + \frac{2}{5} = 41 + \frac{2}{5} = 41\frac{2}{5}.$$

The expression on the far right, $41\frac{2}{5}$, is an abbreviation for the sum $41 + \frac{2}{5}$, and is an example of a *mixed number*. In practice, the operation of expressing an improper fraction as a mixed number is carried out by dividing and using the rule (obtained from the basic division relation):

$$\frac{\text{Dividend}}{\text{Divisor}} = \text{Quotient} + \frac{\text{Remainder}}{\text{Divisor}}.$$

Converting a mixed number to a proper fraction is best accomplished by reversing the steps above. (Many pupils are taught to follow a special rule, which enables them to do the work quickly, but which like all purely mechanical procedures heightens the possibility of error.)

$$41\frac{2}{5} = 41 + \frac{2}{5} = \frac{205}{5} + \frac{2}{5} = \frac{207}{5}.$$

§6. REMARKS ON TEACHING

In the work with fractions in the early school grades, pictorial representations using blocks or other objects are a major teaching aid. Twelve blocks make a good group to work with because the three most common fractional types, halves, thirds, and quarters, can be represented, compared, and added or subtracted. Rectangular lengths can also be used. "Pie slices" are among the common devices, $\frac{1}{2} + \frac{1}{4}$ being shown as follows:

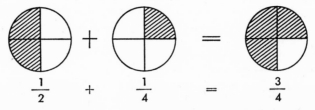

Disks of cardboard or heavier materials are available commercially, cut up into sectors of different sizes, so that common fractions can be represented. Thinner divided disks, with special backings, can be placed on flannel boards.

It is usual to introduce multiplication by first considering the multiplication of a fraction by a natural number:

$$4 \times \frac{1}{2} = \frac{1}{2} + \frac{1}{2} + \frac{1}{2} + \frac{1}{2} = \frac{1+1+1+1}{2} = \frac{4}{2} = 2.$$

The idea of ½ *of* 4 is usually separately introduced as a partitioning conception:

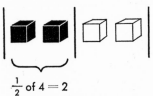

$$\frac{1}{2} \text{ of } 4 = 2$$

It may then be suggested that since $4 \times \frac{1}{2} = 2$, it is reasonable to assume $\frac{1}{2} \times 4 = 2$. Hence ½ of 4 can be taken as meaning $\frac{1}{2} \times 4$. The conception of the general multiplication of fractions can then be gradually built up.

After a pupil has learned the "area" or "two-way array" representation of natural number multiplication, as discussed in Chapter 3, he can be shown a similar representation for the multiplication of fractions:

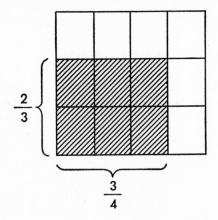

$$\frac{2}{3} \times \frac{3}{4} = \frac{2 \times 3}{3 \times 4} = \frac{6}{12} = \frac{1}{2}$$

6 Black Rectangles out of 12

give a representation of $\frac{1}{2}$

PROBLEM SET 3 (§5–§6)

In problem work involving fractional representation, sketch squares instead of three-dimensional blocks, shading the squares that form the representation. The following, for example, is a representation of ¾ in the form ⁶⁄₈:

◪ ◪ ◪ ◪ ☐ ☐ ◪ ◪

In Problems 1–20, represent each fraction in the form requested. Vary your choice of "blocks," sometimes picking a consecutive group and at other times spotting them here and there.

	Fraction to be Represented	Form		Fraction to Be Represented	Form
1.	$\frac{1}{2}$	$\frac{1}{2}$	11.	$\frac{2}{3}$	$\frac{4}{6}$
2.	$\frac{1}{2}$	$\frac{2}{4}$	12.	$\frac{2}{3}$	$\frac{8}{12}$
3.	$\frac{1}{2}$	$\frac{3}{6}$	13.	$\frac{3}{4}$	$\frac{6}{8}$
4.	$\frac{1}{2}$	$\frac{4}{8}$	14.	$\frac{3}{4}$	$\frac{9}{12}$
5.	$\frac{1}{2}$	$\frac{6}{12}$	15.	$\frac{5}{6}$	$\frac{10}{12}$
6.	$\frac{1}{3}$	$\frac{1}{3}$	16.	$\frac{3}{5}$	$\frac{6}{10}$
7.	$\frac{1}{3}$	$\frac{2}{6}$	17.	$\frac{3}{8}$	$\frac{3}{8}$
8.	$\frac{1}{3}$	$\frac{3}{9}$	18.	$\frac{3}{8}$	$\frac{6}{16}$
9.	$\frac{1}{3}$	$\frac{4}{12}$	19.	$\frac{5}{8}$	$\frac{15}{24}$
10.	$\frac{1}{3}$	$\frac{8}{24}$	20.	1	$\frac{4}{4}$

In Problems 21–29, picture each addition or subtraction in terms of fractional representations as was done in §5. Use the smallest possible base set in each case (LCM).

21. $\dfrac{1}{5} + \dfrac{2}{5}$ 22. $\dfrac{1}{2} + \dfrac{1}{4}$ 23. $\dfrac{1}{2} + \dfrac{1}{3}$

24. $\dfrac{3}{4} + \dfrac{1}{6}$ 25. $\dfrac{1}{4} + \dfrac{3}{8}$ 26. $\dfrac{3}{8} + \dfrac{5}{12}$

27. $\dfrac{4}{5} - \dfrac{1}{5}$ 28. $\dfrac{5}{8} - \dfrac{1}{4}$ 29. $\dfrac{5}{6} - \dfrac{3}{8}$

30. Picture the operation of Problem 22 in terms of "pie slices." (§6).
31. Picture the operation of Problem 25 in terms of "pie slices."
32. Picture the operation of Problem 28 in terms of "pie slices."
33. Picture the operation of Problem 23 in terms of "pie slices."
34. Picture the operation of Problem 24 in terms of "pie slices."
35. Picture the following multiplications on a rectangular grid as shown at the end of §6.

(a) $\dfrac{1}{2} \times \dfrac{3}{4}$ (b) $\dfrac{2}{3} \times \dfrac{3}{8}$ (c) $\dfrac{2}{3} \times \dfrac{2}{5}$ (d) $\dfrac{3}{4} \times \dfrac{5}{7}$

36*. Picture the following, duplicating or triplicating the base set, as necessary:

(a) $\dfrac{1}{2} + \dfrac{3}{4}$ (b) $\dfrac{3}{2} + \dfrac{5}{3}$ (c) $\dfrac{2}{3} + \dfrac{3}{4}$ (d) $2 - \dfrac{2}{3}$

§7. THE RULES FOR FRACTIONS

We collect here the various rules needed for handling fractions, most of which have been developed during the preceding discussion. Taken in conjunction with the earlier rules for operating with whole numbers, the listed rules suffice for all manipulations with fractions (powers and roots excepted).

THE RULES FOR FRACTIONS

In Groups **A** and **B**, the numbers n, a, b, c, d, are whole numbers and no number appearing in a denominator is zero.

A. Special   1. $n = \dfrac{n}{1}$ 2. $\dfrac{a}{b} = a \div b$ 3. $\dfrac{a}{b} = \dfrac{na}{nb}$

B. Operations*   1. $\dfrac{a}{n} + \dfrac{b}{n} = \dfrac{a+b}{n}$ 3. $\dfrac{a}{b} \times \dfrac{c}{d} = \dfrac{ac}{bd}$

               2. $\dfrac{a}{n} - \dfrac{b}{n} = \dfrac{a-b}{n}$ 4. $\dfrac{a}{b} \div \dfrac{c}{d} = \dfrac{a}{b} \times \dfrac{d}{c}$

C. Manipulation   The above rules hold when the various numerators and denominators are themselves fractions.

D. Laws   The five basic laws of arithmetic, commutative, associative, and distributive, hold for fractions.

* These generalize, in the obvious ways, to cases of three or more fractions.

To show how the rules are used, we give several typical numerical examples, and cite the rule used at each step. Thus **A3** signifies that the step is justified by Rule **A3**: $a/b = na/nb$. (**CA3**) refers to a manipulation of type $f_1/f_2 = ff_1/ff_2$, fractions f, f_1, f_2 replacing the whole numbers n, a, b of the original Rule **A3**. Some steps shown in the examples would ordinarily be omitted or performed mentally.

Example 1. Reduce to lowest terms: (a) $^{28}\!/_{35}$; (b) $^{561}\!/_{935}$.

Work.   (a) $\dfrac{28}{35} = \dfrac{4 \times 7}{5 \times 7} = \dfrac{4}{5}$;   (**A3**)

             (b) $\dfrac{561}{935} = \dfrac{3 \times 187}{5 \times 187} = \dfrac{3}{5}$.   (**A3**)

(GCD's may be found from factors or by the Euclidean division rule.)

Example 2. Multiply: $5 \times \dfrac{2}{3}$.

Work. By (**A1**), $5 = \dfrac{5}{1}$.   By (**B3**), $\dfrac{5}{1} \times \dfrac{2}{3} = \dfrac{10}{3}$.

Example 3. Express as a single fraction: $4\frac{2}{3}$ (see §5).

Work. $4\dfrac{2}{3} = 4 + \dfrac{2}{3} = \dfrac{4}{1} + \dfrac{2}{3} = \dfrac{12}{3} + \dfrac{2}{3} = \dfrac{14}{3}$.   (**A1, A3, B1**)

Example 4. Express $^{384}\!/_{65}$ in "mixed" form (see §5).

Work. $\dfrac{384}{65} = \dfrac{5 \times 65 \; + \; 59}{65} = 5 + \dfrac{59}{65} = 5\dfrac{59}{65}.$ **(B1, A3, A1)**

$$\begin{array}{r} 5 \\ 65\overline{)384} \\ 325 \\ \hline 59 \end{array}$$

(In practice, the answer is written at once by inspection of the division work.)

Example 5. Combine: $\dfrac{5}{8} - \dfrac{3}{20}.$

Work. LCM $(8,20) = 40.$

$$\dfrac{5}{8} - \dfrac{3}{20} = \dfrac{25}{40} - \dfrac{6}{40} = \dfrac{19}{40}. \quad \textbf{(A3, B2)}$$

$$\begin{array}{l} 8 = 2 \times 2 \times 2 \\ 20 = 2 \times 2 \times 5 \\ \hline \text{LCM} = 2 \times 2 \times 2 \times 5 \end{array}$$

Example 6. Divide: $\dfrac{35}{16} \div \dfrac{49}{24}.$

Work.

$$\dfrac{35}{16} \div \dfrac{49}{24} = \dfrac{35}{16} \times \dfrac{24}{49} = \dfrac{35 \times 24}{16 \times 49}$$

$$= \dfrac{5 \times 7 \times 2 \times 2 \times 2 \times 3}{2 \times 2 \times 2 \times 2 \times 7 \times 7} = \dfrac{5 \times 3}{2 \times 7} = \dfrac{15}{14}. \quad \textbf{(B4, B3, A3)}$$

In practice, factors are divided out at once:

$$\begin{array}{c} ^{5} \quad ^{3} \\ \dfrac{\cancel{35}}{\cancel{16}} \times \dfrac{\cancel{24}}{\cancel{49}} = \dfrac{15}{14} \\ ^{2} \quad ^{7} \end{array} \qquad \left[\text{i.e., } \dfrac{35}{16} \times \dfrac{24}{49} = \dfrac{5}{16} \times \dfrac{24}{7} = \dfrac{5}{2} \times \dfrac{3}{7} = \dfrac{15}{14} \right]$$

Example 7.   Simplify: $25\dfrac{3}{5} \div 4\dfrac{1}{3}.$

Work.   METHOD A

$$25\tfrac{3}{5} \div 4\tfrac{1}{3} = \dfrac{25\tfrac{3}{5}}{4\tfrac{1}{3}} = \dfrac{25 + \tfrac{3}{5}}{4 + \tfrac{1}{3}} \quad \textbf{(CA2)}$$

$$= \dfrac{15 \times (25 + \tfrac{3}{5})}{15 \times (4 + \tfrac{1}{3})} \quad \textbf{(CA3)} \qquad \begin{array}{l}\text{Note that} \\ \text{LCM } (3,5) = 15.\end{array}$$

$$= \dfrac{375 + 9}{60 + 5} \quad \textbf{(D: also Example 2)}$$

$$= \dfrac{384}{65} = 5\dfrac{59}{65} \quad \text{(Example 4)}$$

METHOD B

$$25 + \frac{3}{5} = \frac{125}{5} + \frac{3}{5} = \frac{128}{5}; \qquad 4 + \frac{1}{3} = \frac{12}{3} + \frac{1}{3} = \frac{13}{3} \quad \text{(Example 3)}$$

$$\frac{128}{5} \div \frac{13}{3} = \frac{128}{5} \times \frac{3}{13} = \frac{128 \times 3}{5 \times 13} = \frac{384}{65} = 5\frac{59}{65} \qquad \text{(CA2; Examples 6, 4)}$$

Example 8.   Multiply: $25\frac{3}{5} \times 4\frac{1}{3}$.

Work. METHOD A

Use the scheme of Example 7B:

$$25\frac{3}{5} \times 4\frac{1}{3} = \frac{128}{5} \times \frac{13}{3} = \frac{128 \times 13}{5 \times 3} = \frac{1664}{15} = 110\frac{14}{15}.$$

METHOD B

$$25\frac{3}{5} \times 4\frac{1}{3} = \left(25 + \frac{3}{5}\right)\left(4 + \frac{1}{3}\right)$$

$$= 25 \times 4 + \frac{3}{5} \times 4 + 25 \times \frac{1}{3} + \frac{3}{5} \times \frac{1}{3} \quad \textbf{(D)}$$

$$= 100 + \frac{12}{5} + \frac{25}{3} + \frac{1}{5} \quad \textbf{(A1, B3, A3)}$$

$$= 100 + 2 + 8 + \frac{3}{5} + \frac{1}{3} \quad \textbf{(B1, A3, A1, B1)}$$

$$= 110 + \left(\frac{9}{15} + \frac{5}{15}\right) = 110\frac{14}{15} \quad \textbf{(A3, B1)}$$

Example 9.   Combine: $\frac{2}{3} - \frac{1}{10} + \frac{4}{45}$.

Work.   LCM $(3,10,45) = 90$.

$$\frac{2}{3} - \frac{1}{10} + \frac{4}{45} = \frac{60}{90} - \frac{9}{90} + \frac{8}{90} = \frac{59}{90}$$

$$3 = 3$$
$$10 = 2 \times 5$$
$$45 = 3 \times 3 \times 5$$
$$\overline{\text{LCM} = 2 \times 3 \times 3 \times 5}$$

(A3, B2, B1)

PROBLEM SET 4 (§7)

Work each problem in the manner of the illustrative Examples 1–9 of §7, at each step citing the rule that justifies the work.

1.   Reduce to lowest terms:

     (a) $\frac{42}{56}$ (b) $\frac{36}{84}$ (c) $\frac{286}{598}$ (d) $\frac{437}{943}$

2. Multiply:

(a) $3 \times \frac{4}{7}$ (b) $\frac{3}{4} \times 5$ (c) $20 \times \frac{5}{8}$ (d) $\frac{2}{3} \times 6$

3. Express as single fractions:

(a) $2\frac{2}{5}$ (b) $10\frac{1}{2}$ (c) $63\frac{3}{4}$ (d) $111\frac{1}{9}$

4. Express in mixed form:

(a) $\dfrac{11}{3}$ (b) $\dfrac{59}{8}$ (c) $\dfrac{303}{10}$ (d) $\dfrac{1190}{73}$

5. Combine and reduce:

(a) $\dfrac{2}{3} + \dfrac{1}{6}$ (b) $\dfrac{5}{12} + \dfrac{3}{20}$ (c) $\dfrac{7}{24} + \dfrac{5}{16}$

6. Combine and reduce:

(a) $\dfrac{2}{3} - \dfrac{1}{6}$ (b) $\dfrac{7}{8} - \dfrac{5}{12}$ (c) $\dfrac{13}{30} - \dfrac{7}{20}$

7. Combine and reduce:

(a) $\dfrac{1}{2} - \dfrac{1}{6} + \dfrac{1}{9}$ (b) $\dfrac{7}{8} - \dfrac{1}{12} + \dfrac{5}{6}$

8. Simplify

(a) $\dfrac{20}{33} \div \dfrac{35}{12}$ (b) $\dfrac{18}{35} \div \dfrac{24}{49}$

9. Simplify in two ways (Example 7, §7): $4\frac{3}{4} \div 5\frac{1}{6}$.

10. Simplify in two ways (Example 8, §7): $8\frac{1}{4} \times 5\frac{1}{3}$.

9

Decimals

§1. THE BACKGROUND

Old European textbooks display horrendous problems involving fractions like

$$\frac{231,976}{50,872,371}.$$

As future clerks and tradesmen labored with these monstrosities, their schoolroom frustrations must have grown so intense as to dwarf those which plague the pupils of today and which are so much the concern of our educational specialists.

Why did the old-time schoolmen foist such numerical complexities upon their pupils? They may have felt that work tedium was good for the mind—or for the soul. Yet actually they had no other choice. Before decimals were invented, the practical computer had no way to avoid dealing with cumbersome fractions.

A Belgian, Simon Stevin, introduced the idea of *decimal fractions* in the book *La Disme*, published in 1585. We have seen that the Babylonians had the first notions of this sort, making particular use of the "sexagesimal" fractions $\frac{1}{60}$ and $\frac{1}{3600}$. But Stevin combined the idea of using fractions whose denominators are powers of the number base (10) with the modern place value conception. The combination was a brilliant stroke. Nowadays we generally use the common or ratio form of fractions, like $\frac{3}{5}$, only when the fraction is a simple one. Otherwise we prefer the decimal form.

Merchants, artisans, and others were slow to accept the new form. It was hard to agree on a standard notation. The following notations, shown for the number $3^{14}\!/_{100}$, were among those tried and discarded:

$$3\textcircled{1}1\textcircled{1}4\textcircled{2} \qquad 3{,}1'4'' \qquad 3/\overline{1}\,\overset{1}{\overset{}{\underline{4}}}\overset{2}{} \qquad 3/\dot1\,\dot4 \qquad 3/\underline{14}$$

At present, the decimal point (dot .) is used as the "separatrix" in the United States and in England, but the English write it higher up than

155

we do. In Belgium, France, Germany, Italy, and the Scandinavian countries, a comma is used instead. Scandinavians also print the fractional part in smaller type than the integral part:

$$\text{U. S.,} \quad 3.14 \qquad \text{France, etc., } 3,14$$
$$\text{England, } 3{\cdot}14 \qquad \text{Scandinavia, } 3,_{14}$$

We use a still different notation when writing checks, $3\underline{^{14}}$ instead of 3.14, having found this a greater protection against misreading or alteration.

§2. DECIMAL FRACTIONS

A decimal fraction is a fraction whose denominator is a power of ten (*1, 10, 100, 1000, etc.*)

Thus $^{314}\!/_{100}$, $^5\!/_1$, $^{17}\!/_{1000}$ are decimal fractions. Except for those equal to whole numbers, like $^5\!/_1 = 5$, we customarily write decimal fractions in *decimal form*: 3.14 instead of $^{314}\!/_{100}$; .017 in place of $^{17}\!/_{1000}$. The denominator is discarded and a *decimal point* inserted between two digits of the numerator so as to make the number of digits on its right equal to the "exponent" of the power of ten which formed the denominator. (This exponent or index equals the number of zeros in the written power: $10^0 = 1$, $10^1 = 10$, $10^2 = 100$, $10^3 = 1000$, etc.) The number of digits following the point is called the number of *decimal places* in the number. The number 3.14 is given to two decimal places.

Examples. $^{31425}\!/_{1000} = 31.425$

(three decimal places, corresponding to the three zeros in 1,000); and

$$^{24}\!/_{10000} = .0024$$

(four decimal places, corresponding to the four zeros in 10,000).

When a number is written in decimal form, its *place-value structure* may be seen to be as in Figure 24, the number 204.3708 being used in illustration.

Sometimes the place names are used in reading the number: "Two Hundred Four *and* Three Thousand Seven Hundred Eight Ten-Thousandths." (The "and" signifies the addition of the whole number portion and the fractional portion.) The more usual way of reading is: "Two – oh – Four *point* Three – Seven – oh – Eight."

The decimal form helps us judge the relative sizes of numbers. Only a glance is needed to tell which of two numbers is the greater. The decimal form simplifies computation enormously: Handling decimals is much like handling whole numbers, the complications of fractions being by-passed.

What common fractions can be written as decimal fractions? The prime factors of ten are 2 and 5. The various powers of ten are thus products of 2's and 5's. Hence a fraction can be converted to a decimal

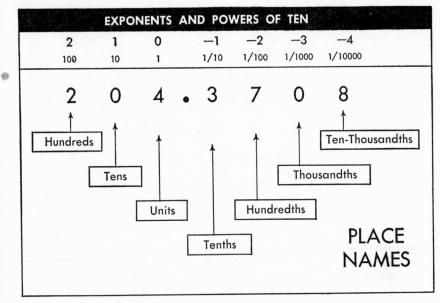

Fig. 24   Place-Value Structure of a Decimal Expression

fraction only if the prime factors of its denominator (when the fraction is written in lowest terms) include only 2's and 5's. With $\frac{3}{40}$, for example, we have $40 = 2 \times 2 \times 2 \times 5$. Hence 40 is a divisor of $1000 = 2 \times 2 \times 2 \times 5 \times 5 \times 5$, and $\frac{3}{40} = \frac{75}{1000} = .075$.

From the above we see that the much-used fraction $\frac{1}{3}$ cannot be expressed as a decimal fraction. We make the best of this awkward situation by using approximations. In a given practical situation we may not mind making an error of $\frac{1}{30}$. Then we may use .3 in place of $\frac{1}{3}$, because

$$\frac{1}{3} - .3 = \frac{1}{3} - \frac{3}{10} = \frac{10}{30} - \frac{9}{30} = \frac{1}{30}.$$

The error can be cut down by increasing the number of decimal places, .33 approximating $\frac{1}{3}$ with an error of $\frac{1}{300}$, etc. The effect of using such approximations will be discussed in Chapter 12.

§3.   DECIMAL ARITHMETIC

Shifting the decimal point one place multiples or divides a number by ten. (Why?) Shifting it several places therefore multiplies or divides it by as many tens as places shifted. Thus 21470 is $10 \times 10 \times 10 = 1000$ times as large as 21.47, while .2147 is $10 \times 10 = 100$ times smaller.

Addition and Subtraction.   Arrange the numbers in a column with decimal points lined up vertically. Add or subtract as though the numbers were whole numbers. Insert a decimal point in the answer in position below the others:

7.14	*Add as though*	7140
306.008	*the numbers were:*	306008
2150.		2150000
2463.148		2463148

The following analysis shows why the scheme works:

$$7.14 + 306.008 + 2150 = 7.140 + 306.008 + 2150.000$$
$$= \frac{7140}{1000} + \frac{306008}{1000} + \frac{2150000}{1000}$$
$$= \frac{2463148}{1000} = 2463.148$$

Multiplication. Multiply as though the numbers were whole numbers. The sum of the numbers of decimal places in the given numbers gives the number of decimal places in the answer.

$$
\begin{array}{r}
46.52 \\
\times \quad 2.3 \\
\hline
13956 \\
9304 \\
\hline
106.996
\end{array}
\qquad
\begin{array}{l}
\text{2 places} \\
\text{1 place} \\
\\
\\
\text{3 places}
\end{array}
$$

Reason

$$2.3 \times 46.52 = \frac{23}{10} \times \frac{4652}{10 \times 10}$$
$$= \frac{23 \times 4652}{10 \times 10 \times 10}$$

Division. Before dividing, multiply both divisor and dividend by as many tens as needed to produce a whole-number divisor. This will not change the value of the quotient, and is effected just by moving decimal points. Place the decimal point for the quotient vertically above its new position in the dividend. In the following examples, crosses ($\times$) indicate the new positions of the decimal points after the multiplication by 100.

$$29.6 \div 2.28$$

$$
\begin{array}{r}
12. \\
2.28_\times \overline{)29.60_\times} \\
22\ 8 \\
\hline
6\ 80 \\
4\ 56 \\
\hline
2\ 24
\end{array}
\qquad\qquad
\begin{array}{r}
12.982 \\
2.28_\times \overline{)29.60_\times 000} \\
22\ 8 \\
\hline
6\ 80 \\
4\ 56 \\
\hline
2\ 240 \\
2\ 052 \\
\hline
1880 \\
1824 \\
\hline
560 \\
456 \\
\hline
104
\end{array}
$$

If the division process does not terminate at some stage with a zero remainder, then it may be continued as far as is wished. The work at the left above corresponds to the whole-number division of 2960 by 228:

$$\frac{29.6}{2.28} = \frac{2960}{228} = 12 + \frac{224}{228} = 12\frac{224}{228}.$$

The work at the right corresponds to:

$$\frac{29.6}{2.28} = \frac{2960}{228} = \frac{1}{1000} \times \frac{2960000}{228}$$

$$= \frac{1}{1000}\left(12982 + \frac{104}{228}\right)$$

$$= 12.982 + \frac{104/228}{1000}$$

This result could be written as $12.982\frac{104}{228}$, the fraction $104/228$ being understood to be in the same decimal place as the integer 2 to its left, *thousandths*. But such a form is confusing and should never be used. The division should always be carried out to a point at which the error term, $104/228000$ in this case, may for the purpose at hand be disregarded. The question of how the error term may be expressed then becomes irrelevant.

General Computation. In calculating the value of an expression involving the multiplication and/or division of several decimal numbers, computers sometimes disregard all decimal points, then place the point in the final answer by making a crude estimate of its size. This scheme is especially useful when calculations are made upon instruments or machines, such as the slide rule, which has no built-in provision for handling decimal points.

Consider the problem

$$x = \frac{93.6 \times 2.346}{.0718}.$$

This might be worked as follows:

$$936 \times 2346 = 2196 \ldots, \text{(actually 2195856)}$$
$$2196 \div 718 = 306 \ldots \quad .$$

But

$$x = \frac{100 \times 2}{.07} = \frac{200}{.07} = \frac{20000}{7} = \frac{21000}{7} = 3000 \text{ (roughly)}.$$

Hence

$$x = 3060 \text{ (approximate answer)}.$$

The idea of making crude estimates of the size of an answer is of considerable importance. Pupils should be urged to make such estimates in connection with most of their computational work. Not only are estimates valuable as gross checks, but making them serves to focus the attention of pupils upon the sizes of the numbers being dealt with. This keeps them closer to the realities behind the "paper" problems.

PROBLEM SET 1 (§1–§3)

1. Can a fraction with a denominator of 14 be written as a decimal fraction? *Answer:* No, since 14 contains the factor of 7, no multiple of which can be a power of 10 (= 2 × 5) according to the fundamental theorem of arithmetic of §9, Chapter 7.

2. Which of the following forms represent decimal fractions? (a) $1\frac{3}{8}$; (b) $\frac{7}{10}$; (c) $\frac{5}{6}$; (d) $5\frac{7}{25}$; (e) $37\frac{1}{256}$; (f) $\frac{2}{15}$.   *Answers:* (a), (b), (d), (e)

3. How closely does the decimal .67 approximate the fraction $\frac{2}{3}$?

4. Write in decimal form: (a) $\frac{3}{100}$; (b) $\frac{3}{80}$; (c) $273\frac{1}{10}$; (d) $\frac{2}{25000}$.
   Answers: (b)   .0375; (d)   .00008

5. Write as a fraction in lowest terms: (a)   .4; (b)   12.4; (c)   .035.
   Answers: (a) $\frac{2}{5}$; (c) $\frac{7}{200}$

6. Multiply: 80.43 × 1371.2.

7. Multiply: .0036 × 27.2.

8. Carry out the division 21.4 ÷ 3.5 to two decimal places, and use the resulting remainder to express the difference between your answer and the true quotient of 21.4 by 3.5.   *Answer:* $\frac{3}{700}$

*§4.   STANDARD FORM

When very large or very small numbers have to be dealt with, various devices may be used to avoid long strings of zero digits serving just as place fillers between the significant digits of the number and the decimal point.

The *World Almanac* cites the "Public Debt of the United States" for the fiscal year 1954 as $271,259,599,108. In a news story, it might be felt that $271,000,000,000 would be a sufficiently accurate figure to use. But rather than put in all the zeros, the reporter would likely write "271 billion dollars." In similar fashion, a technician working with radar or with a high-speed electronic computing machine may speak of a time interval of "35 microseconds" instead of .000035 seconds.

A general mathematical device is that of expressing numbers in **standard form** (also known as "scientific" form). The first step is to find the number between 1 and 10 that "corresponds" to the given number. This is found by moving the decimal point to a position just to the right of the first non-zero digit (reading from left to right) of the given number. It is suggested that this corresponding number between 1 and 10 may be named the *dekapart* ("ten-part") of the given number.

Given	*Corresponding Number*
Number	*between 1 and 10*
	(dekapart)
214	2.14
21,400	2.14
5.63	5.63
30.8	3.08
.6	6.
.00083	8.3

This operation of moving the decimal point either multiplies or divides the given number by as many tens as places moved. Hence:

$$214 = 2.14 \times 10^2 \qquad \text{(moved 2 places)}$$
$$21400 = 2.14 \times 10^4 \qquad \text{(moved 4 places)}$$
$$5.63 = 5.63 \times 10^0 \qquad \text{(moved 0 places)}$$
$$30.8 = 3.08 \times 10^1 \qquad \text{(moved 1 place)}$$

$$.6 = 6 \quad \times \frac{1}{10^1} \qquad \text{(moved 1 place)}$$

$$.00083 = 8.3 \quad \times \frac{1}{10^4} \qquad \text{(moved 4 places)}$$

The notation 10^0 may be unfamiliar to the student. In advanced algebra, the definition $a^0 = 1$ (a = any positive number) is introduced and justified by showing how it fits in with other exponential ideas. We will take $10^0 = 1$ on faith. Let us also on faith take a *negative* exponent as meaning "take the reciprocal":

$$10^{-1} = \frac{1}{10^1} = \frac{1}{10}; \qquad 10^{-2} = \frac{1}{10^2} = \frac{1}{100}; \qquad 10^{-3} = \frac{1}{10^3} = \frac{1}{1000}; \qquad \text{etc.}$$

Then we may write:

$$.6 = 6 \quad \times 10^{-1} \qquad \text{(moved 1 place)}$$
$$.00083 = 8.3 \times 10^{-4} \qquad \text{(moved 4 places)}$$

It is apparent that a negative exponent will appear *only when the given number is less than one.*

The forms listed at the right in our examples are the *standard forms.* The exponent of 10 is called the *characteristic* of the given number. If the corresponding number between 1 and 10 is called the "dekapart," as suggested, we have:

$$\text{Number} = \text{Dekapart} \times 10^{\text{Characteristic}}$$

In computing with numbers in standard form, we make use of simple rules for multiplying and dividing powers of ten. The product or quotient of two powers of ten is again a power of ten. For the product, the exponent is the *sum* of the two exponents. For the quotient, it is the *difference:*

$$10^2 \times 10^3 = 10^5$$

because $(10 \times 10) \times (10 \times 10 \times 10) = 10 \times 10 \times 10 \times 10 \times 10,$

$$\frac{10^5}{10^2} = 10^3$$

because $\dfrac{10 \times 10 \times 10 \times 10 \times 10}{10 \times 10} = 10 \times 10 \times 10.$

Example 1.   Compute $(295000) \times (.00621)$.

Work. $(295000) \times (.00621) = (2.95 \times 10^5) \times (6.21 \times 10^{-3})$
$= (2.95) \times (6.21) \times 10^5 \times 10^{-3}$
$= 2.95 \times 6.21 \times 10^2$
$= 18.3 \times 10^2$
$= 1.83 \times 10^3$ (standard form)
$= 1830$, approximately.

"Log" tables list the *logarithms* of numbers between 1 and 10. The logarithms of numbers outside this range may be found with the aid of standard forms:

$$\log 243 = \log (2.43 \times 10^2) = \log 2.43 + \log 10^2$$
$$= \log 2.43 + 2 = .386 + 2 \qquad (= 2.386).$$

$$\log .0076 = \log (7.6 \times 10^{-3}) = \log 7.6 - 3 = .881 - 3.$$

In general: log of number = log of dekapart + characteristic.

*PROBLEM SET 2 (§4)

1. Write in standard form:

    (a) 820   (e) 373,000,000
    (b) 82,000   (f) 52.4
    (c) .82   (g) .00000029
    (d) .0082

2. Write in ordinary form:

    (a) 2.6×10^3 (c) 5.081×10^1 (e) 2.81×10^{-1}
    (b) 3.62×10^5 (d) 7.2×10^{12} (f) 3.7×10^{-3}

3.   The sun is about 9.3×10^7 miles away. Light travels at about 1.86×10^5 miles per second. How long does it take for the light from the sun to reach the earth?   *Answer:* About $8\frac{1}{3}$ min.

4.   A radio station is broadcasting on 1000 kilocycles (marked either 10 or 100 on your AM band). This means that $1000 \times 1000 = 10^6$ waves pass your antenna each second. Their velocity is the same as that of light, about 1.86×10^5

miles per second. How long is one wave, in feet? How long is one wave from an FM station broadcasting on 100 megacycles (1 megacycle = 1 million cycles)?

Answer: The FM wave is 10 ft. long, less 2 in.

5. The sun's mass is about 2.2×10^{27} tons. The mass of a hydrogen atom is about 3.7×10^{-21} lb. If the sun were all hydrogen (which it isn't, quite), about how many atoms would it contain?

6. If a plant grows 2 inches per day, what is its average rate of growth per second?   *Answer:* 2.3×10^{-5} in./sec.

§5. RATIO

In introducing fractional ideas, we considered the notion of a **ratio** of one number to another, as of 3 to 2. This at first provided no more than a way of stating how one set compared with another in relative size. Within the enlarged number system of the fractions, however, such ratios may be interpreted as quotients and thereupon treated as numbers. We define:

The ratio of the number a *to the number* b *is the quotient* a ÷ b. This ratio is more often written in the fractional form *a/b*.

In common usage, some ratios are referred to as such, and others are called *rates*. The latter term is often used when dissimilar "units" are involved. If an auto travels 120 miles in 3 hours, for example, we compute its average *rate* of speed by forming the ratio of 120 to 3, $^{120}\!/_3 = 40$, and we cite the result as "40 miles per hour." Similarly a price *rate:* "$4\frac{1}{2}$¢ per pound." Or a production *rate:* "2,000 widgets per day." However, if 8 of 10 members attend a club meeting, then the *ratio* of attendance is $^8\!/_{10} = .8$. The answer is itself a "pure number," .8, with no "units" appended. The 1956 Chevrolet with standard transmission has a gear *ratio* of 3.70, meaning that in high gear the motor makes 370 revolutions for each 100 revolutions of the wheels.

A statement that two ratios are equal is called a **proportion.** Thus:

$$\frac{3}{2} = \frac{12}{8}.$$

In fractional terms this reads awkwardly: "Three halves equals twelve eighths." The language of proportion is more expressive: *3 is to 2 as 12 is to 8.* In older days, the notation 3:2::12:8 was often used, a form which has now happily vanished.

Noting that he has traveled 12 miles during the last 30 min. and that he still has 8 miles to go, an autoist may ask himself how long this will take at the same rate. In effect, he is trying to "solve" the proportion

$$\frac{?}{30} = \frac{8}{12}.$$

But 8 is to 12 as 2 is to 3, hence as 20 is to 30:

$$\frac{?}{30} = \frac{8}{12} = \frac{2}{3} = \frac{20}{30}.$$

So the driver may anticipate that the rest of the trip will require 20 min.

Much mental juggling of this sort goes on during the normal round of daily activities, as we compare prices of cans of different sizes in the supermarket, as we revamp to the family's needs recipes designed to serve different numbers, as we "build it ourselves" in the basement workshop, as we scan the multitudes of comparative figures scattered through the newspaper.

We also spend a great deal of time reflecting upon things that may or may not happen. Often we ascribe numerical *probabilities* to these uncertain events. A coin can fall in two ways, each as "likely" as the other. The number of ways that it can fall "heads" is 1. The number of ways it can fall tails is 1. Hence we say the *odds* for heads are even (1 to 1). The total number of ways the coin can fall is $1 + 1 = 2$. The *probability* or "chance" of the coin's falling heads is $\frac{1}{2}$, the ratio of the ways for heads to the total ways. Similarly, if it is known that of 24,386 people who have contracted the dread disease "mathophilia," 5,476 have died, we estimate the probability that a person who contracts the disease will die as the ratio $^{5476}\!/_{24386} = .22$ (approximately). In less clear-cut circumstances, we still make probability estimates and back them with hard cash: "I will put up \$5 to your \$3 that Senator Phogbound is re-elected." The tacit hypothesis here is that the probability of the Senator's election is at least $\frac{5}{8}$.

The usefulness of maps and diagrams depends upon the geometric similarity between these representations and the real objects (in projection), that is, upon the maintenance of a proportion: The ratio between two measurements on the map must equal the ratio between corresponding measurements on the object. This relationship is also the basis of the sense of reality which we get from photographs.

Example 1.   One store sells potatoes at 29¢ for 6 lb., another store at 36¢ for 8 lb. Compare.

Work.   The ratios giving the prices per pound are

$$\frac{29}{6} \quad \text{and} \quad \frac{36}{8}.$$

These may be compared by reduction to a common denominator:

$$\frac{29}{6} = \frac{116}{24} > \frac{108}{24} = \frac{36}{8}.$$

Therefore "36¢ for 8 lb." represents a lower price. It is of course also feasible to express each ratio as a decimal, then compare:

$$\frac{29}{6} = 4.83 > 4.50 = \frac{36}{8} \text{ (cents per lb.)}$$

Example 2. On a house plan, 2 in. represents 5 ft. A room length measures $7\frac{3}{16}$ in. on the plan. What is the length?

Work. We have these proportions:

$$\frac{\text{Length in feet}}{5} = \frac{7\frac{3}{16}}{2} \quad \text{or} \quad \frac{\text{Length in feet}}{7\frac{3}{16}} = \frac{5}{2}.$$

Either may be solved by multiplying on both sides by the denominator of the ratio at the left:

$$\text{Length} = \frac{5 \times 7\frac{3}{16}}{2} = \frac{35\frac{15}{16}}{2} = \frac{34\frac{31}{16}}{2} = 17\frac{31}{32} \text{ (ft.).}$$

Another scheme is to observe successively:

2 in.	represents	5 ft.,
1 in.	represents	$\frac{5}{2}$ ft.,
$7\frac{3}{16}$ in.	represents	$7\frac{3}{16} \times \frac{5}{2} = 17\frac{31}{32}$ ft.

§6. PERCENT

Many ratios or rates represent comparisons of a "part with a whole," hence of a smaller number with a larger. In these as well as in a great many more general comparisons, the rates are proper fractions, less than 1, but usually more than $\frac{1}{100}$. It is convenient to express such rates as *multiples of* $\frac{1}{100}$.

We write the symbol % as an abbreviation for multiplying by $\frac{1}{100}$, reading it "percent" (from the Latin: *per centum* = "out of a hundred"). Thus:

$$\text{"Twenty percent" or } 20\% \text{ means: } 20 \times \frac{1}{100} = .2.$$

To convert a number from decimal to percent form, or vice versa, move the decimal point two places in the appropriate direction, bearing in mind that the percent symbol % means "hundredths":

$$.24 = 24\%; \quad .436 = 43.6\%; \quad 6\% = .06.$$

In converting a fraction to a percent, it is usually simpler to multiply by 100 before dividing:

$$\frac{2}{9} = \frac{200}{9}\% = 22\% \text{ (approx.)}; \quad \frac{1}{3} = \frac{100}{3}\% = 33\frac{1}{3}\%.$$

Though the percent notion is most useful with numbers in the .01 to 1 range, it may be used with any number:

$$.00032 = .032\%; \quad .005 = .5\% \text{ or } \frac{1}{2} \text{ of } 1\%; \quad 2.3 = 230\%.$$

If a city increases its population from 4 million to 5 million in a decade, then the absolute increase is 1 million, while the relative increase is the ratio of 1 million to 4 million, or $\frac{1}{4}$ = .25. The *percent* of increase is 25%. If an auto weighs 4000 lb., of which 2200 is on the front wheels and 1800 on the rear, the percent of weight on the rear is 45% ($^{1800}\!/_{4000}$ = $\frac{9}{20}$ = $^{45}\!/_{100}$). If a firm sells $200,000 worth of goods and makes a profit of $12,000, then the percent of profit (based on sales) is 6%. If a man pays $80 in taxes on a house valued at $12,000, then the percent of tax is $\frac{2}{3}$ of 1%.

In the general language of percent, a ratio is called the *rate*, its numerator the *percentage*, its denominator the *base:*

$$\text{Rate} = \frac{\text{Percentage}}{\text{Base}}.$$

Thus if an invested sum of $300 earns $24 interest in one year, the base and the percentage are 300 and 24, respectively, so that the rate is:

$$\frac{24}{300} = \frac{8}{100} = .08 = 8\% \quad (\text{``annual interest rate''}).$$

The multiplied-out form is most commonly seen:

$$\text{Percentage} = \text{Rate} \times \text{Base}.$$

No mathematical relationship receives more wear and tear at the hands of the human multitude than this one.

In practical work, the percentage formula is seldom used explicitly. The term "percentage" is apparently a confusing one, and is used incorrectly more often than not. The following examples show common procedures for working the "three types" of percentage problems: to find the "rate," the "percentage," and the "base" (given the other two quantities in each case).

Example 1.   Enrollment in a course dropped from 396 to 351. What was the percent of decline?

Work.   The drop was 396 − 351 = 45. We must find what percent 45 is of 396, the original amount or "base":

$$\frac{45}{396} = \frac{4500}{396}\,\% = 11.4\%.$$

Example 2.   A merchant advertises "30% off" on every item in the store. What will be the sale price on an item regularly sold for $2.96?

Work.   The reduction is 30% of 2.96, the "of" meaning "times," as with fractions:

$$30\% \times 2.96 = .30 \times 2.96 = .89 \text{ (nearest cent)}.$$

The sale price is 2.96 − .89 = 2.07 ($).

Example 3.   Invested at 6%, a sum of money earns $42 in interest in a year. What was the sum?

Work. The problem is: 6% of Sum = 42.

If   6% × Sum = 42,

Then   1% × Sum =   7   (dividing by 6).

Since $\frac{1}{100}$ of the sum is $7, the sum is $700.

NOTE. The algebraic approach would be:

$$.06x = 42; \qquad x = \frac{42}{.06} = \frac{4200}{6} = 700.$$

Taxes often involve—or used to involve—small percents. It has been suggested that the symbol ‰ might be used as an abbreviation for multiplying by $\frac{1}{1000}$. Then 1‰ of $1 would be $\frac{1}{1000}$ of $1, or $\frac{1}{10}$ of a cent, a unit already named "1 mil." Hence the symbol ‰ could be read "per-mil," the amount produced by a "permil" rate being called a "permillage." A real estate tax rate of "18 mils" ($18 per $1000 valuation) could be referred to as an 18‰ rate. A .342 batting average could be stated as 342‰. (Still another possibility would be to use ‰ as an abbreviation for $\frac{1}{10,000}$.)

Example 4. John Jones' yearly income is $5000. He expects to pay out: $700 for income taxes; $900 for rent; $1500 for food; $400 for transportation (auto); $300 for clothes; $550 for household equipment, TV, furnishings, and repairs; $300 for recreation and miscellaneous; $350 for insurance and savings. Construct a table showing the percentage distribution of his anticipated expenditures, so that his budget may be compared with others based on different incomes. Display the distribution pictorially by a "pie" chart.

Work. Compute the ratio of each expenditure to Jones' total income (base) and express these ratios as percents. Use a protractor to construct the pie chart. Since 100% is to be represented by the full circle, 360°, there are 3.6° to each 1%. The 30% expenditure for food is therefore represented by a sector whose central angle is 30 × 3.6° = 108°. (A "bar" chart also makes an effective exhibit.)

JOHN JONES' BUDGET	Dollar Amounts	Percents
Food	1500	30
Rent	900	18
Tax	700	14
Household	550	11
Car	400	8
Insurance	350	7
Clothes	300	6
Recreation	300	6
	5000	100

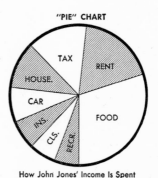

"PIE" CHART

How John Jones' Income Is Spent

Example 5.   William Green, salesman, receives a commission of $7\frac{1}{2}\%$ on his sales. He agrees to pay an assistant 30% of his own "take." What net rate will this give him?

Work.   He keeps 70% of $7\frac{1}{2}\%$ of his sales. But $70\% \times 7\frac{1}{2}\% = 70\% \times 7.5\% = .7 \times .075 = .0525 = 5.25\%$. His future net earnings will amount to $5\frac{1}{4}\%$ of his sales.

Example 6.   If a man's salary is increased by 32%, and at the same time the cost of living goes up 20%, how much is his position improved?

Work.   The problem cannot be solved precisely unless it is known just how the general statistical index called "the cost of living" is related to the living habits of the particular man concerned.   To simplify the situation, let us suppose that the man spends his whole income on pork chops, the price of which has risen 20%.   The same quantity of chops that formerly cost him $100 now cost him $120. Since he now has $132 instead of $100 to spend, he gets $^{132}\!/_{120}$ = 1.1 times as many chops. His gain is 10%.

Example 7.   If two men are precisely similar in their physical structure, but one weighs 40% more than the other, how do their heights compare?

Work.   On the basis of the improbable hypothesis cited, the weights will compare as the volumes, and these as the *cubes* of the heights. Hence the ratio of the heights will equal the cube root of the ratio of the weights:

$$\sqrt[3]{\frac{140}{100}} = \sqrt[3]{\frac{1400}{1000}} = \frac{11.2}{10} = 1.12 = 112\% \text{ (approx.)}.$$

The heavier man is about 12% taller than the other.

PROBLEM SET 3 (§5–§6)

1.   Two cans of tomatoes hold 1 lb. 10 oz. and 1 lb. 2 oz., respectively. What is the ratio of the weight of the contents of the larger can to that of the smaller?

2.   If the cans in Problem 1 are of the same brand, and are priced at 38¢ and 27¢, respectively, which is the better buy?

3.   The weight of the contents of the smaller can in Problem 1 is what percent of the weight of the contents of the larger can?

4.   A $2\frac{1}{4}$ in. $\times$ $2\frac{1}{4}$ in. (film size) camera has a 36° angle of view. The angle subtended by the moon is about $\frac{1}{2}°$. What will be the diameter of the image of the moon on a contact print?

5.   The owner of the camera in Problem 4 makes an enlargement from a section of his negative in order to get a print on which the moon's image is $\frac{1}{3}$ inch in diameter. What is his enlarging ratio?   *Answer:* $^3\!/_3$.

6.   A model auto is to be made with an 8-in. wheelbase. The full-sized car has a 128-in. wheelbase. What is the scale of the model.   *Answer:* $\frac{1}{16}$.

7.   If the model in Problem 6 is an *exact* copy, and the full-size car weighs 3600 lb., what does the model weigh?   *Answer:* About 14 oz.

8.   The odds against Kalif. State in its annual grid classic with Oak Ridge U., are estimated at 5 to 4. What is the estimated probability that Kalif. State will win?

9.   The probability of your being dealt an aceless bridge hand is about .3. State the odds against your receiving such a hand.   *Answer:* 7 to 3

10.   The number of possible poker hands is 2,598,960. (number of combinations of 52 things taken 5 at a time). The number of possible "straight flushes" is 40. What are the odds against your being dealt a straight flush?

11.   If the cost of living rises 80% while rents rise only 60%, by what percent have rents declined relative to the cost of living?   *Answer:* About 11% ($^{20}\!/_{180}$)

12.   A shopkeeper marks up all his prices 50%. Later he cuts them by 50%. His final prices are what percent of his original prices?   *Answer:* 75%

13.   As in Problem 12, a markup of 60% is followed by a cut of 40%. These two changes are equivalent to a single markup or cut of what percent?

Answer: 4% cut

14.   Assume that for each sex taken separately, strength is proportional to weight, but that a woman is 30% weaker than a man of the same weight. How heavy is a woman whose strength equals that of a 140-lb. man?

Answer: 200 lb.

15.   A grocer keeps separate tabs on his sales under these heads: Meat, Vegetables, Tobacco, General. In one day, his receipts under these heads total $48, $40, $8, $64, respectively. Show the percentage distribution of his receipts by a table; also by a "pie" chart.

10

The Number
Scale

§1. NEGATIVE NUMBERS

Among primitive peoples living today, some tribes have few words
to tell of their needs. Even so, these words include number names. We
may from this surmise that *whole numbers* probably played a role in pre-
history, before the Great Idea dawned upon man that he might forever
freeze his speech and gesture in stone and clay. *Fractions* too were devised
in ancient times. The Egyptians used them even in an era when their
"written" language still took the picture form.

But the *negative numbers* have few roots in the deep past. All along
the course of history, right up to the sixteenth century, we find only
scattered instances of anyone's daring to entertain the notion that a
negative number could be a respectable mathematical object.

In a manuscript dated 1225, the Italian mathematician Fibonacci obtained a
negative answer to a financial problem, and interpreted this to mean a loss, even
as we do today. Before Fibonacci, some Hindu mathematicians had used the loss,
or debt, notion. Few others followed these leads.

Yet for many centuries computers had manipulated additive and subtractive combinations, using symbols corresponding to our plus and minus
signs to link the numbers in them. The Chinese had even used black number rods for the numbers tagged with plus signs, and red rods for those
tagged with minus signs. And the "rules of signs" had been worked out.

So it would appear that the negative numbers were not actually
"invented," as such. It just took a long time for them to be recognized.
The operation of subtraction essentially implied their "existence," as
the operation was not universally possible without them. The invention
of this operation in early times had made it certain that mathematicians
would one day seek a larger number system *closed* under the operation,
as the systems of whole numbers and fractions were not. (A system is
"closed" under an operation if performing the operation upon any object

of the system again leads to an object of the system. Since 5 cannot be subtracted from 2, the system of the whole numbers is not closed with respect to the operation of subtracting 5.)

But at the time, no one wanted the negative numbers, nor felt they were needed. They were overlooked, or pushed aside as impossible annoyances.

The conception of the negative numbers presented itself to the mathematician like a stray kitten on his doorstep, yearning for a home. Distracted by its persistent plaintive mewing, the mathematician at last yielded to the inevitable. With as good grace as he could muster, he quelled the repulsion that seized him at the sight of the unkempt critter, admitted it to his sanctum, and nourished it. Lo! It grew to a sleek beauty, the prize of the household.

Confronted with a numerical form like $2 - 5$, a medieval mathematician could readily reject it as "meaningless" or "absurd" without giving the matter a second thought. But he also dealt with algebraic forms, like $a - b$. He added, subtracted, multiplied, divided, and took powers of such forms, all the while certain that he was accomplishing something useful by his efforts. How frustrating for him to discover at the end of a series of such manipulations that in the particular problem being worked on, the number a was less than the number b! In such a case the form $a - b$ which he had so deftly handled could mean nothing, so that his work had been sheer nonsense.

In the sixteenth century, mathematicians finally began to accept these new numbers that so clamored for recognition. In 1545, Cardan used them as roots of equations, and stated rules for their manipulation. Other prominent mathematicians followed suit. Within a hundred years they were well established.

Cardan called them *false* numbers, revealing his own misgivings about them. Others came to call them *negative* numbers (i.e., "non-numbers"), stressing the greater legitimacy of the older tried-and-true numbers by reference to the latter as the "affirmative" or *positive* numbers. Other examples of names given new numbers have suggested like distrust: *irrational* ("unreasonable") numbers, *imaginary* ("unreal") numbers, *surds* ("inaudible" or "mute" numbers). No wonder it took a hundred years for the mathematical public to become friendly to them! Modern public relations experts and ad writers would have graced them with adjectives like "super," "cosmic," "stellar," and would have gained quick popular acceptance for them.

As it became apparent that the negatives had useful roles to play and as numerous concrete or practical interpretations of them turned up, the suspicions gradually evaporated. The fantastic became the acceptable and finally the commonplace.

§2. THE RATIONAL NUMBER SYSTEM

The system of the fractions embraces all the whole numbers (0, 1, 2, 3, . . .) and all the quotients of pairs of whole numbers ($\frac{2}{3}$, $5\frac{1}{8}$, etc.), except that zero may not be the divisor.

Let us tag each such fraction by two labels, a $+$ and a $-$, the same "plus" and "minus" symbols that we use for indicating addition and subtraction. The non-zero fractions tagged with a $+$ are the **positive** numbers. The non-zero fractions tagged with a $-$ are the **negative** numbers. Both $+0$ and -0 are taken to be the same number, **zero**, 0.

All these are the **rational numbers.** It is helpful to picture them as distributed in size order along the entire extent of a line, which then forms an **axis,** or **number scale:**

The line is directed toward the right, the **positive direction,** the numbers increasing as one so moves along the line. When sketching the axis, always mark the position of the *origin*, or zero point, and of the point marked $+1$, the *unit point.* With the integers placed, all the other rationals may be located with respect to them. Thus the rational number $-\frac{5}{2}$ is associated with a point lying halfway between those marked -3 and -2.

Each number and its negative, like $+3$ and -3, are symmetrically located with respect to the origin. They lie at the same distance, 3, from the origin, but on opposite sides. This common distance is called the **absolute value** or the **numerical value** of both numbers. To denote it, box in the numeral between vertical bars:

$$|+3| = |-3| = 3.$$

Since the positive rationals are just like the fractions that we had before, we generally omit the plus sign in writing them: $+3 = 3$.

Suppose we tried to get along without the new negative numbers. Our number scale would then be only a half-line, beginning abruptly at zero, and extending infinitely to the right. Surely such a "one-way" structure represents an incomplete system. For this is a "two-way" world, to say the least: in it, processes proceed both backward and forward. Now in constructing a number system, our major aim is to provide an effective instrument by which we can measure and describe such processes. We need at least a two-way number system to match the structure of our two-way world. What we need we supply.

Nowadays, negative numbers are everywhere before us. Sometimes we use them explicitly, as in citing a temperature reading of $-14°$.

More commonly in everyday life we use them implicitly, as when we say that the temperature is "14 below zero." Our language often shows that we have the two-way scale in mind, as we distinguish between:

3 miles west — 3 miles east
3 hours ago — 3 hours hence
3 floors up — 3 floors down
left — right
to — fro

And we frequently recognize that we are dealing with the same kind of two-way structure, even though no physical directions may be involved, in the case of opposites like:

profit — loss
credit — debt
export — import
acid — base
excitation — inhibition
yellow — blue
extravert — introvert

We may map these variables—economic, chemical, biological, physiological, psychological—along the number scale, then study their interplay in a precise *quantitative* fashion.

In tackling problems that involve two-way notions, we can sometimes arrange the work in terms of positive numbers alone. It may be possible to break down the work into one-way steps, then combine the separate results by adding and subtracting. But as the number of such stages in a problem increases, this method becomes unwieldy.

In our leisurely perception of everyday life, it may seem satisfactory to picture the separate steps of a to-and-fro motion, as though we were watching a tennis ball pass back and forth across a net.

But as the several billion wheels of our civilization whirl, the points on them move up and down and to and fro many times a second. To try to analyze these motions with the aid only of the one-way positive numbers would seem a hopeless venture.

Worse yet, the electric current in our television antennas oscillates to and fro several hundred million times per second. In describing this process mathematically, we cannot change the $+$ and $-$ signs in our equations so rapidly. We must have symbols that do their own sign-changing automatically, that is, symbols that range in value over the full two-way number scale. Without the scale, we would have no radio sets, much less TV. For Maxwell would then have been unable to carry out the fundamental electrodynamical analysis which he performed around 1870. Without this basic work in pure science which showed the way, Hertz would scarcely have conceived of producing electric waves, and the notion of an electronic tube in an oscillating circuit would certainly never have materialized. Radio communication would now exist only as a device of the fancy discussed on the pages of our "science-fiction" magazines.

§3. OPERATIONS

As noted in §2, we write 3 and +3, etc., interchangeably. That is, we agree to treat the positive rationals just like the fractions or naturals to which they correspond. We agree, for example, that $(+3) + (+2) = +5$ because $3 + 2 = 5$, and that $(+2) \times (+3) = +6$ because $2 \times 3 = 6$. In this way we ensure that the system of the rational numbers shall be a true *extension* of the system of the fractions.

What further agreements need we make about ways of combining rationals? What shall be the values of expressions like $(+3) + (-2)$, $(-2) \times (+3)$, $(+3) - (-2)$? In one sense, we may lay down such arbitrary rules as appeal to us; in another sense, our freedom of choice is severely limited. The rules must as a group be consistent, none contradictory with the rest. Furthermore—and this is all-important—the chosen scheme must turn out to be *useful*.

A criterion of utility is often hard to apply. Sometimes the only way to tell which is the most useful of several plans is to try out each over long periods of time. Even then posterity may eventually reverse the decision. In the present case, however, we have already observed the crucial roles played by the five commutative, associative, and distributive laws in rendering positive number arithmetic simple and useful. *If possible*, then, let us require that the entire system of the rationals shall be subject to these laws.

In addition, we must in some way explicitly describe the relationship between the negatives and the positives. So far, the two-way symmetrical conception on which we have based our approach is only intuitive in our minds. We must translate into mathematical terms our feeling that the negatives are the "mirror images" of the positives. This is not hard to do. We simply require the following:

BASIC RELATION

If N is any positive rational number,

$$N + (-N) = 0.$$

The above requirements can be met. When they are, it turns out that we have no further freedom of decision. They wholly determine the structure of the rationals. We will not carry out a formal development of this theory, but will cite some numerical examples illustrating how the requirements may be applied to derive familiar rules of operation with "signed numbers."

Example 1. Show that $5 + (-2) = 5 - 2 = 3$.

Work. Add 2 to the expression $5 + (-2)$, then simplify by the "basic relation":

$$[5 + (-2)] + 2 = 5 + [(-2) + 2] = 5 + 0 = 5.$$

Hence:

$$5 + (-2) = 5 - 2.$$

Example 2. Show that $5 - (-2) = 5 + 2 = 7$.

Work. Write: $x = 5 - (-2)$.

Then $x + (-2) = 5$.

As in Example 1, we may show that $x + (-2) = x - 2$, so that

$$x - 2 = 5 \quad \text{and} \quad x = 5 + 2.$$

Example 3. Show that $(-3) + (-2) = -(3 + 2) = -5$.

Work. Add $3 + 2$ to $(-3) + (-2)$:

$$[(-3) + (-2)] + (3 + 2) = [(-3) + 3] + [(-2) + 2] = 0.$$

Hence if $N = 3 + 2$, then because $(-N) + N = 0$, we have:

$$(-3) + (-2) = -N = -(3 + 2).$$

Example 4. Show that $2 \times (-3) = -(2 \times 3) = -6$.

Work. Add 2×3 to $2 \times (-3)$.

$$2 \times (-3) + 2 \times 3 = 2 \times [(-3) + 3] = 2 \times 0 = 0.$$
$$\therefore \quad 2 \times (-3) = -(2 \times 3).$$

Example 5. Show that $(-2) \times (-3) = 2 \times 3 = 6$.

Work. Add $(-2) \times 3$ to $(-2) \times (-3)$:

$$
\begin{aligned}
(-2) \times (-3) \;\; + \;\; (-2) \times 3 &= (-2) \times [(-3) + 3] \\
&= (-2) \times 0 \\
&= -(2 \times 0) \quad \text{(Show as in Ex. 4)} \\
&= -0 = 0.
\end{aligned}
$$

Now if we denote $N = 2 \times 3$, then from Example 4, we see that $(-2) \times 3 = -N$. Hence $(-2) \times (-3) = N = 2 \times 3$.

PROBLEM SET 1 (§1–§3)

1. Draw a straight line segment a little over 6 in. long, and scale it from -3 to $+3$, as in the figure of §2. On it mark the approximate positions of the points corresponding to these numbers:

(a) $+\frac{5}{2}$ (c) $-2\frac{1}{2}$ (e) 1.7 (g) 0.5

(b) $\frac{2}{3}$ (d) $-\frac{2}{3}$ (f) $-.75$ (h) $-2\frac{3}{8}$

2. Write the absolute value of each number of Problem 1.

3. Under what conditions is the absolute value of $3 - x$ equal to $x - 3$?

4. Several directional opposites, like "3 miles west–3 miles east" are cited in §2. Cite three more such instances.

5. Several nondirectional opposites, like "acid–base" are cited in §2. Cite three more such instances.

6. Which of the following quantities might best be measured by signed numbers and which by positives alone?

    (a)   Population of countries

    (b)   Daily change in the price of a stock

    (c)   Daily minimum temperature at Moscow, U.S.S.R.

    (d)   Fat content of milk

    (e)   Monthly net profit of a resort hotel

    (f)   Yards gained by a football team, down by down

    (g)   Acceleration of a car during a trip

    (h)   Level of a river

7. Are the following sets of numbers "closed" (§1) under the operations specified?

    (a)   Whole numbers (0, 1, 2, . . .); under addition

    (b)   Integers; under subtraction

    (c)   Integers; under division

    (d)   Rationals; under division

    (e)   Positive rationals; under division

    (f)   Odd naturals; under addition

    (g)   Positive integers; under multiplication

    (h)   Negative integers; under multiplication

    (i)   Numbers of form $3n/4$ (n a natural number); under addition

    (j)   Same set as in (i); under multiplication

8. Explain the assertion made in the first paragraph of §3, that the agreement to treat the positive rationals like the fractions to which they correspond ensures that the system of the rationals shall be an extension of that of the fractions.

9. Write the basic relation, $N + (-N) = 0$, in these specific cases:

    (a) $N = 3$ (b) $N = -3$ (c) $N = 0$ (d) $N = -\frac{5}{3}$

10. As in Example 1 of §3, show that $6 + (-4) = 6 - 4$.

11. Show that $2 + (-5) = 2 - 5$. By adding 3 to $2 + (-5)$, show that $2 + (-5) = -3$, hence that $2 - 5 = -(5 - 2) = -3$.

12. Show that $2 - (-3) = 5$.

13. Show that $(-4) + (-2) = -6$.

14. Show that $3 \times (-4) = -12$.

15. Show that $(-3) \times (-4) = 12$.

16. Show that $(-12) \div 3 = -4$. (*Hint:* Division is inverse to multiplication.)

17. Show that $(-12) \div (-3) = -4$.

18.* Show that the product of any two rational numbers must be a rational number. *Hint:* Denote two rationals by a/b and c/d, the letters denoting integers. Discuss the structure of the product ac/bd.

19.* Show that the sum of any two rational numbers must be a rational number.

20.* Show that there is a rational number between any two rational numbers.

§4. SIGNED NUMBER ARITHMETIC

By generalizing the procedures used in the Examples of §3, we could derive the *Rules of Signs*, cited below, as well as the algebraic rules for removing parentheses, here omitted.

RULES FOR COMBINING SIGNED NUMBERS

1. To subtract a number, change its sign and add.

2. To add two "minus" numbers, add their absolute values and tag the result with a minus sign.

3. To add a "plus" and a "minus" number, write their absolute values and subtract the smaller value from the larger. Tag the result with the sign of the number of larger value.

4. To multiply or divide two numbers, multiply or divide their absolute values. Tag the result with a plus or minus sign according as the numbers have "like" or "unlike" signs.

Example 1. Add 2.34 and -7.80.

Work. Use Rule 3.

$$\begin{array}{r} 7.80 \\ -\ 2.34 \\ \hline 5.46 \end{array}$$

Answer: -5.46

Example 2. Subtract -3.6 from 6.8.

Work. Use Rule 1.

$$\begin{array}{r} 6.8 \\ +\ 3.6 \\ \hline 10.4 \end{array}$$

Answer: 10.4

Example 3. Subtract 5 from -7.

Work. Use Rule 1, then use Rule 2 implicitly, "thinking" $7 + 5 = 12$, but writing as shown:

$$\begin{array}{r} -7 \\ +\ -5 \\ \hline -12 \end{array}$$

Answer: -12

Example 4. A bank teller lists sums taken in and paid out, tagging them by plus and minus signs, respectively. His list shows ($): $+21$, -59, $+120$, -15, -40. What is his cash increase?

Work. To add the listed numbers, we first rearrange and group them (associative and commutative laws of addition):

$$[21 + 120] + [(-59) + (-15) + (-40)].$$

The negative numbers sum according to Rule 2. Then Rule 3 gives

$$141 + (-114) = 27. \qquad\qquad Answer: \$27$$

Example 5. What is the sign of

$$\frac{(-29)^3 \times (-7)^2 \times (3.46)}{-5.42} \, ?$$

Work. To determine the sign of such a product-quotient combination, we need only to count the number of minus signs. If the result is even, the whole expression is plus; if odd, minus. (For according to Rule 4, every pair of minuses produces a plus.) Note that the powers are products: $(-29)^3 = (-29) \times (-29) \times (-29)$, $(-7)^2 = (-7) \times (-7)$. Since the count gives six minuses, we conclude:

$$\frac{(-29)^3 \times (-7)^2 \times (3.46)}{-5.42} = +\frac{29^3 \times 7^2 \times 3.46}{5.42}.$$

Example 6. The temperature, now $24°$, is falling at the rate of $3°$ per hour. What will it be in 2 hr?

Work. To illustrate the principle involved, we will use negatives in place of subtracting. The time rate of *rise* of temperature is $-3°$ per hour. The total rise in 2 hr. is $2 \times (-3) = -6$. Adding this to the present amount gives $24 + (-6) = 18$. *Answer:* $18°$

Example 7. The temperature, now $24°$, has been falling at the rate of $3°$ per hour. What was it 4 hr ago?

Work. The total rise in -4 hr. is $(-4) \times (-3) = +12$, and $24 + (+12) = 36$. *Answer:* $36°$

§5. A PICTORIAL MODEL

The number scale itself furnishes an excellent model for portraying operations with signed numbers. Imagine the scale laid along a road running from west to east (positive direction), the origin placed at the center of a town. The numbers $+1$, $+2$, $+3$, . . . designate mileposts to the east (E) of the town; the numbers -1, -2, -3, . . . go with mileposts to the West (W).

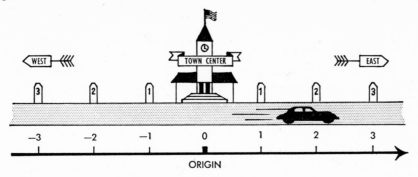

Fig. 25   Number Scale Laid along a Road

We now associate numbers with *displacements;* +5 corresponds to a displacement or movement of 5 miles toward the east; −2 to a displacement of 2 miles to the west. The sum, $5 + (−2)$, is represented by a displacement of 5 miles to the east, followed by one of 2 miles to the west. The result is a displacement of 3 miles to the east: $5 + (−2) = 3$.

In picturing the displacement operation we may use arrows, or "vectors," as shown in Figure 26. The absolute value of a number gives the length of the arrow representing it; the arrow points to the right or left according as the number is positive or negative. To diagram a sum, we draw the first arrow with its tail at the origin, the second with its tail at the head of the first. The student may use such diagrams as objective aids to his understanding or he may take them as bases for kinaesthetic imagery: He

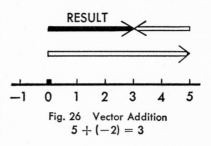

Fig. 26   Vector Addition
$5 + (−2) = 3$

may trace the movements in the air with a finger, or he may pace forward and backward.

Now let us regard a minus sign, whether it designates a negative number or a subtraction, as a *direction-changing operator.* In dealing with both $5 + (−2)$ and $5 − 2$, we will think of the positives 5 and 2 as being the numbers involved, and we will take the minus sign in front of the 2 in either expression as a signal to reverse the direction of the "2-arrow" before chaining it onto the "5-arrow." From this point of view, Figure 26 represents both $5 + (−2) = 3$ and $5 − 2 = 3$.

Consider the expression $3 − (−2)$. According to the operator point of view, the two minuses twice reverse the direction of the 2-arrow, giving it a final positive, right-hand direction. The diagram is shown in Figure 27. It also serves for $3 + 2$. Figure 28 shows the diagram for $2 + (−5) = 2 − 5$.

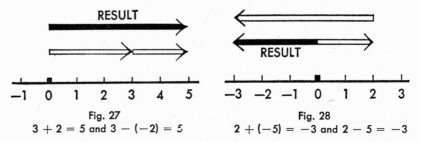

Fig. 27

$3 + 2 = 5$ and $3 - (-2) = 5$

Fig. 28

$2 + (-5) = -3$ and $2 - 5 = -3$

The direction-changing idea is also applicable to products and quotients, though arrow diagrams can no longer be used. In the case of the product $(-3) \times (-2)$, the numerical values involved are 3 and 2, whose product is 6. Each minus gives a change of "direction," from $+$ to $-$, then $-$ to $+$. (*Answer:* $+6$.)

Imagine that a car is being driven along the road of Figure 25. To get nice numbers to work with, let us wink at the speed laws, saying that the car is traveling at a constant speed of 2 miles per minute, also that it passes the town center (origin) at 12 noon, taken as "time zero."

We can compute the distance driven in miles from the town center by the relation

Distance = Speed × Time.

After 3 min., the car is $2 \times 3 = 6$ miles from the town center. *But which way*—east or west? Perhaps the car ran over a chicken 3 min. ago. Where was it then?

Were we restricted to positive numbers, we should have to describe these different directional situations by four separate formulas. With signed numbers, one equation does the whole job. We write it

$$d = vt,$$

vt being algebraic shorthand for the product $(v) \times (t)$. In this formula, t denotes the number of minutes reckoned from time zero (12 noon), being $+$ for times later than time zero, $-$ for earlier times. The velocity v equals the speed $+2$ if the car is traveling east, but is taken as -2, the negative of the speed, if the car is traveling west. Similarly, d is $+$ or $-$ according as the car is east or west of the town center.

We illustrate each of the four directional situations:

1. Car travels east. Where is it 3 min. after 12 noon?
    Formula: $d = vt = 2 \times 3 = 6.$ *Answer:* 6 miles east
2. Car travels east. Where was it 3 min. before 12 noon?
    Formula: $d = vt = 2 \times (-3) = -6.$ *Answer:* 6 miles west
3. Car travels west. Where is it 3 min. after 12 noon?
    Formula: $d = vt = (-2) \times 3 = -6.$ *Answer:* 6 miles west
4. Car travels west. Where was it 3 min. before 12 noon?
    Formula: $d = vt = (-2) \times (-3) = 6.$ *Answer:* 6 miles east

These illustrations suggest that the rules we use for multiplying signed numbers are the ones naturally suited to the handling of simple problems in directional motion. In more complex engineering and dynamical situations, the rules are indispensable.

PROBLEM SET 2 (§4–§5)

In Problems 1–20 combine according to the Rules of Signs.

1. $36.3 + (-8.7)$
2. $21.2 + (-57.6)$
3. $-63 + 120$
4. $(-12.3) + (-25.6)$
5. $\frac{3}{4} + (-\frac{3}{4})$
6. $39 - (-7)$
7. $2.63 - (-3.37)$
8. $-20 - 8$
9. $-14.2 - (-40.2)$
10. $10\frac{1}{2} - (-8\frac{1}{3})$

11. $2 - 8 - 9 + 20 - 6$
12. $-6 - 7 - 15 + 20$
13. $5 \times (-3)$
14. $(-7) \times 4$
15. $(-20) \div 5$
16. $(-24) \div (-8)$
17. $8 - [2 \times (-3)]$
18. $(-1)^{62}$
19. $2 \times (-2) \times (-1) \times (-1) \times 2 \times 2$
20. $[(-4) \times 5] \div [(-2) \times (-3)]$

21. The nurse in charge of a blood bank lists numbers of pints coming in from donors (+) and going out for transfusions (−). Her list runs: $-3, +1, -4, +2, +2, -2, -6, -4, +1$. What is the net increase in pints of blood?

22. Over a period of a week the daily changes in a stock quotation were $+\frac{3}{4}, -\frac{1}{8}, -1\frac{1}{8}, +2, +\frac{1}{2}, -3\frac{3}{8}, 0$. What was the net increase?

23. Demonstrate in detail how the associative and commutative laws are used to effect the following reduction: $7 - 4 - 2 + 5 = (7 + 5) - (4 + 2)$.

24. Now 60°, the temperature is rising at a rate of 2° per hour. What will it be in 6 hr.? What was it 6 hr. ago? (In both cases, use the formula Change = Time × Rate, the positive time direction being toward the future and a positive rate being a rate of increase, as in Examples 6, 7, of §4.)

25. Now 60°, the temperature is falling at a rate of 2° per hour. What will it be in 6 hr.? What was it 6 hr. ago?

26. Along an east-west road, an auto travels east (positive direction) at 40 miles per hour. The car passes milepost No. 250 at 2 P.M. Where was it at 11 A.M.? (Use signed numbers, substituting into the formula $d = vt$, as in §5.)

27. Along the road of Problem 26, an auto travels west at 40 miles per hour, passing milepost No. 210 at 1 P.M. Where was it at 11.30 A.M.?

Answer: At milepost No. 270

28. A body thrown upward at time $t = 0$ with a speed of 80 ft per second, will have its velocity subsequently given by $v = 80 - 32t$. Find v when $t = 3$. What is the physical meaning of the answer?

29. The generator in a car charges the battery as needed (+), and starting, running, and the use of accessories discharge it (−). Discuss how this process may operate during a short trip, relating the discussion to the signed number conception.

30.* When a body moves under the impulsion of a force acting on it, the "work" done on the body over a short distance is found by multiplying the distance by the portion of the force that is applied in the direction of the motion. Both these factors are "signed" quantities. On an amusement-park roller coaster, a car follows a winding up-and-down path which returns it to its starting-point. Were there no friction and were the car released at the highest point of the path (with a slight push), the car would travel around indefinitely. The work done by gravity on the car during a complete circuit adds up to zero. How can this be? (Also consider the case of a simple pendulum, say a 25-lb. ball of iron at the end of a 100-ft. wire. Such a pendulum will oscillate for days with little appreciable diminution in amplitude.)

§6. WHY WE NEED IRRATIONAL NUMBERS

In everyday life we can put up with many inaccuracies. The extent of the error that may be tolerated depends upon the situation. A man may cut the grass a day or two earlier or later than he planned, but if he wishes to leave a bus at a certain stop, the leeway is cut to seconds. It is a matter of small concern if the housewife prepares one tablespoon too many of mashed potatoes for dinner, but an extra teaspoon of salt in the stew may spoil the meal. The novice mechanic who grinds an extra hundredth of an inch from the cylinder wall of an automobile motor will be urged to seek another trade.

A similar situation is found in the scientific laboratory. No physicist can nor ever will be able to measure the length of a metal bar "exactly." He may be able to measure it to the nearest .00000000001 in. For practical purposes such approximate measurement is fully adequate.

Do the finite decimals, then, furnish an adequate practical number system? With them we may approximate any exact value as closely as we please, to the nearest .1 unit, or the nearest .01 unit, or the nearest .001 unit, . . . , or the nearest 00000000000000000001 unit, . . . — there is no limit to the minuteness of the error-range which we may enforce.

Now possibly *absolute precision* of measurement is never entirely *necessary*, but there are many circumstances in which such exactness is highly convenient. We often wish to state the sizes of groups accurately, in terms of natural numbers. In preparing a dessert recipe, the cook could just as well apportion the ingredients on the theory that 8.003 people were to be served instead of exactly 8. But what would we think of the guest who observed that "about 8.003 people" were seated at the table? Monetary accounts and other inventories are supposed to be exact, to facilitate checking, and for legal and other reasons.

When we use natural numbers as precise measures, we will often find ourselves also compelled to use fractions as precise measures. If 12 rolls are to be distributed equally among 3 people, each person must get just ⅓ of the dozen, not .3 (30%), nor .33, nor .333, etc. This is still a case of theoretical convenience rather than practical necessity. Who cares whether he receives 4 rolls or 4.00000000007 rolls?

The system of the finite decimals lacks many exact fractions: ⅓, 2/7, etc. Hence it is inadequate to serve as a basic number system.

The rational number system is our next most promising candidate. Yet, over two thousand years ago, the Greeks found it too to be inadequate.

From the sixth grade on, we meet a profuse variety of applications of the simple geometry of the Euclidean plane, from shopwork and common arts and crafts to machine design and analytical dynamics. At the very least, we would wish our number system to tie in with this geometry, so that exact numerical lengths could be assigned to all line segments, circular arcs, etc. The Greeks discovered that the rational numbers did not meet this requirement, as we shall now see.

Consider this problem (Fig. 29): Given a right triangle with legs each of unit length, how long is the hypotenuse?

Our first step in attacking the problem is to assume that it has an answer, i.e., that there really is a number that exactly measures the length of the hypotenuse. We denote this unknown number by x, as marked on the figure. We mark the mid-point of the hypotenuse and inspect the shaded right triangle whose leg length is $\frac{1}{2}x$. This triangle is similar to the original, because it is also a 45°–45° right triangle.

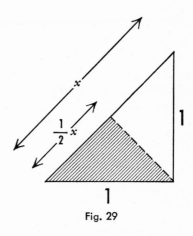

Fig. 29

Hence the corresponding sides of the two triangles are in proportion:

$$\frac{\frac{1}{2}x}{1} \quad \frac{1}{x}.$$

Multiplying both sides by $2x$ gives

$$x^2 = 2 \quad \text{so that} \quad x = \sqrt{2}.$$

We may approximate the value of $\sqrt{2}$ with a finite decimal, say 1.41, by applying some square root extraction process, then use the decimal value in whatever practical application is under consideration. (For example, the sides of the triangle may represent bridge girders.)

In §7 we will show that *there is no rational number whose square is* 2. With respect just to the rational number system, therefore, the work set forth above is sheer nonsense! If we chose to limit ourselves to that number system, we would be compelled to replace the simple geometry in which there can exist right triangles with legs of equal length by some far more complicated theoretical geometrical system—one with which, to be sure, we could in some way derive the final decimal result 1.41, but at a heavy cost in complication of conceptual theory and algebraic effort. It is for essentially utilitarian reasons, therefore, that we seek a further enlargement of the number system, beyond the rationals.

§7.   IRRATIONALITY OF $\sqrt{2}$

There is no rational number whose square is 2.

Sometime before 430 B.C., a Greek mathematician, probably a member of the group called *Pythagoreans*, made this outstanding mathematical discovery. It was the forerunner of many famous "impossibility proofs" that have made their impact felt upon the course of Western culture. The other proofs have been given in modern times, but most of them relate to problems left unsolved by the Greeks —squaring the circle, doubling the cube, trisecting the general angle, proving the parallel postulate.

When the Pythagoreans learned of the proof, consternation swept their ranks. The philosophy of this famous school of Greek thinkers stemmed from the dictum that "number rules the universe." Here, *number* had reference only to the natural numbers and to their ratios, the positive rationals. That the dominion of number did not even embrace geometry—this must have been as shocking to the Pythagoreans as though the sun had chosen to vanish overnight or water had ceased to be wet. Even so, they and their successors recognized the fundamental and profound importance of the new knowledge. Plato said, "He who does not know the proof of the incommensurability of the diagonal of the square with its side, is not a man but a beast." Euclid included a proof in his *Elements*.

The discovery had an unfortunate consequence. It quite likely led Greek mathematicians to take the devious detour that finally brought them to a dead end insofar as arithmetic and algebra were concerned. Since geometric magnitudes had turned out not to be universally measurable in terms of their number scheme, they set about developing a "geometric algebra." They interpreted operations like adding and multiplying geometrically, carrying them out as constructions with line segments, surfaces, and volumes. They could not make use of relations involving fourth and higher powers; cubing a line segment to produce a volume was as far as they could go. Euclid's Book V dealt with proportions. To develop the subject in geometric terms he had to establish some thirty propositions. Today, with an efficient numerical algebra, we handle that theory in a few lines.

In the proof to follow we will need this fact: *A natural number is even or odd according as its square is even or odd.* To show this, first note that by taking $n = 1, 2, 3, \ldots$ successively, we get all the even naturals from the form $2n$ and all the odd naturals from the form $2n - 1$. Square each form:

SQUARES OF EVENS   SQUARES OF ODDS
$$(2n)^2 = 4n^2 \qquad (2n - 1)^2 = 4n^2 - 4n + 1$$

Since $4n^2$ is divisible by 2, the square of an even natural is even. Since $4n^2 - 4n$ is divisible by 2, the square of an odd natural is odd. Hence if the square of a natural number is known to be even, the number cannot be odd (since then its square will be odd) and so must be even. Likewise, a natural whose square is odd must itself be odd.

THEOREM. *There is no rational number whose square is* 2.

Proof. Let us suppose that there is some positive rational number whose square is 2. If we can demonstrate this supposition to be impossible, then we will have proved the theorem. (We need not worry about the negative case, for a negative rational whose square was 2 would be numerically equal to a positive rational with square 2.)

Let x denote such a positive rational ($x^2 = 2$). Since the positive rationals are the non-zero fractions, x is the quotient of some two natural numbers. Now we may reduce any fraction to a *lowest term form* and thus express x in this way:

$$x = \frac{P}{Q}. \quad \begin{cases} \text{The quotient of two natural numbers } P \text{ and } Q \text{ which are prime} \\ \text{to each other, i.e., have 1 as their only common factor.} \end{cases}$$

From $x^2 = 2$ we get

$$\frac{P^2}{Q^2} = 2, \qquad \text{so} \qquad P^2 = 2Q^2.$$

The equation $P^2 = 2Q^2$ states that P^2 is even. According to our earlier result, therefore, *P is even*. This means that $P/2$ is a natural number which we will call I. Then $P = 2I$, and

$$2Q^2 = P^2 = (2I)^2 = 4I^2 \qquad \text{whence} \qquad Q^2 = 2I^2.$$

So Q^2 is even, and therefore Q *is even*.

We have shown that *both* P and Q are *even*, which directly contradicts the previous stipulation that P and Q are prime to each other. What forced us into this impossible predicament was our initial assumption that there was some positive rational with square 2. Hence that assumption is itself impossible.

Our modern **real number system** is an extension of the rational number system. A larger aggregate, it *does* include a number whose square is 2, written $\sqrt{2}$, also one whose square is 3, written $\sqrt{3}$, and many other *irrational* numbers.

Put yourself in the position of a mathematician who has at his disposal only the rational numbers and who is constructing from them candidates for admission to a new, larger "real number system." From your point of view the expression $\sqrt{2}$ is thus not yet a number. But you have O.K.'d its application for membership. It is a "number-to-be."

Can $\sqrt{2} + 1$ be rational? If it is, call it R. Then $R - 1 = \sqrt{2}$, so that $R - 1$ is not rational. But $R - 1$ is a difference of rationals and so must be rational (for a difference of fractions can be rewritten as a single fraction). This contradiction shows that there is no rational number of the form $\sqrt{2} + 1$. By similar argument, no form $a + b\sqrt{2}$, with a,b rational and $b \neq 0$, can represent a rational. Yet there are as many such forms as there are rationals. So there are at least as many numbers-to-be missing from the rational system as there are numbers in the system.

Any root combination you may write (avoiding even roots of negatives) is likely to represent such a missing number-to-be:

$$\sqrt{2} + \sqrt{3}; \; \sqrt[3]{2}; \; \sqrt{2\sqrt{3} - \sqrt[3]{71}}; \; \sqrt{2 - \sqrt[5]{3}}.$$

There are various algebraic procedures that generate many other candidates. And there are certain special number candidates of major mathematical importance that are wholly nonalgebraic: π, for example, representing the ratio of the circumference of a circle to its diameter.

As a matter of fact, yours is a hopeless task. The large portion of the numbers-to-be cannot be singled out and identified. The only way to get the all-inclusive number system which you aim toward is by a gross approach that gives the whole in one fell swoop. Such a scheme is described in §8.

§8. THE REAL NUMBER SYSTEM

Consider the number scale used as a model in §5. It is a line along which the integers are evenly marked, both ways from the origin. Imagine that the finite decimals are also marked at appropriate positions along it. These pepper the line evenly and "densely."

The *tenths* separate the line into equal segments, any consecutive ten of them making up a unit length. The *hundredths* likewise give an even separation, and include the tenths. The *thousandths* include both tenths and hundredths. The set of *all* the finite decimals may thus be thought of as lying evenly or homogeneously along the line. Furthermore, choose any tiny segment of the line and you will find within it a finite decimal marker (infinitely many, in fact). For example, any segment of length one-millionth includes 9 or 10 ten-millionth markers. For this reason the decimals are said to lie "densely."

The finite decimals reveal the "pattern" of the entire line, even as the separate tiny dots of light on a TV picture-tube screen give a total image to the viewer. Of course these decimals miss many positions on the line, including many rational positions. Thus ⅓ is missed, for this corresponds to an *infinite* decimal, .333... .

It turns out that *all* positions on the line may be exactly described by using *infinite decimals*. Conversely, every infinite decimal describes some position. This is a key to the all-inclusive number system which we seek and which we call the *real number system*.

DEFINITION. **The real numbers are the infinite decimals.**

Certain infinite decimals display an unending string of consecutive nines. Each of these represents the same number as does some finite decimal. Thus .36999... = .37. We do not regard as infinite a decimal that displays an unending string of zeros (.37000...).

It is not hard to see that any given position on the line can be described by some infinite decimal. Let P be a point of the line. Suppose P lies between the 0 and 1 marks. By a simple geometric construction, we can divide the segment from 0 to 1 into ten equal segments whose ends are accordingly marked as tenths: .0, .1, .2, .3, . . . , .9, 1.0. If P is one of these marked points, then its position is decimally given at once. If not, then P falls between some consecutive two of them. Say it falls between the points marked .7 and .8. In such case, .7 is taken as a *first decimal approximation* to the number that is to be assigned to P.

With the segment from .7 to .8 divided into ten equal segments (hundredths), a *second decimal approximation* may be found, say .73. This process continues, at each step furnishing a more accurate approximation. The infinite process gives an infinite decimal. This decimal is uniquely determined: any requested digit, say the twenty-sixth, can be found.

On the other hand, let an infinite decimal be given, .333..., for example. This describes a position between the marks at .3 and .4, also between those at .33 and .34, also between those at .333 and .334, and so on. Imagine that a pair of pincers is placed with its jaws at .3 and .4. The left jaw moves to .33, the right to .34. Then to .333 and .334, and so on. As the decimal places are run through, the pincers close. Wholly closed at last, both jaws fall at an exact position on the line, that which is described by the infinite decimal.

The above discussion is not mathematically "rigorous." A sound treatment requires more technical mathematical machinery than can be suitably developed here. One of the simplest rigorous approaches makes use of *sets* of rational numbers. A positive real number can be defined as an "unbroken" set of rationals. Such a set is one which includes every rational that lies between any two rationals which belong to it, thus forming a kind of "arrow" or "vector" of rationals. For example, the set of all positive rationals with squares less than 2 is a "$\sqrt{2}$-arrow" (§5). It is easy to define sums and products for such arrows, hence for the real numbers. The decimal representation can then be derived. Such an approach is entirely numerical, dependent in no way upon geometry.

The real number system is the basis of analytical mathematics. In mathematical usage the word "number" ordinarily means "real number."

Since the real numbers match **(1-1)** the points of a line, any line can be taken as a complete continuous *number scale*. There is in this way seen to be an intimate connection between geometry and arithmetic or algebra, a relat: onship that is constantly exploited in mathematical application. Our books, magazines, and newspapers, for example, display many *graphs*, showing how two numerical variables are related. The graph is the geometric equivalent of a lengthy numerical table or algebraic formula.

PROBLEM SET 3 (§6–§8)

1.   Draw a line segment of unit length (length = 1 unit). With this as base, erect a right triangle of altitude 1 (1 unit). As noted in §4, the hypotenuse of this triangle will be of length $\sqrt{2}$. Now use this hypotenuse as base and on it erect another right triangle of altitude 1. Show its hypotenuse to be of length $\sqrt{3}$. Continue this procedure until you have constructed a segment of length $\sqrt{18}$. (If your constructions are accurate, the successive altitudes of the triangles will form a polygonal spiral turning through a total angle of 364°47′.)

2.   Draw a circle of diameter 3. Draw a diameter. Draw a chord perpendicular to this diameter and dividing it in the ratio of 2 to 1. Show that the length of the chord is twice $\sqrt{2}$.

3.* Construct a line segment of length $\sqrt[4]{2}$.

4.* Let P be a point of the line segment AB. Denote $\overline{AP} = x$ and $\overline{AB} = l$. If P is such that $l/x = x/(l - x)$, then P is called a "golden section" of AB. Show that if $x = 1$, then $l = \frac{1}{2}(1 + \sqrt{5})$. Construct a rectangle of length l and width x. The Greeks considered such a rectangle to have an especially pleasing shape.

5.   In the quotation of §7, Plato used the term "commensurable." Look up the meaning of this term, and explain Plato's reference.

6.   Prove $\sqrt[3]{2}$ irrational.

7.   With the aid of the prime-product theorem (§8, Chap. 7), prove that if p^2 is divisible by 3, so is p. Then prove $\sqrt{3}$ irrational.

8.* In the base-three numeral system, squares end in 0 or 1, because $0^2 = 0$, $1^2 = 1$, $2^2 = 11$. Hence if $2Q^2 = P^2$, Q^2 and P^2 must both end in 0. Explain these statements, then use them to prove $\sqrt{2}$ irrational. (*American Mathematical Monthly*, vol. 63, no. 4, April, 1956, page 247.)

9.* Frame a proof of the irrationality of $\sqrt{2}$ according to the scheme outlined in Problem 8, but with respect to the base-ten system.

10.   A given number may when represented in numeral systems with certain bases have a finite "decimal type" of expansion, while having an infinite such type of expansion with respect to other bases. In base ten, for example, $\frac{1}{3} =$ .333..., while in the base three $\frac{1}{10} = .1$. Give other instances.

11.   Will every rational number have a finite "decimal type" of expansion with respect to some numerical base? What is the least base with respect to which the number $\frac{7}{24}$ (base-ten representation) has such a finite expansion? 2/13?

Latter Answer: 13

12.* Consider each kind of combination listed below. Some of them will always produce an irrational number. Identify these cases and prove. The rest will sometimes produce an irrational, sometimes a rational, depending on the numerical values selected. In these cases cite numerical examples giving each type of result. (*Illustrations:* " $\sqrt{\text{Irrational}}$ " always produces an irrational, since if for some irrational number I and rational number $R = a/b$, $\sqrt{I} = R$, then $I = R^2 = a^2/b^2 = rational$, a contradiction. But "Irrational ÷ Irrational" may produce either a rational or an irrational. Thus $\sqrt{2} \div \sqrt{2} = 1$, while $\sqrt{6} \div \sqrt{3} = \sqrt{2}$.)

 (a) Irrational + Irrational
 (b) Irrational + Rational
 (c) Non-zero Rational × Irrational
 (d) $\sqrt{\text{Rational}}$

13.* Prove the following: Given any two irrational numbers, there is some rational number lying between them. *Hint:* It is sufficient to consider two irrationals lying between 0 and 1. (Why?) There must be some first place in which their decimal expansions differ.

14. Assuming $\sqrt{2}$ irrational, show $3\sqrt{2} - 8$ irrational. Will the same type of argument serve for $\sqrt{2} + \sqrt{3}$?

15. Is any real number "next" to another?

16. Probably no one has ever made use of a decimal expansion running beyond the one-hundredth place. Why don't we just agree to stop there, so as to avoid the difficulty of dealing with irrationals?

*§9. REPEATING DECIMALS

Some infinite decimals "repeat." In such a decimal there appears a certain finite sequence or "block" of digits. The rest of the decimal is simply the unending repetition of that same block of digits.

This is a handy notation: Write the block to be repeated only once, placing a dot over each of its digits. *Examples:*

$$.\dot{3} \quad = \quad .333...$$
$$23.0\dot{7}\dot{2} = 23.072072072...$$
$$5.0\dot{7}\dot{2} = 5.0727272...$$

The repeating decimals all turn out to represent rational numbers. To get the fractional form, multiply by the power of ten whose exponent equals the number of digits in the block. Then subtract the original number. To find a fractional form for $.\dot{3}$, for example, let $N = .\dot{3}$. Then

$$
\begin{array}{lll}
10N = 3.\dot{3} & (= 3.333...) \\
- \quad N = .\dot{3} & (= .333...) \\
\hline
9N = 3 & \text{so that} & N = \tfrac{3}{9} = \tfrac{1}{3}.
\end{array}
$$

Example 1. Find a fractional form for $.34\dot{1}\dot{7}$.

Work. Let $N = .34\dot{1}\dot{7}$.

$$
\begin{array}{lll}
100N = 34.17\dot{1}\dot{7} & (= 34.171717...) \\
- \quad N = .34\dot{1}\dot{7} & (= .341717...) \\
\hline
99N = 33.83 & \text{so that} & N = \dfrac{3383}{9900}
\end{array}
$$

The converse statement may be more surprising: Every rational number expands into a repeating decimal! This is easily seen by examining the division process used to express a fraction as a decimal. (Recall also that the infinite equivalent of a finite decimal will be repeating. *Example:* .27 = .26$\dot{9}$).

Illustration.   We express ¾ as a repeating decimal.

	List of Remainders	*Explanation*
.4 2 8 5 7 1		Only proper fractions need be
7)3.	3	considered. Once a remainder is
2 8		duplicated, the portion of the di-
2 0	2	vision included between the equal
1 4		remainders must repeat thereafter.
6 0	6	Some remainder must be dupli-
5 6		cated, for the number of possible
4 0	4	remainders, zero included, is only
3 5		equal to the divisor. (If a bag con-
5 0	5	tains only red, white, and blue
4 9		balls, and four balls are drawn,
1 0	1	some two must be like-colored.)
7		
3	3	Hence ¾ = .$\dot{4}$2857$\dot{1}$.

Evidently the set of rational numbers is identical with the set of the repeating decimals:

$$\{\text{Repeating Decimals}\} = \{\text{Rationals}\}.$$

From this we conclude that *every nonrepeating decimal represents an irrational number.* Here are two such irrationals:

$$.1\,0\,1\,0\,0\,1\,0\,0\,0\,1\,0\,0\,0\,0\,1\,0\,0\,0\,0\,0\,1\ldots$$
$$.1\,2\,3\,4\,5\,6\,7\,8\,9\,1\,0\,1\,1\,1\,2\,1\,3\,1\,4\,1\,5\ldots$$

It is left to the student to detect the "rules" followed in writing these, also to verify that neither decimal is repeating.

Let us imagine that a machine has been set up to write decimals between 0 and 1. The machine selects at *random* one of the ten digits 0, 1, 2, . . . , 9 to be the tenths digit of the decimal number. This takes ½ min. By similar random choice the machine produces the hundredths digit in ¼ min., the thousandths digit in ⅛ min., and so on. Our magic device produces an entire infinite decimal in exactly one minute (½ + ¼ + ⅛ + · · · = 1). Is it likely that this decimal will turn out to represent a *rational* number? With each digit chosen at random, there would seem to be a negligibly small chance that the decimal will be repeating. Apparently *there are many more irrationals than rationals.*

One further number classification is of some interest. An *algebraic* number is a real number which is a solution of some algebraic equation, like $x^7 - 3x^4 + 8 = 0$. Other real numbers are termed *transcendental*. All rationals are algebraic, being solutions of "linear" equations. Thus $-\frac{5}{18}$ is the solution of $18x + 5 = 0$. Some irrationals are algebraic. Thus $\sqrt{2}$ is a solution of $x^2 - 2 = 0$. But most irrationals are transcendental. The number π was shown by Lindemann in 1882 to be a transcendental. Here is a decimal transcendental:

$$.110001000000000000000001\ldots$$

The "ones" occupy the places numbered 1!, 2!, 3!, etc., where $1! = 1$, $2! = 1 \times 2 = 2$, $3! = 1 \times 2 \times 3 = 6$, etc.

*PROBLEM SET 4 (§9)

1. Derive fractional forms (lowest terms) for these repeating decimals:

   (a) $.\dot{1}$ (c) $.\dot{6}$ (e) $3.\dot{2}\dot{7}$ (g) $.58\dot{3}$
   (b) $.0\dot{1}$ (d) $.1\dot{6}$ (f) $.08\dot{3}$ (h) $.\dot{0}7692\dot{3}$

   Answers: (b) $\frac{1}{99}$, (h) $\frac{1}{13}$

2. Verify: (a) $4 \times .\dot{3} = 1.\dot{3}$, (b) $\dot{7} + \dot{8} = 1.\dot{6}$.
3. Express as repeating decimals:

   (a) $\frac{2}{3}$ (c) $\frac{3}{11}$ (e) $\frac{8}{13}$ (g) 5
   (b) $\frac{1}{11}$ (d) $\frac{5}{7}$ (f) $\frac{1}{2}$ (h) $\frac{5}{12}$

   Answers: (c) $.\dot{2}\dot{7}$, (f) $.4\dot{9}$

4. From a bag full of red and white socks, how many socks must you draw out (blindly) in order to be sure of getting two of the same color? How is this notion applied in §9?
5. Discuss the proof that every rational number expands into a repeating decimal, using $\frac{5}{13}$ in illustration (as $\frac{3}{7}$ was used in the text).
6. Three examples of nonrepeating decimals, representing irrationals, were cited in the text. Give two more examples.
7. Give arguments to show that your examples in Problem 5 are truly nonrepeating.
8. Show the following to be algebraic numbers:

   (a) $\frac{2}{3}$ (c) $1 + \sqrt{2}$
   (b) $\sqrt{3}$ (d) $\sqrt{2} - \sqrt{3}$

9. Show that with the binary system $\frac{1}{11} = .0\dot{1}$.
10.* In the binary numeral system $1 = .\dot{1}$ (just as in the decimal system $1 = .\dot{9}$). But $.\dot{1} = \frac{1}{10} + \frac{1}{100} + \frac{1}{1000} + \cdots$, equivalent to $\frac{1}{2} + \frac{1}{4} + \frac{1}{8} + \cdots$ in base ten. Does this justify the assertion $\frac{1}{2} + \frac{1}{4} + \frac{1}{8} + \cdots = 1$?

11

Using Units

§1. MEASURING

By classifying and by quantifying, man arranges his universe in an orderly way. He names and numbers whatever he can.

All of us run our lives according to the numerical labels on clocks and watches, rulers and mileposts, price tags and pay checks. These are *measurements*—37 min., 26.3 in., 85¢.

Whether it be a person, a city, an atom, a stick of wood, or what you will, every "object" has many measurable aspects or properties. (Even emotions and attitudes can be studied in terms of measurements of objective attributes: chemical and electrical changes in the human body; questionnaire results; etc.) "Weight" is a measurable property of physical objects. "Blood pressure" is a measurable property of human beings.

Some measuring is just counting: size of a group of people, cost of a purchase. Here, only the positive integers are used. In many cases, however, a continuous portion of the real number scale is needed. A yardstick graduated in inches makes use of the portion from 0 to 36. An outdoor thermometer may display the portion from -40 to $+120$. *The real number scale is a kind of universal measuring stick*. The kinds of measurement quantities best suited to mathematical manipulation are those which most resemble the real number line in their structure, those which are homogeneous, continuous, and *additive* (§2).

Measurable properties will be called **measures,** for short. *Length,* for example, is a measure. So are time, weight, area, cost, and so on. With each such measure are associated various specific scaling schemes, or kinds of **units.** We may measure a length in inches. But we may also measure it in feet, in meters, even in light-years.

REMARKS ON TERMINOLOGY. In mathematical applications, we encounter a jumble of numerical and measurement expressions. The adjectives *pure* and *concrete* are often used to help us distinguish between the two types. The term *pure number*, for example, is applied both to number symbols and to numbers. A measurement expression may be called a "concrete form" or a "concrete expression," and the physical quantity denoted by the expression may be called a "concrete quantity." Consider the formula giving the circumference of a circle in terms of its radius, $c = 2\pi r$. Here, 2 and π are pure numbers, and the letter r is to be replaced by a concrete form, "3 in." say, denoting a concrete quantity, a length.

Many concrete quantities can be "scaled," so that their values form a continuous portion of the real number line. These are called *denominate quantities*. Examples of denominate forms: 3 in., 7 sq. ft., 150 gal., 60 kw-hr. Nondenominate quantities often have a "cardinal" or "ordinal" character, referring precisely or imprecisely to the sizes of sets or to a rank order. *Examples:* 3 people, 2½ hamburgers, No. 2 on the best-seller list. Some concrete forms are nothing more than codes: "Social Security No. ———." These latter have little or no mathematical significance.

In a strict sense, only denominate quantities have "units." On the elementary level, however, we customarily apply the notion of "units" more generally, extending it to include "people," "hamburgers," "best-seller list rank," etc. Suppose that 2 men work 3 hr. each and 5 men 4 hr. each, on a construction project. The number of *man-hours* worked is 2×3 $+$ 5×4 $=$ 26. This is a measure of total work effort. The technician may prefer to consider the units to be associated with the 26 simply as *hours*, the numbers 2 and 5 being regarded as "weighting factors." From the elementary point of view, however, it is probably more desirable to take the "man-hour" as the unit, a derived unit of product type (§4).

§2. ADDITIVE MEASURES

Length is an *additive* measure. This means that a length can be found by measuring a part, then the remainder, and adding the two results. Lay a 2-ft. and a 3-ft. rule end to end in a straight line and you have, in effect, a 5-ft. rule. So we write

$$2 \text{ feet} + 3 \text{ feet} = 5 \text{ feet}.$$

We continually make statements of this sort. Yet they are always potentially unsafe. A person who steps 2 ft. west, then 3 ft. east, has indeed moved through a total of 5 ft.—yet he is only a foot from where he started. Evidently the statement "2 ft. + 3 ft. = 5 ft." applies to distances moved along a path, but is not generally true when taken to refer to the spatial displacements given by the movements.

Many limitations must be borne in mind. Suppose that a rubber strip is measured while it is being stretched. Partial measurements (2 ft. and 3 ft.) must be made simultaneously; their computed sum (5 ft.) gives the correct total length just as the same instant.

Compare these two statements:

$$2 \text{ feet} + 3 \text{ feet} = 5 \text{ feet}. \qquad (M)$$
$$2 \ + \ 3 \quad = \quad 5. \qquad (N)$$

The labels M and N signify that the one is a relation involving *measurement*, the other a pure *number* relation.

There is an enormous difference between these two kinds of statements.

An M-statement can only be *conditionally true*. An N-statement can be *universally true*. Once having agreed upon the definition and notation for the real numbers, we must grant that the statement $2 + 3 = 5$ is true today, tomorrow, and for all time; true here, there, and everywhere; true in this, in that, and in all applications. We may use the relation $2 + 3 = 5$ generally and freely. But whenever we contemplate using the relation 2 ft. + 3 ft. = 5 ft., we must carefully examine the particular physical situation that is involved and must make a judgment as to whether the relation will or will not be true under the circumstances.

For each M-statement below, can you describe a situation in which the statement is true and another in which it is not?

1. 2 pints + 3 pints = 5 pints.
2. 2 years + 3 years = 5 years.
3. 2 volts + 3 volts = 5 volts.

Hints: With (1), consider the mixtures water-water, water-alcohol, water-sugar, air-air. With (2), consider concurrent prison terms, also two children's ages. With (3), consider series and parallel hookups.

We are all careless in our use of language. To a certain extent this is inevitable. Absolute precision of speech is impossible. Whenever two persons employ identical language forms, they both have in mind somewhat different meanings. Sometimes the difference is gross—as when a Soviet and an American spokesman both talk of "freedom" or "peace." Then communication may be hampered or even made impossible. In using M-statements we take a risk of tumbling into pitfalls just as we do when using ordinary language.

Many people find it difficult to distinguish between M-statements and N-statements. Some others just can't be bothered or don't wish to make the effort. Their troubles are legion. In simple situations a modicum of common sense may sometimes rescue them. Having two chains each capable of supporting 50 lb., even the most mathematically and scientifically illiterate individual will likely use them in parallel if he must lift 100 lb., rather than fasten them end to end. And this person will probably not take twice as much medicine as his doctor prescribes, so as to heal himself twice as quickly. Yet he might try to grow twice as many tomatoes in his garden by putting in twice as many plants as recommended. He might suppose that a beam of twice the dimensions of another is only twice as strong, or if not this, that the strength/weight ratio is the same for the two. In general, people display a marked tendency to regard simple numerical relations as having the character of universal physical laws, $2 + 3 = 5$ being taken to mean $2(\ ) + 3(\ ) = 5(\ )$, where almost anything can be filled in the blanks.

When read aloud, some false mathematical statements (N-type) sound like plausible M-statements. An unthinking student may write $3^2 + 4^2 = 7^2$ because this is read as:

$$3 \text{ squared} + 4 \text{ squared} = 7 \text{ squared.}$$

This horrendous kind of mathematical blunder has also been attributed to the assumption of the "universal distributive law," according to which $f(x_1 + x_2) = f(x_1) + f(x_2)$ for every expression or function $f(x)$. Actually, the only "continuous" function which satisfies that relation is the proportional type $f(x) = cx$, c being any numerical constant. But students continue to write $\sqrt{16 + 9} = \sqrt{16} + \sqrt{9} = 4 + 3 = 7$, $\frac{1}{2} + \frac{1}{3} = 1/(2+3) = \frac{1}{5}$, $\sin 30° + \sin 30° = \sin 60°$. Occasionally common sense calls a halt—they do not write $(1 + 2) + (1 + 3) = (1 + 5)$!

Some measures are not additive. The life and social sciences provide many examples. Psychological variables, for example, often combine "logarithmically." Thus when the C notes of three consecutive octave ranges are sounded, they seem evenly separated in pitch to the ear. Yet their actual frequencies jump by multiplication instead of addition. They are in ratio 1, 2, 4 rather than 1, 2, 3. Sound intensity is commonly measured in *decibels* (db.). This too is a nonadditive measure. It is *never* true that 40 db. + 40 db. = 80 db. In fact, under the appropriate circumstances (like-pitched sounds heard simultaneously), the correct relationship is

$$40 \text{ decibels} + 40 \text{ decibels} = 43 \text{ decibels.}$$

Nonadditive measures, however, can usually be related to basic additive measures, and so more easily handled. In the case of the decibel, we have db. = $10 \log i$, where i denotes the sound power per unit normal area, in micromicrowatts per square meter (m). The statement $10,000m + 10,000m = 20,000m$ is equivalent to the statement 40 db. + 40 db. = 43 db.

§3. ADDING AND SUBTRACTING MEASUREMENTS

"Only like quantities may be added or subtracted."

School texts lay much stress upon this rule. Although it serves a useful purpose, the rule is inaccurate and incomplete, even so misleading as to invite general misunderstanding.

"Like quantities" are measurements expressed in *the same units:* "2 ft." and "3 ft." are like quantities, but "2 ft." and "36 in." (or "2 ft." and "3 lb.") are not. Taken literally, the rule asserts that "2 ft." and "36 in." may not be added. Yet the following statement is surely a sensible one:

$$2 \text{ ft.} + 36 \text{ in.} = 5 \text{ ft.}$$

The crux of the matter is that the numerical coefficients 2 and 36 do not in this case add to give the coefficient 5 of the sum quantity. With *like* quantities the coefficients do add:

$$2 \text{ ft.} + 3 \text{ ft.} = 5 \text{ ft.} \qquad \text{Coefficients: } 2 + 3 = 5.$$

It is this additive property of the coefficients which the rule is supposed to suggest:

$$x \text{ units} + y \text{ units} = (x + y) \text{ units}.$$

In words: *When two like quantities are added, the result is a third like quantity whose numerical coefficient is the sum of the coefficients of the given quantities.*

As a reminder, or mathematical Commandment to the young pupil, the simple proscription *"Don't add unlike quantities"* can be given. The emphasis is then where it belongs, upon *process* rather than *conception*. For although it makes sense to speak of the sum of two distances even if one is given in miles and the other in feet, the *practical procedure* of combining is to express each distance in the same units, miles, feet, inches, or what you will. Then and then only will it be possible to find the sum just by adding the attached numbers.

EXAMPLES OF ADDITIVE COMBINATIONS MAKING

Sense	*Nonsense*
2 ft. + 3 ft.	2 ft. + 3 lb.
2 ft. + 3 in.	2 + 3 sec.
2 boys + 3 boys	2°F. + $6

Combinations that involve different kinds of objects make sense or not, according as we choose. From the standpoint of *set union*, for example, we may regard "2 cows + 3 sheep" as a meaningful expression, one referring to a set whose elements are cows and sheep. By "changing the units" we could even perform an addition operation: "2 animals + 3 animals = 5 animals."

To change the units of a measurement, express it first as a product: coefficient times 1 of the unit. Replace the 1 unit by the equivalent number of new units, and simplify. This is easier done than said!

$$3 \text{ ft.} = 3 \times (1 \text{ ft.}) = 3 \times (12 \text{ in.}) = 36 \text{ in.}$$

It is very often convenient to leave a measurement in mixed sum form: "2 ft. + 3 in." instead of "2¼ ft." or "27 in." In fact, we use the mixed form so much that we leave out the plus sign, writing

2 ft. 3 in. (or 2′3″)	instead of	2 ft. + 3 in.
5°36′	instead of	5° + 36′.
2 hr. 6 min. 45 sec.	instead of	2 hr. + 6 min. + 45 sec.

Example 1.   Express 8000 sec. in terms of hr., min., sec.

Work.

$$8000 \text{ sec.} = 8000 \times (\tfrac{1}{60} \text{ min.})$$
$$= 133 \text{ min. } 20 \text{ sec.}$$
$$= 133 \times (\tfrac{1}{60} \text{ hr.}) \, 20 \text{ sec.}$$
$$= 2 \text{ hr. } 13 \text{ min. } 20 \text{ sec.}$$

$$\frac{8000}{60} = 133 + \frac{20}{60}$$

$$\frac{133}{60} = 2 + \frac{13}{60}$$

Example 2. $2'10'' + 5'6'' = ?$

Work. Apply the "like quantity" procedure separately with respect to the ft. and in.

$$
\begin{array}{l}
2 \text{ ft. } 10 \text{ in.} \\
\underline{5 \text{ ft. } \ \ 6 \text{ in.}} \\
7 \text{ ft. } 16 \text{ in. } = 8 \text{ ft. } 4 \text{ in.} \qquad\qquad\qquad (16 = 12 + 4) \\
\phantom{7 \text{ ft. } 16 \text{ in. }} = 8'4''
\end{array}
$$

We may justify the above process by writing out the mixed forms in full:

(2 ft. + 10 in.) + (5 ft. + 6 in.) = (2 ft. + 5 ft.) + (10 in. + 6 in.) = etc.

Is the addition of measurements commutative and associative?

Example 3. $200 \times (3 \text{ lb. } 13 \text{ oz.}) = ?$

Work.

$$
\begin{array}{l}
200 \times (3 \text{ lb. } + 13 \text{ oz.}) \\
\quad = (200 \times 3) \text{ lb. } + (200 \times 13) \text{ oz.} \\
\quad = 600 \text{ lb. } + 2600 \text{ oz. } = 600 \text{ lb. } + 2600 \times (\tfrac{1}{16} \text{ lb.}) \\
\quad = 762 \text{ lb. } 8 \text{ oz.} \qquad\qquad [2600 \ \ = \ \ 16 \times 162 \ \ + 8]
\end{array}
$$

Can you justify the "distributive" relation used in the first step?

Example 4. $35'6'' \div 8.$

Work.

$$
\frac{35 \text{ ft. } 6 \text{ in.}}{8} = \frac{32 \text{ ft. } + 42 \text{ in.}}{8} = 4'5\tfrac{1}{4}''
$$

PROBLEM SET 1 (§1–§3)

1.   List a dozen measures, citing one system of units used with each. *Example:* Time (minutes).

2.   Consider the relation 8 in. + 7 in. = 15 in. Describe two sets of circumstances, both involving an 8-in. and a 7-in. measurement, such that the relation holds in the one but not in the other.

3.   Same as Problem 2 for 20 lb. + 30 lb. = 50 lb. [forces].

4.   Same as Problem 2 for 3 gal. + 4 gal. = 7 gal.

5.   Same as Problem 2 for 2 hr. + 3 hr. = 5 hr.

6.   Same as Problem 2 for 20 miles/hr. + 3 miles/hr. = 23 miles/hr.

7.   Is weight an additive measure? Can you find the weight of a large sack of marbles with the aid of a scale which can weigh only a portion at a time?

8.   Is area an additive measure? Illustrate by discussing the problem of finding how much wallpaper to buy to cover the walls of a room. (Wallpaper rolls are about half a yard wide.)

9.   If a child gets a certain amount of pleasure from eating a half-pint of ice cream, will he likely get twice the pleasure from eating a full pint? Devise two such illustrations of your own.

10.   Are two 6-in. diameter hot-air furnace pipes equivalent to a single 12-in. pipe?

11.   In each case, can it make sense to "add" two measurements in the units cited?

(a)	Apples and pears	(d)	Pounds and ounces
(b)	Boys and girls	(e)	Miles and hours
(c)	Feet and acres	(f)	Quarts and dollars

12.   Can it be appropriate to add two temperature measurements (in the sense that the sum can be interpreted as the temperature of something)? Ages? Blood pressures? Birth rates? Life expectancies? Population densities? Populations? Shoe sizes?

13.   Express each of these "compound" measurements in terms of the larger unit named:

(a)	2 hr. 20 min.	(e)	8°24′
(b)	6 ft. 9 in.	(f)	2 yr. 5 mo.
(c)	12 lb. 6 oz.	(g)	2 gal. 3 qt.
(d)	3 weeks, 5 days	(h)	3 reams, 200 sheets

Answer: (c) $12\frac{3}{8}$ lb.

14.   Express each measurement in Problem 13 in terms of the smaller unit named.   *Answer:* (c)   198 oz.

15.   Express each in compound form:

(a)	40 in.	(c)	17 days	(e)	100 sec.
(b)	50 oz.	(d)	29 pt.	(f)	10,000 sec.

Answer: (d)   3 gal. 2 qt. 1 pt.

16.   Combine as indicated:

(a)   2 ft. 10 in.   (b)   10 hr. 35 min.
     $+$ 4 ft. 7 in. $-$ 2 hr. 50 min.

17.   Combine as indicated:

(a)   35°17′42″   (b)   3 gal. 3 qt.
     $+$ 23°50′38″ $-$ 1 gal. 1 qt. 1 pt.

18.   If 30 lb. 6 oz. of flour is to be divided equally among 12 persons, how much does each get?

19.   Thirty chairs are placed in a row, with centers 2 ft. 5 in. apart. Find the total distance from center of first to center of last.   *Answer:* 70 ft. 1 in.

20.   Justify the "distributive" relation

$$4 \times (2 \text{ hr. } 5 \text{ min.}) = 8 \text{ hr. } 20 \text{ min.}$$

Suggestions: Time, in hours, is an additive measure. The given form may be regarded as a sum of four terms, each equal to $(2 + \frac{5}{60})$ hr.

§4. NEW MEASURES FOR OLD

We choose certain measures as *basic,* then derive others by multiplication or division.

Length and *time* are always regarded as basic measures. The day is a natural time unit. We take various numbers of days or split the day into parts to get some other unit systems: 7 days = 1 week, 24 hr. = 1 day, 60 min. = 1 hr., etc.

The world has chosen the *meter* as the principal unit of length. The "official" meter is the distance between two marks on a platinum-iridium bar kept in the International Bureau of Weights and Measures, near Paris. Other length units are defined in terms of this standard. By decree of Congress, our inch is such that 39.37 inches exactly equals one meter. From the inch we obtain the foot, yard, mile, and other familiar distance units.

The meter is the fundamental unit in the *metric system,* which will receive further attention in §6. The meter was originally defined as a ten-millionth of a quarter of the earth's circumference (quadrant distance from Pole to Equator). This proposal was made shortly before 1800 by a committee of mathematicians, at the request of the French government. During the tumultuous upheaval of the Revolution, surveying parties laboriously and dangerously pursued the task of measuring an arc of the meridian between Dunkirk and Barcelona. Despite the care taken in the work, errors entered—and indeed would enter today in such an undertaking. The present meter, therefore, must be regarded as essentially an arbitrarily chosen standard rather than a "natural" choice like the day. We are no longer dependent upon a marked standard. Were all our scales destroyed overnight, we could duplicate the lost meter as the length of a train of 1,552,734.8 waves of red cadmium light.

Speed is a *derived* measure. We find its value by dividing a distance value by a time value. Thus if a car travels 800 ft. in a 10-sec. interval, we form the quotient $800/10 = 80$ and say that the "average speed" is 80 *feet per second.* (To pass from this conception to that of the speed at an instant, we must consider the value "approached" by the quotient as the time interval shrinks.) We write the unit of speed in such a way as to suggest the division process by which the speed is found:

A unit of speed: 1 ft./sec.

Let a car travel at 80 ft./sec. for 4 sec. Moving 80 ft. in every second, it will obviously go 4 × 80 ft. = 320 ft. in the 4 sec. In a more formal approach to the same problem, we now put down the worded formula,

Distance = Speed × Time,

then fill in the given quantities:

$$\text{Distance} = 80 \, \frac{\text{ft.}}{\text{sec.}} \times 4 \text{ sec.}$$

If we treat the unit names like numerical quantities, then we get a "cancellation" of the "sec." appearing in the numerator with the "sec." in the denominator (sec./sec. = 1!!):

$$\textbf{Distance} = 80 \, \frac{\text{ft.}}{\cancel{\text{sec.}}} \times 4 \, \cancel{\text{sec.}} = 320 \text{ ft.}$$

Handling unit names like numbers thus gives a kind of automatic scheme for obtaining the units of the answer.

Suppose that a farmer offers a 60-lb. bag of potatoes for sale at a price of \$5.70, agreeing to sell smaller portions at a proportional (prorated) price. It is then convenient to calculate a *price per pound;*

$$\frac{570 \text{ cents}}{60 \text{ lb.}} = 9\tfrac{1}{2} \text{¢/lb.}$$

Here too is a derived measure, the unit being 1 cent per pound. If 24 pounds are purchased, the price is:

$$9\tfrac{1}{2} \, \frac{\text{cents}}{\text{lb.}} \times 24 \text{ lb.} = 228 \text{ cents} = \$2.28.$$

A purchaser who buys \$2.00 worth gets

$$200 \text{ cents} \div 9\tfrac{1}{2} \, \frac{\text{cents}}{\text{lb.}} = \frac{200}{9\tfrac{1}{2}} \text{ cents} \times \frac{\text{lb.}}{\text{cents}} = \frac{400}{19} \text{ lb.} \approx 21 \text{ lb.}$$

(Read the wavy equality sign as "approximately equals.")

In the above illustrations, the unit forms *tell exactly how to find the quantity to which they refer.* The form "ft./sec." correctly suggests that a speed is found by dividing a distance value by a time value. But in more complicated cases the forms cannot be taken so literally. Consider *acceleration,* or "rate of change of speed." A car which increases its speed by 2 ft. per second during every second of its motion is said to have an acceleration of "2 ft. per second per second," or (2 ft./sec.)/sec. This is customarily abbreviated as "2 ft./sec.²" But the acceleration of an object can never be found by dividing a distance value by the square of the corresponding time value. In the simplest case, that of uniform acceleration, the acceleration is twice that quotient.

Two different kinds of measures may have like unit forms. The product 3 ft. × 4 lb., for example, may refer to *work* or to *torque.* In the first instance, a force of 4 lb. acts on a body over a 3-ft. moved distance, expending 12 ft-lb. of energy. In the other, a 4-lb. force is applied at a lever-arm distance of 3 ft., producing a 12 lb-ft. turning effect.

Still another quantity having the form "force × distance" is the *ton-mile,* a unit used by shippers to measure transportation effort. In the case of birth rates, death rates, radio signal frequencies, etc., we may in popular usage regard them as expressed in different units, yet technically they all share the same form, "1 ÷ time."

As new measures are constructed out of old ones, the new unit forms reflect the corresponding multiplications or divisions. This observation leads to the following rule:

RULE OF UNITS

When unit names are written into an equation and treated "like numbers," then the units must "check" on both sides of the equation.

That is, after simplification, the left and right members of the equation must display identical unit forms. We may have "ft." equated to "ft.," "cents" to "cents," or "ft./sec." to "ft./sec." We may not have "ft." equated to "sec." Also, before checking, we should express all lengths in terms of some one length unit, etc., so that we avoid ending with "ft." equated to "in.," etc.

The Rule of Units is of fundamental importance in practical application. We use it to determine the units of the final answer to a problem. We also use it as an aid in setting up the problem. A pupil who has trouble remembering the relation Distance = Speed × Time may be led to it by reminding himself that speed can be given in miles per hour, hence must be "multiplied" by hours to get miles.

In a very short problem, unit names may be written in all along the way, as we did in the illustrations above. In a long problem, the writing in of units will clutter up the work and should be avoided. Rewrite the first expression or equation with the unit names written in, delete numerical values, and simplify, so as to find the units of the answer or to check the form. In either case, be *consistent:* never drop units on one side of an equation while retaining them on the other. (When the work has been put down *sans units,* the units of the final answer may be shown in parentheses.) Here are instances of sound and unsound procedure in finding the distance covered by a car traveling at 30 miles per hour for 2 hours:

O.K.	O.K.	OBJECTIONABLE
$\text{Distance} = 30 \dfrac{\text{miles}}{\text{hr.}} \times 2 \text{ hr.}$	$\left[\dfrac{\text{miles}}{\text{hr.}} \times \text{hr.} = \text{miles} \right]$	$30 \dfrac{\text{miles}}{\text{hr.}} \times 2 \text{ hr.}$
		$= 30 \times 2$
$= 60 \text{ miles}$	$30 \times 2 = 60 \text{ (miles)}$	$= 60 \text{ miles}$

A college mathematics professor will almost invariably require his students to confine their handling of units wholly to the sidelines, so that all their operational procedures will be purely numerical.

Area and volume are usually defined directly rather than as derived measures. Thus a one-foot-square surface may be taken as a standard.

The area of a general surface can then be expressed in terms of the number of such surface units that it contains. The unit of area is termed "1 square foot." A rectangle of dimensions 3 ft. by 4 ft. can be split into $3 \times 4 = 12$ such squares and so has an area of "12 square feet." The area formula for a rectangle thus involves a product of length measurements. So does the formula for other plane figures and curved surfaces. It is therefore convenient to regard the unit of area as derived from the product 1 foot $\times$ 1 foot, abbreviated "1 ft.^{2}" Similarly, we take as a unit of volume: 1 cubic foot = 1 ft.^{3}

Example 1.   A pound of sugar costs 12¢. Sugar provides 3 calories per gram. What is the cost per 100 calories?

Work.   To get 100 calories, we require:

$$100 \text{ cal.} \div 3 \text{ cal./gm.} = \frac{100}{3} \text{ gm.} = \frac{100}{3} \times \left(\frac{1}{454} \text{ lb.}\right) = \frac{100}{1362} \text{ lb.}$$

This costs:

$$\frac{100}{1362} \text{ lb.} \times 12 \frac{\text{cents}}{\text{lb.}} = \frac{1200}{1362} \text{ cents} \approx \frac{7}{8} \text{ cents}$$

The computation could be performed in a single operation:

$$12 \frac{\text{cents}}{\text{lb.}} \times \frac{1}{454} \frac{\text{lb.}}{\text{gm.}} \times \frac{1}{3} \frac{\text{gm.}}{\text{cal.}} = \frac{4}{454} \frac{\text{cents}}{1 \text{ cal.}} = \frac{400}{454} \frac{\text{cents}}{100 \text{ cal.}} \approx \frac{7}{8} \frac{\text{cents}}{100 \text{ cal.}}.$$

If the computation were to be repeated for a variety of foods, it would pay to set up a formula:

$$c = \frac{100n}{454g}$$

where n = number of cents per pound, g = number of calories per gram, c = number of cents per 100 cal. But note that the units will not *check* in the formula unless the "lb./gm." units attached to the constant 1/454 are taken into account. Many common formulas contain such "concealed" units.

Example 2.   Water weighs 1 gram per cubic centimeter. What does it weigh in pounds per cubic foot?

Work.   The density of water is:

$$1 \frac{\text{gm.}}{\text{cm.}^3} = 1 \frac{1/454 \text{ lb.}}{(1/30.5 \text{ ft.})^3} = \frac{(30.5)^3}{454} \frac{\text{lb.}}{\text{ft.}^3} \approx 62.5 \frac{\text{lb.}}{\text{ft.}^3}.$$

Hence a cubic foot of water weighs about 62.5 lb.

REMARKS.   The matter of writing units into equations is controversial. Engineers and physical scientists do not hesitate to write units in whenever this seems desirable. Mathematicians studiously avoid putting units in, though insisting upon full descriptions, with units specified, of all physical quantities that are symbolized in the work. A reason for this "purism" is that the theories underlying mathematical operations are framed in terms of numerical variables, and would become unduly and unnecessarily complicated in terms of measurement variables. (*M*-statements are more hazardous to use than *N*-statements.) There may also be the feeling that it is easier for a student to see the mathematical pattern of his work and to understand and correct his errors when the work is in number and number operation terms, without the further complication of units. So the college mathematics professor usually requires his students to treat the units as an aspect of the problem apart from the numerical or algebraic manipulation. Typically, the professor would like to see this approach followed from the beginning, in the elementary grades and onward.

On the other hand, some professional educators and writers on arithmetic tend to overdo the writing in of units. They also often introduce confusing or unnecessary conceptions, and employ misleading terms. We have already noted that the "like quantities" rule is seldom presented correctly in texts on arithmetic. These texts also generally apply such adjectives as "concrete" and "denominate" to *numbers* instead of just to expressions or to quantities, a practice that encourages serious misunderstanding. They allow a "concrete number" to be multiplied by an "abstract number" (2 × 3 ft. = 6 ft.), but object to the multiplication of two "concrete numbers" (2 ft. × 3 ft. = 6 sq. ft.)! The entire subject of units is a tricky one to deal with. Unless the theory is soundly put, both pupils and teachers are likely to lose their mental bearings and be blocked in their approach to understanding the ways in which mathematics can be applied to real problems. (A clear mathematical "philosophy" is not just the luxury of an abstract thinker, but an important practical tool in itself.)

Writing units into equations may aid the young pupil to gain a keener sense of the realities of the problem, by keeping it upon what for him is a more concrete level. The forfeit to be paid is that he must gradually be weaned away from the practice, in high school and perhaps in college. Is this a high price?

PROBLEM SET 2 (§4)

In Problems 1–5, cite an appropriate unit for measuring each quantity named. In some cases several choices are possible. In some other cases the measurement is wholly numerical, no physical units being involved.

1. (a) Price of string beans (bulk display in grocery)
   (b) Price of rolls (bakery)   *Answer:* ¢/12
   (c) First-class postage rate
   (d) Coverage of a wall paint   *Answer:* sq. ft./gal.

2. (a) Grade on a spelling test   *Answer:* Pure number. No units.
   (b) Death rate in a country   *Answer:* 1/(1000 yr.) *or* . . .
   (c) Typing speed
   (d) Yield of a wheat field

3. (a) Heating rate of a furnace   *Answer:* B.T.U./hr.
   (b) Quantity of household electricity used in a month
   (c) Air movement rate of an attic fan
                                          Answer: cu. ft./min.
   (d) Batting average

4. (a) Homicide rate in a city
    (b) Gas consumption of an auto
    (c) Size of a house   *Answer:* sq. ft.
    (d) Property tax rate   *Answer:* Pure number. No units.

5. (a) Passenger volume of an air line   *Answer:* miles *or* passenger-miles
    (b) Rating of a water pump
    (c) Caloric value of steak   *Answer:* cal./4 oz.
    (d) Vitamin B content of a cereal

6. Cite four quantities other than those listed in problems 1–5, and give appropriate units for measuring them.

7. The freight-carrying activity of a railroad may be measured in ton-miles per year. The *ton-mile* is of the form "force × distance." Is it therefore a unit of physical work in the same sense as is the foot-pound? (*Hint:* Force is a directed quantity. In what directions do the forces act in the two cases?)

8. In newspaper parlance, a "line" is a measure of area. Fourteen (14) lines make a "column inch," which is a rectangle 2 in. wide by 1 in. deep. Advertising "force" is measured in "circulines," this being the product of the number of lines in an ad and the circulation of the paper. What is the force of a full-page ad (8 × 20, i.e., 8 columns of 20 in.) in a paper with a circulation of 20,000? Of a 3 × 8 ad in a paper with 80,000 circulation? (*Latter Answer:* 26,880,000 circulines). Should the cost of an ad be proportional to its circuline force?

9. A power mower is propelled at 1½ miles per hour and cuts a 16-in. strip (overlap allowed for). What is its cutting rate in square feet per hour? With no allowance for turns, how long will it take to mow a 60-ft. by 80-ft. plot?

10. A standard package of 80 9-in. by 9-in. floor tiles of a certain type costs $11.36. What is the cost per square foot? With no allowance for wastage, what will be the cost of the tiles needed for a 12-ft. by 18-ft. room?

11. Algernon Kallikak is supposed to take 6 milligrams of Vitamin Q per day. The preparation comes in syrup form, the label stating that one tablespoon provides the normal daily portion of 2⅓ milligrams of the vitamin. How long should Mr. Kallikak's 12-fluid-ounce bottle last him? To lay in a month's supply, how much should he buy?   *Latter Answer:* 38⁴⁄₇ fluid oz.

12. According to an almanac, about 212,000 cu. ft. of water pours over Niagara Falls per second, 94% of this over Horseshoe Fall (Canada), the rest over American Fall (U.S.). Horseshoe Fall is 160 ft., American Fall 167 ft. high. A cubic foot of water weighs about 62½ lb. A pound of water dropping one foot acquires one foot-pound of energy, and 550 ft-lb. per second equals one horsepower. If all of Niagara's energy could be harnessed, what horsepower would be available?   *Answer:* 3.86×10^6 horsepower

§5.   THE SPIRIT OF MATHEMATICAL APPLICATION

Mrs. Jones intends to buy some apples. Standing before the fruit displays in the grocery, she looks over the apples and considers the cost of the purchase. In its full totality, the situation involving Mrs. Jones and the apples is enormously complex. Each apple is a nonhomogeneous object whose superficial outward aspects, shape, color, and so on, are even in themselves too extensive for a complete description. Thousands of such objects are in Mrs. Jones' vicinity. There are people nearby, moving in devious spatial paths with variable velocities.

Amid the swarm of activity bombarding her with sights, sounds, odors, tastes, and feelings, and in spite of the many vague thoughts and notions that continually flit through her mind, Mrs. Jones easily singles out a simple mathematical relation that bears upon her "problem." Deciding to buy 3 lb. of apples and noting a tag that reads "11¢/lb.," she computes $3 \times 11 = 33$ and concludes that the purchase will cost 33¢.

Mrs. Jones has made use of a process called *abstraction*. With a complex situation confronting her, she has "isolated" a tiny bit of it, focusing her attention on just two quantities which need to be taken into account to find the purchase cost. Her experience and training tell her that no other factors are relevant. She knows she need not measure the sizes of the apples, nor consider their colors and arrangement, nor recall the present phase of the moon, nor look up the 1950 population of Mexico City.

We are all well accustomed to abstraction of this sort. It underlies our conscious perception, thought, and behavior. Faced with a problem situation, whether of the common everyday variety or of a technical or scientific type, we always try to locate simple elements or familiar patterns within the complex context of the full situation. In the sciences these "patterns" are groups of "laws" which we have formulated about the behavior of material things. Mathematical patterns are systems involving abstract relation-forms like $\sqrt{27}, 2 + 3 = 5, y = kx^2, e^{-y} \sin 2\pi x$, etc. (See Chap. 3, §2, last two paragraphs.)

The function of the mathematician is to discover types of relations that occur widely in man's dealings with Nature, and to analyze their patterns so that they may be recognized wherever they occur and may be made use of in application. The simplest types may be expected to show up most frequently. Thus the arithmetic of the natural numbers is everywhere in demand, and we use the real number scale nearly as often— many times a day. When our concern is with space and form, we find ourselves dealing with lines, circles and triangles, planes, spheres, cylinders, cones, and rectangular boxes. Centered upon such topics, the mathematical studies of the grades and of early high school provide a general educational base needed by everyone. As the centuries have rolled on, we have found ourselves dealing in increasingly complicated ways with Nature, so that the subject field of mathematics has grown enormously. No other field of study is of such broad scope, either in regard to the accumulation of knowledge or to the variety of research directions.

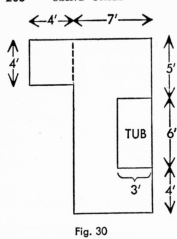

Fig. 30

Illustration 1. Mr. Beamish wishes to lay 9-in. by 9-in. tiles covering a bathroom floor of the shape and dimensions given in Figure 30. The tub is flush with the floor. How many tiles will he need?

The principal abstraction has already been performed: the passage from the complex real-life situation to the geometric diagram of Figure 30. Next it is necessary to recognize that the figure is composed of rectangular portions, one 4 ft. by 4 ft., another 7 ft. by 15 ft., the third 3 ft. by 6 ft. The problem of covering must be interpreted as one of area, the required area being the sum of the areas of the first two rectangles, less that of the third:

$$4 \times 4 \ + \ 7 \times 15 \ - \ 3 \times 6 \ = \ 16 + 105 - 18 = 103 \text{ (sq. ft.)}.$$

Since the area of a tile is

$$\frac{3}{4} \times \frac{3}{4} = \frac{9}{16} \text{ (sq. ft.)},$$

the minimum number needed will be

$$103 \div \frac{9}{16} = 103 \times \frac{16}{9} \approx 183.$$

Of course this will not be enough, because of cutting to fit at edges, etc. Perhaps 17 dozen should be bought.

Illustration 2. Archibald Oates wishes to estimate the height of a tall tree in his yard. What data are relevant? Need we identify the species: maple, oak, elm, etc.? Should the number of leaves or branches be counted? Is the time of day important? The tree is sixty years old, four times as old as Oates' daughter, who is blond and who expects to become a schoolteacher.

Whether or not certain factors are relevant depends also upon the method of estimation which Oates selects—the particular abstraction he makes. If he should begin by measuring the length of the tree's shadow on the ground, with the intention of using nautical tables to find the angle of the sun's rays, then the time of day would become relevant.

Let us suppose that what Oates actually does is to stand away from the tree at A, considering A, B, C, as vertices of a large triangle in space, where B and C mark the tree's foot and top, respectively (Fig. 31). He plans to measure the ground distance $\overline{AB}$ and the angle at A, then to draw a scale diagram of $\triangle ABC$ on paper, reading off the value of the height $\overline{BC}$. Of course if the ground slopes appreciably or if the tree leans badly, other measurements will have to be taken (additional relevant factors). But even in the simplest case, with level ground and vertical tree, when Mr. Oates lays his measuring tape along AB, it will not lie precisely straight. In the second diagram, AB has been drawn a little wavy

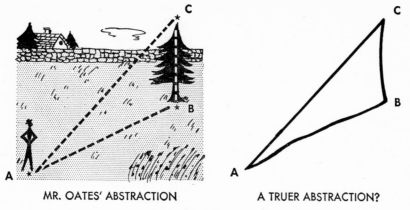

MR. OATES' ABSTRACTION   A TRUER ABSTRACTION?

Fig. 31

(exaggerated) and BC curved away from the vertical. Is this a truer abstraction, more closely representative of the real situation? If the second figure is indeed truer and if, nevertheless, Mr. Oates bases his calculations upon the simpler figure, can he be sure that his result for $\overline{BC}$ will fall near the true value? (This is often a hard question to answer. Small differences sometimes have a gross effect on the total outcome. "For want of a nail . . . ")

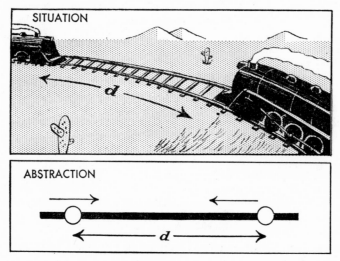

Fig. 32

If two trains rush toward each other along a single track, and we wish to determine when they will collide, we may abstract the trains as "particles" moving along a straight line (Fig. 32). If a sled slides down a straight incline of smooth ice, we may abstract the sled as a "particle" moving along a line and acted on by two forces, its own weight and the frictional resistance. But a rubber ball that *rolls* down an incline cannot correctly be abstracted as a "particle." Additional factors become relevant for the analysis of rolling motion: the ball has to be treated as a sphere of a certain size and mass. Making appropriate abstractions in real life situations calls for a great deal of experience and training, for both "common-sense" and technical know-how. A major share of the time spent by pupils upon their mathematical and scientific studies is devoted to learning how to abstract correctly.

From the earliest grade levels on, mathematics textbooks include many problems designed to convey the flavor of real life situations. Of course the problems can only suggest the situations in bare outline. They cannot describe the full context and bewildering variety of actual events and activities. It is up to the pupil and his teacher to practice visualizing this larger context, as well as to seek illustrative material directly from their own experiences. Unless this is done, a pupil may do all the textbook work, perhaps even get near-perfect grades, yet find his training meaningless and useless to him. (The too enthusiastic teacher, however, must be cautioned against giving her pupils an overdose of "project" and other motivational activity, while neglecting the systematic development of basic skills. A balanced program is essential.)

Illustration 3.   A truck driver is bent on beating a train to a crossing. When the truck, moving at 50 miles per hour, is 100 ft. from the crossing, the train, moving at 60 miles per hour, is 140 ft. away. What will happen?

If truck and train were "particles" moving as described, the truck would clearly beat the train (since 100 is twice 50, while 140 is more than twice 60). But in view of the small margin of safety, we can hardly neglect to take lengths and widths into account. (Even the precise shapes of front or rear of truck or train may turn out to be relevant.) Let us regard train and truck as rectangular boxes, the train 8 ft. wide and 400 ft. long, the truck 6 ft. wide and 30 ft. long. Also assume the truck to be moving right along the center line of the road. Now, will (1) the truck beat the train, (2) the train hit the truck, (3) the truck hit the train, (4) the train beat the truck? In case there is a collision, just what portion of truck or train is struck?

PROBLEM SET 3 (§5)

1.   A certain forced-air furnace unit is to be supplied with warm-air runs (pipes carrying heated air driven through the furnace by a blower) having a total cross-section area of about 210 sq. in. (manufacturer's recommendation). Round pipes of diameters 4½″, 6″, 7″, and 8″ are available for this purpose. The following list gives the sizes of the rooms to be heated, width × length × height, also the number of pipes to be run to them. Assume that a room should receive heat in proportion to its cubic capacity, except that the bathroom should receive half again as much and the kitchen a third less. Distribute pipe sizes to the rooms so as to get as good a balance of heat as possible:

Rooms

1.	Living Room	(2 pipes)	$15' \times 20' \times 9'$
2.	Dining Room	(2 pipes)	$13' \times 18' \times 9'$
3.	Kitchen	(1 pipe)	$13' \times 17' \times 9'$
4.	Bathroom	(1 pipe)	$7' \times 9' \times 8'$
5.	Main Bedroom	(1 pipe)	$14' \times 16' \times 8'$
6.	Second Bedroom	(1 pipe)	$12' \times 14' \times 8'$

Partial Answer: One $4\frac{1}{2}''$ and one $6''$ pipe should go to the dining room.

2. Look up a cake recipe in a cookbook. At prevailing grocery prices, how much will it cost to make the cake (nearest cent)? Be sure to take into account all possibly relevant factors—wastage of various types, cost of gas or electricity, parking or delivery cost, wear and tear on equipment, etc.

3. You plan to build a durable and attractive doghouse, starting from scratch, with new lumber. Discuss the problem of estimating the entire cost of the project.

4. Discuss the problem of determining the annual cost of:

(a) Operating a car   (c) Attending college
(b) Keeping a dog   (d) Pursuing your favorite sport

5. How much does it cost to take a bath?

6. How would you go about estimating the volume of water in a small lake?

7. Estimate the approximate pressure (pounds per square inch averaged over the contact area) which you put upon the ground when standing on it in bare feet. Also find the pressures exerted by some particular automobile. Estimate the pressure exerted by the point of a thumbtack as it is pushed into a drawing board.

8. Select a particular issue of a newspaper or magazine and estimate the number of words in it, advertising excluded.

9. Suppose that you wish to estimate the proportion of students in your college who own a portable radio. You will use a "sampling" technique, directing your inquiries only to a minor portion of the student body. How will you proceed?

10. As in Problem 8, in each case you wish to estimate the proportion of students falling into the given classification. How will you proceed?

(a) Are subject to hay fever
(b) Had two or more colds last year
(c) Are "going steady"
(d) Frequently cheat during examinations

11. If a person consumes 500 more calories daily than he needs, he will normally gain about 2 lb. per week. A girl who needs about 2800 cal. daily wishes to gain at the rate of 3 lb. per week. With the aid of a table giving caloric equivalents (found in many cookbooks), plan a sample day's diet for her.

12. A house in your city is to have a large picture window set in a wall that faces somewhat west of south. The gently sloping roof of the house will extend outward at a location several feet above the window, providing some shielding. It is felt to be desirable that during the month of July, from, say, 10 A.M. to 3 P.M.,

sun time, the solar rays should not strike the floor more than a foot from the wall. Discuss the problem of finding the extent of roof overhang needed to effect this result. If so directed by your instructor, assume some definite dimensional measurements and work toward an approximate solution. (*See* the Spring-Summer, 1957, issue of *House Beautiful's Building Manual*, pp. 196ff.)

§6. U.S. WEIGHTS AND MEASURES

Units of measure commonly used in the United States are summarized in the table at the end of the book. Rarely used units are omitted: rod, chain, gill, hogshead, etc. Popular names are used: "pound" instead of "pound, avoirdupois," "quart" instead of "liquid quart," etc.

We have noted that the *meter* is the fundamental unit of length in the metric system, equivalent to 39.37 in., hence about 10% longer than the yard. The unit of land area is the *are*, the area of a square of side 10 meters. The unit of capacity is the *liter*, the volume of a cube of side $\frac{1}{10}$ meter, about 5% more than a quart. (The *stere*, or cubic meter, is also used.) The mass unit is the *gram*. This is the mass of a cubic centimeter (1 centimeter = $\frac{1}{100}$ meter = .3937 in.) of water at near freezing temperature (4°C.)

With only a few exceptions, names of other metric units are formed by using the Greek and Latin prefixes listed at the right. The prefixes indicate various decimal (tens) multiples of the unit to which they are attached.

A thousand grams, for example, is a *kilogram*, equal to about 2.2 lb. Six-inch rulers often also carry a metric scale, graduated in *centimeters* and in the tenths of these, *millimeters*, of which there are just over 25 to the inch. Land distances are

METRIC PREFIXES	
Prefix	*Value*
Micro	1/1,000,000
Milli	1/1,000
Centi	1/100
Deci	1/10
	1
Deka	10
Hekto	100
Kilo	1,000
Myria	10,000
	100,000
Mega	1,000,000

measured in *kilometers*, 100 kilometers equaling about 62 miles. A *hectare* (hekto-are) is about 2½ acres. A thousand kilograms is called a *metric ton*.

The prefixes "micro" and "mega" are most frequently seen in technical usage. *Micron* is an abbreviation for micrometer. While standard broadcast stations (AM) list their frequencies in *kilocycles*, FM dials are marked in *megacycles*, 88 to 108. The *microsecond* is used in connection with radar ranging and to time atomic bomb explosions. A "megamile" would be a handy unit for interplanetary travelers. Our large length unit is the *light-year*. This is the distance traveled by light in one year, about 6 trillion miles, roughly a quarter of the way to the nearest star.

We live surrounded by numbers, measures of sizes and values. We make many rough estimates day by day. For these, we must keep in mind some approximations and crude relations not given in the table of units. Knowing that 640 acres make a square mile will not help a city dweller visualize the setting of Erskine Caldwell's *God's Little Acre*. He must learn that a football field is about 10% larger than an acre, or that a square of side 70 yards—about half a city block long—encloses slightly more than an acre. There are times when it may be handy for a person to realize that a level, or "struck," bushel is approximately the volume contained by a cylinder 1 ft. high and 15 in. in diameter (historically: 8 in. high, 18½ in. in diameter). Every household head and every businessman needs to know that a month averages 4⅓ weeks. An autoist ought to know that 30 miles per hour is equivalent to 44 ft. per second. It is worth while to know that a knot is one nautical mile per hour. Some other useful relations are listed below:

LIKE QUANTITIES

A meter is about 10% more than a yard.
A liter is about 5% more than a quart.
A half-kilogram is about 10% more than a pound.
There are about 16 kilometers in 10 miles.
A cubic inch is about 16 cubic centimeters.
There are about 28 grams to the ounce.
A grain is about $\frac{1}{16}$ of a gram.
A cubic foot is about 7½ gallons.
Five British gallons equal 6 U.S. gallons.
A dry quart is about 1⅙ (liquid) quarts.
A nautical mile is about 1⅙ (statute) miles.
An acre is a trifle larger than a 40-yard by 120-yard plot.

WEIGHT AND VOLUME OF WATER

A cubic centimeter of water weighs almost exactly a gram.
A cubic inch of water weighs about $\frac{4}{7}$ of an ounce.
A cubic foot of water weighs a little over 60 pounds (62½).
A pound of water occupies about 28 cubic inches.
A fluid ounce of water weighs just over an ounce (4% more).
A pint of water weighs just over a pound (4% more).

Miscellaneous and derived measures are legion, so that we could hardly begin to catalog relations between their units here. The kilowatt and the horsepower, for example, are both units of power having like unit forms: mass $\times$ (length)^2 $\div$ (time)^3. They are commonly associated with electrical and mechanical energy expenditure, respectively. There are many occasions when it is useful to know that a kilowatt is equivalent to about 1⅓ horsepower. Also, a kilowatt is nearly equivalent to 1 B.T.U. (British Thermal Unit) per second. In science and mathematics courses or in general science reading, the student or informed adult gradually picks up this kind of information.

REMARKS ON MASS AND WEIGHT.   If Mr. Gallup's poll-takers should quiz the populace about "mass" and "weight," they would turn up only a few people out of each thousand who could give reasonably lucid explanations of the meanings of the two conceptions. *Mass* is often crudely characterized as a measure of the "quantity of matter" in a body. Better, it is a measure of the "inertia" of a body. It is proportional to the force needed to give the body a constant unit acceleration, say of one foot per second per second. *Weight,* on the other hand, is a measure of the force of gravity upon a body.

An inspector of weights and measures carries a set of "standard weights," which are actually standard masses. Consider the one marked "1 Pound." When the inspector hangs this on a spring scale in a grocery, he expects the arrow to indicate a weight of one pound. If scale and mass were moved to different locations on the earth, the arrow would always point very nearly to the unit mark. (From Equator to Pole, a slight weight increase would register because the poles are closer to the center of the earth and because the earth rotates. A 190-lb. man weighs a pound more at the North Pole than at the Equator.) If the scale were taken to the moon, the one-pound mass would only stretch the spring enough to carry the arrow to the ⅙-lb. mark. And in space far away from planets or stars, the weight would be essentially zero.

Yet anywhere in the universe the one-pound mass would remain a one-pound mass. Standing on a tiny asteroid, a man might balance a locomotive on one hand lifted above his head, estimating its weight as, say, ten pounds. Still, he could not *toss* it anywhere nor move it quickly in any direction, and if he himself were thrown against it, his body would be abruptly halted as by an immovable wall. In other words, though nearly weightless, the locomotive on the asteroid would be just as "massive" as its counterpart on earth. Two colliding locomotives in space, each perhaps "weighing" less than a tennis ball, would not bounce away from each other like two balls, but would crash and crumple just as on earth.

In a uniform gravitational field, as we nearly have all over the surface of the earth, weight is strictly proportional to mass. Hence it is feasible to measure weight and mass in the same units and to speak of them interchangeably, up to a point. Because of this common practice, most of us have gotten the notions accompanying the one conception mixed with those belonging to the other and now find it hard to think of them as two separate conceptions. Only the physicist and the engineer have had to train themselves to make the distinction, as well as to use two different systems of units (weight = mass $\times$ length $\times$ $1/\text{time}^2$).

Nowadays, it is becoming necessary for more of us to deal with these conceptions, and to start to develop an understanding of them at a more elementary level—even in the upper grades. With interplanetary rocket explorations in the offing, there will be incentive for such study. A boy who thinks of mass as synonymous with weight will be hard pressed to conceive how a rocket can be propelled in the weightless void of space.

§7.   OUR MOTLEY UNITS

When the "Man from Mars" inspects the table of U.S. weights and measures, he will surely take it to have been contrived by madmen.

Learning that an *acre* is a unit of area, our visitor will look in vain for a length unit whose square gives the acre. (Such a unit would be about one foot under 70 yd.) The visitor may read in the table that an acre is 10 square chains, a chain being 4 rods and a rod 5½ yd. Entering a grade-school classroom, the Martian may find the children working problems involving rods and chains. Yet he will learn that adults have almost universally forgotten the significance of these measures, never having had occasion to use them.

The Martian will find that "troy" ounces and pounds differ from "avoirdupois" ounces and pounds. The connection between the two systems is furnished by a tiny unit called the *grain*, familiar to most people only if they are reminded that it appears on the label of bottles of aspirin tablets. The Martian will come upon both "dry" and "liquid" measures of capacity, and may wonder why a "fluid ounce" should be used as a unit of capacity when an ounce is a unit of weight.

Finally, the Martian will discover that the relations between similar kinds of units involve a wide assortment of numerical ratios. There are 12 in. to the foot, 16 oz. to the pound, 60 min. to the hour, 7 days to the week. There are certain especially awkward ratios that complicate computation: 5280 ft. to the mile, 231 cu. in. to the gallon.

The motley structure of common units of measure stems from several causes. The evolution of many units can be traced back as far as Babylonian times. From distant beginnings, their histories have run varied and separate courses. They became more or less standardized at different times and places, by custom or by legislation or decree—usually arbitrarily or capriciously, in terms of a monarch's arm-span, a chain of kernels of corn, a soldier's pace. Many fascinating tales are told about the ways our units have developed. A prospective teacher should become familiar with some of these accounts, which may be found in various books on arithmetic or on the history of mathematics.

Possibly on further investigation, the Martian may become less critical regarding the assortment of numerical ratios found between similar units: 12, 16, 60, 7, and others. The carpenter and the builder find the 12-in. foot a most convenient standard, because its fractional parts are so easily determined and handled. With 16 oz. to the pound and 16 fluid oz. to the pint, the efficiency of the binary numeral system comes into play. Fewer weight or volume measure standards are needed than if a 12 or other scale had been chosen.

The division of the week into 7 days is backed by long tradition. Whether this came about quite by accident or whether the physiology of the body played some part, is hard to say. Like all persistent ancient customs, it received religious sanction. (It is sometimes claimed that astrology was responsible for the 7-day week, special mystic significance always having been attached to the number 7. This may be a case of

"Which came first, the chicken or the egg?"—here, the custom or the sanction?) When the French Revolutionary Republic in 1793–1795 legislated and decreed the metric system into existence, there went with it a new calendar and a new set of time units, with 100-min. hours, 10-hr. days, and 10-day weeks. This whole decimal time system perished ignobly within the duodecimal period of 12 years, and was so utterly interred that few people nowadays are aware that such an amazing curiosity was once the law of a land.

Certain awkward types of units appear to be gradually passing out of usage. These include the "dry" measures of capacity. We still meet the "peck" in nursery rhymes but seldom in the market place, though we do buy berries by the dry quart measure. The "troy" and "apothecaries'" weights are little used. But we seem to be stuck with the 5280-ft. mile and the 231-cu.-in. gallon, not to speak of the awful acre.

There is a constant agitation urging that we should make the change to the metric system, which we have seen to be a rational set of measure units fitted to the decimal number scheme. Except for the United States and Great Britain, the world is officially on the metric system. The system is *legal* everywhere. In most scientific work, metric units are used to the virtual exclusion of all others.

Yet we have observed that measure units which are duodecimal or binary in their characteristic ratios have certain advantages despite their poor fit with our decimal numbers. In countries where only the metric system is officially permitted, the populace frequently clings to older units. This cannot be laid just to habit. The human organism is best adapted to sense the doubling of a quantity, next perhaps two doublings, while a tripling, being in between, may be acceptable. The physiological mechanisms of the body are not well suited to apprehend the ten-times jump required by the decimal metric system. It also seems that our inch, foot, and pound are handier base units than their approximate metric equivalents: $\frac{1}{4}$ decimeter, $\frac{1}{3}$ meter, and $\frac{1}{2}$ kilogram. There is serious question, therefore, whether the metric system will, or should, win final world-wide acceptance.

A kind of compromise procedure would be to redefine our familiar units so as to coordinate them with the corresponding metric units. We could retain 12 in. to the foot and 3 ft. to the yard, but redefine the yard to be equivalent to the meter. This would magnify our length units by about 10%. Taking the mile to be 4800 of the new feet would leave it nearly unchanged. Or we could change it drastically, to 3000 or 6000 (new) feet, to make it equivalent to one or two kilometers. Inflating the quart by 5% would equate it to the liter, and loading the pound by 10% would equate it to the half-kilogram.

Should the world ever adopt a number system based on 6, 8, or 12 instead of 10, there would be little question that a system of units coordinated with the new number scheme should and would be adopted simultaneously. It is only the innate cumbersomeness of our number base, 10, that renders metric measurement subject to serious criticism.

PROBLEM SET 4 (§6–§7)

In Problems 1–5, convert to the new units indicated.

1. (a) 1 pint = ? tablespoons
    (b) 60 nautical miles = ? miles   *Answer:* 69.0 miles
    (c) 30,000 square feet = ? acres   *Answer:* Just over $1\frac{1}{16}$ acres
    (d) 1 cup = ? cubic inches

2. (a) 1 cubic foot = ? gallons
    (b) 6000 yards = ? miles   *Answer:* Just over $3\frac{2}{5}$ miles
    (c) 1 cubic yard = ? bushels   *Answer:* 21.7 bushels
    (d) 365 days = ? seconds

3. (a) 1 foot = ? decimeters   *Answer:* 3.048 decimeters
    (b) .01 inch = ? microns   *Answer:* 254 microns
    (c) 100 meters = ? yards
    (d) 100 miles = ? kilometers

4. (a) 1 hectare = ? acres
    (b) 1 square foot = ? square centimeters
    (c) 40 cubic yards = ? steres   *Answer:* 30.6 steres
    (d) 1 liter = ? fluid ounces   *Answer:* 33.8 fluid oz.

5. (a) 1 metric ton = ? pounds
    (b) 1 ounce = ? grams   *Answer:* 28.4 gm.
    (c) 1 cubic inch = ? cubic centimeters
    (d) 1 gram = ? grains   *Answer:* 15.4 grains

6. Show that a month averages $4\frac{1}{3}$ weeks.

7. Show that 30 miles per hour = 44 ft. per second.

8. Look up the definition of a nautical mile, then show its length to be about 6080 ft.

9. How many common 5-grain aspirin tablets are needed to provide an ounce of aspirin?

10. A dry pint is what percent larger than a pint?

11. Light, radio and TV signals, and other electromagnetic waves travel at 3.00×10^{10} cm. per second in the vacuum of space, and only just a trifle more slowly in air. TV Channel 4 corresponds to a 66 to 72 megacycle frequency (frequency = number of cycles, or waves per second). What is the length in inches of a single wave?   *Answer:* 164 in. to 179 in.

12. In the case of visible light, wave lengths are often measured in millimicrons (mμ). Green light has a wave length of 510 mμ. What is its frequency?
Answer: 5.88×10^{16}

13. To the nearest ten billion miles, how long is a light-year?

14. A certain oil has a density equal to 90% that of water (specific gravity

= .90). About how much does a barrel of it weigh? Use one of the approximate weight and volume relations listed in §6. *Answer:* About 235 lb.

15. If *you* were to step into a partially filled rectangular bathtub, 2 ft. wide by 4 ft. 2 in. long by 1 ft. 6 in. deep, and submerge your body completely, by how many inches would the water level rise?

16. Under our calendar, a day is added each fourth year, except in century years indivisible by 400. Over a long period, how will the average number of days in a year agree with the 365.2422 figure cited in the table (at the end of the book) as the number of days in a tropical solar year?

In Problems 17–20, describe the meaning of each measure named, and cite a numerical case involving it. Consult reference books where needed. Example of a satisfactory answer: "The grade of a road is the ratio of its vertical 'rise' to its horizontal 'run' . . . [Define 'rise' and 'run' and perhaps include a diagram.] . . . The ratio is usually stated as a percent. A road that ascends 12 ft. in a level distance of 100 ft. has an average 12% grade."

17.   (a) Caliber (gun)   (d) Degree-day
      (b) Life expectancy   (e) Carat (gem)
      (c) Man-hour   (f) Shoe size, as 7B

18.   (a) Traffic count   (d) Tire size, as 6.70–15
      (b) Pollen count   (e) Tire pressure, as "28 lb."
      (c) Blood count   (f) I.Q. (intelligence quotient)

19.   (a) Specific heat   (d) f-number (photo lens)
      (b) Viscosity   (e) Magnitude of a star
      (c) Mach number   (f) Latitude and longitude

20.   (a) Weight of paper, as 16 lb.
      (b) Size of nails, as "tenpenny"
      (c) Guage and denier (hosiery)
      (d) Pitch and timbre (musical note)
      (e) Binocular rating, as 7 × 50
      (f) Blood pressure, systolic and diastolic

12

Computational
Topics

§1. POWERS

POWER NOTATION: **BASE**^{Exponent} *(The exponent tells how many times the base is taken as a factor.)*

As successive additions of the same number lead to the idea of multiplication $(3 \times 2 = 2 + 2 + 2)$, so successive multiplications lead to the idea of taking **powers.** We write:

$$2^1 = \qquad\quad 2 \qquad\quad = 2 \qquad \text{(First power of 2)},$$
$$2^2 = \qquad 2 \times 2 \qquad = 4 \qquad \text{(2 Squared)},$$
$$2^3 = \quad 2 \times 2 \times 2 \qquad = 8 \qquad \text{(2 Cubed)},$$
$$2^4 = 2 \times 2 \times 2 \times 2 = 16 \qquad \text{(Fourth power of 2), etc.}$$

Squares and cubes appear in problems about areas and volumes, as well as in other common applications. When higher powers turn up, the payment of careful attention to the meanings of the power forms will often save much numerical labor.

Example 1. Express $2^3 \times 2^5$ as a power of 2.

Work. By definition:

$$2^3 \times 2^5 = (2 \times 2 \times 2) \times (2 \times 2 \times 2 \times 2 \times 2).$$

In a sequence of multiplications, the associative law permits us to group the factors at will, i.e., to remove or insert parentheses as convenient. The above expression thus gives the product of $3 + 5 = 8$ two's:

$$2^3 \times 2^5 = 2 \times 2 \times 2 \times 2 \times 2 \times 2 \times 2 \times 2 = 2^8.$$

Example 2. Evaluate 2^8.

Work. Instead of performing seven multiplications ($2 \times 2 = 4$; $2 \times 4 = 8$; etc.), let us take a hint from Example 1, this time breaking down instead of combining. *Three* multiplications give us $2^4 = 16$.   Hence:

$$2^8 = 2^4 \times 2^4 = 16 \times 16 = 256.$$

Example 3.   Evaluate: $\dfrac{5 \times 4^{10}}{4^7}$.

Work.   The seven denominator factors of 4 can be divided into seven of the ten numerator factors of 4, leaving three of them:

$$\frac{5 \times 4^{10}}{4^7} = 5 \times 4^3 = 5 \times 64 = 320.$$

Example 4.   Evaluate: $2^3 \times 5^3$.

Work.

$$2^3 \times 5^3 = (2 \times 2 \times 2) \times (5 \times 5 \times 5)$$
$$= (2 \times 5) \times (2 \times 5) \times (2 \times 5) = 10^3 = 1000.$$

Example 5.   Evaluate: $(\tfrac{2}{3})^3$.

Work.

$$\left(\frac{2}{3}\right)^3 = \frac{2}{3} \times \frac{2}{3} \times \frac{2}{3} = \frac{2 \times 2 \times 2}{3 \times 3 \times 3} = \frac{8}{27} \quad \left(= \frac{2^3}{3^3}\right).$$

Consideration of the general case leads to the common rule: *To raise a fraction to a power, raise numerator and denominator to the power, etc.*

§2.   ROOTS

Let us regard the taking of a given power as an *operation* that may be performed upon numbers. Then the *inverse operation* is that of taking the corresponding root. The following diagrams, like others in §6 of Chapter 3, demonstrate the inverse relationship:

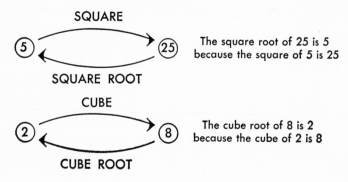

SQUARE

The square root of 25 is 5
because the square of 5 is 25

CUBE

The cube root of 8 is 2
because the cube of 2 is 8

SQUARE ROOT

CUBE ROOT

A square root is indicated by the radical symbol $\sqrt{}$. Thus: $\sqrt{25} = 5$. With higher roots, an index is placed on the radical to show the order of the root: $\sqrt[3]{8} = 2$; $\sqrt[4]{16} = 2$; etc.

In elementary applications, it is almost always adequate to take account only of positive roots of positive numbers. This is the only case we will treat. It can be proved that any positive number has one and only one positive root of each order. This theorem is too technical to establish here, and we assume it in all that follows.

Many simple problems call for finding a square root. Two sides of a right triangle, for example, may be known, with the third to be determined by using the Pythagorean relation. Since this involves the squares of the sides, the final step of the work will be the extraction of a square root.

There exists an "exact" procedure, called the *Square Root Algorithm*, by which the successive digits of the root are found, one by one. This rule was at one time commonly taught in the upper elementary grades. In many school systems nowadays, the practice is to postpone the topic to the ninth grade. This is not necessarily an instance in which standards have been "lowered." It is quite difficult to explain why the rule works, even to pupils who have had some experience in algebra. With today's emphasis on "meaning," educators generally object to presenting a rule that must be followed mechanically, without understanding. But whatever the practice in the school system, every upper grade teacher of arithmetic should be familiar with the algorithm and be ready to demonstrate it to pupils showing curiosity or aptitude.

When the square root rule is postponed, an approximate "division method" is often taught in its stead. And in any case, the use of *tables* is taught. In shop, field, office, and laboratory, roots are read from tables or on slide rules, or occasionally are computed by rule or by the division scheme. (The cube and higher roots are always found by approximate methods. There is an "exact" cube root rule, but it is too cumbersome to be practical.)

Examples 4 and 5 of §1 illustrated the following properties of powers:

1. A power of a product is the product of the powers of the factors;
2. A power of a quotient is the quotient of the powers of the numerator and denominator.

Roots of products and quotients have similar properties:

$$\sqrt{9 \times 16} = \sqrt{9} \times \sqrt{16} = 3 \times 4 = 12.$$
$$\sqrt{\frac{16}{9}} = \frac{\sqrt{16}}{\sqrt{9}} = \frac{4}{3}.$$

INDICATION OF PROOF: $\sqrt{a^2b^2} = \sqrt{(ab)^2} = ab = \sqrt{a^2} \cdot \sqrt{b^2}$.

Powers and roots of sums and differences may *not* be reduced according to any similar simple rules:

$$3^2 + 4^2 \neq (3 + 4)^2 = 7^2 = 49. \ (!!)$$

Instead: $3^2 + 4^2 = 9 + 16 = 25.$

$$\sqrt{9 + 16} \neq \sqrt{9} + \sqrt{16} = 3 + 4 = 7. \ (!!)$$

Instead: $\sqrt{9 + 16} = \sqrt{25} = 5.$

§3. SQUARE ROOT TABLES

SQUARE ROOT TABLE

N	$\sqrt{N}$	$\sqrt{10N}$
1	1.0	3.2
2	1.4	4.5
3	1.7	5.5
4	2.0	6.3
5	2.2	7.1
6	2.4	7.7
7	2.6	8.4
8	2.8	8.9
9	3.0	9.5
10	3.2	10.0

Multiplying a number by 100 only multiplies its square root by 10. (Because $\sqrt{100N} = \sqrt{100} \times \sqrt{N} = 10\sqrt{N}$.) Consequently, tables of square roots are usually arranged in the form shown at the right. The column headed $\sqrt{N}$ gives the roots of the numbers 1, 2, . . . , 10. The column headed $\sqrt{10N}$ gives the roots of the numbers 10, 20, . . . , 100.

Consider a number between 1 and 10, say 3. We read directly $\sqrt{3} \approx 1.7$ in the $\sqrt{N}$ column. The "hundreds multiples" of 3 will have roots that are "tens multiples" of $\sqrt{3}$:

$$\sqrt{300} = \sqrt{100 \times 3} = \sqrt{100} \times \sqrt{3} = 10\sqrt{3} \approx 10(1.7) = 17$$
$$\sqrt{30{,}000} = \sqrt{10{,}000 \times 3} = \sqrt{10{,}000} \times \sqrt{3} = 100\sqrt{3} \approx 100(1.7) = 170$$

$$\sqrt{.0003} = \sqrt{.0001 \times 3} = \sqrt{\frac{1}{10{,}000}} \times \sqrt{3} = \frac{1}{100}\sqrt{3} \approx \frac{1}{100}(1.7) = .017, \text{etc.}$$

(The curly equality sign $\approx$ is read "is approximately equal to.")

The "odd tens multiples" of 3 are "hundreds multiples" of 30, and will have roots that are "tens multiples" of $\sqrt{30}$:

$$\sqrt{30} = \qquad\qquad\qquad\qquad\qquad \approx 5.5$$

$$\sqrt{3{,}000} = \sqrt{100 \times 30} = \sqrt{100} \times \sqrt{30} = 10\sqrt{30} \approx 10(5.5) = 55.$$

$$\sqrt{.3} = \sqrt{\frac{1}{100} \times 30} = \sqrt{\frac{1}{100}} \times \sqrt{30} = \frac{1}{10}\sqrt{30} \approx \frac{1}{10}(5.5) = .55, \text{etc.}$$

All standard tables permit *interpolation*, the effect of which is to give results that could be read directly only in a table ten times as large. From our small square root table, we may determine roots to one decimal place for numbers between 1 and 10 given to tenths (1.0, 1.1, 1.2, 1.3, . . . , 9.9, 10.0) and for numbers between 10 and 100 given to units (10, 11, 12, . . . , 99, 100). In general, the table may be used to obtain square roots "accurate to two figures" (see §8) for numbers given accurate to two figures.

It is presumed that the student is familiar with the ordinary process of linear interpolation, but an example is furnished to dispel any haziness that may cloud his memory. Let the task be to find $\sqrt{3.8}$. Locate and copy down the nearest tabular entries, those for $N = 3$ and $N = 4$, as shown below. Mentally neglect the decimal point and note that 38 is $\frac{8}{10}$ of the way from 30 to 40. Hence in the root column we wish to go $\frac{8}{10}$ of the way from 17 to 20. Since $\frac{8}{10}$ of 3 is 2 (nearest whole value), we arrive at 19. So $\sqrt{3.8} \approx 1.9$. Set down in full, the work looks like this:

$$
10 \left\{ 8 \left(\begin{matrix} N \\ 3.0 \\ 3.8 \\ 4.0 \end{matrix} \right. \quad \begin{matrix} \sqrt{N} \\ 1.7 \\ \boxed{1.9} \\ 2.0 \end{matrix} \right) 2 \right) 3 \qquad .8 \times 3 = 2.4
$$

PROBLEM SET 1 (§1–§3)

1. Express each as a single power:

   (a) $3^2 \times 3^4$ (c) $x^2 \cdot x^3$

   (b) $(\frac{2}{5}) \times (\frac{2}{5})^3$ (d) $8^{20} \div 8^{17}$ *Answer:* (c) x^5

2. Evaluate:

   (a) 2^{10} (c) $4^5 \times 5^5$

   (b) $(6 \times 3^7) \div 3^5$ (d) $(.2)^{10}$ *Answer:* (d) $2^{10} \times 1/10^{10} = \cdots$

3. Verify that the volume of air in a spherical balloon of diameter 10 in. is approximately 524 cu. in. ($V = \frac{4}{3}\pi r^3$).

4. The energy radiated from a hot body is proportional to the fourth power of its "absolute temperature." If the sun were half again as hot as it is, how many times more energy would it radiate?

5. Compare the energy radiated by a unit area heated to the temperature of boiling water (373° abs.) with that of a unit area heated to the temperature of the tungsten filament of an ordinary light bulb (about 3100° abs.).

Answer: Approx. ratio 1:4800

6. In a half-hour an executive makes ten "yes" or "no" policy decisions. Among how many courses of action did he choose?   *Answer:* 1024

7. You had two parents. Each of them had two parents, and so on. How many different ancestral lines have you extending back ten generations? Is it possible that all your thirtieth generation ancestors (reached by different lines) were distinct individuals?   *Latter Answer:* No.

8. If you could triple your capital daily, beginning with one cent on the first day of the month, how much would you have on the thirtieth day?

9. If you could fold a sheet of paper 40 times, first one way and then the other alternately, the final result being a one-inch square, how large would the sheet have been initially?

10.   A germ colony doubles its number every 2 hr. 24 min. How long will it take a culture of a hundred germs to grow to one of a billion?

Answer: About 56 hr.

11.   Draw diagrams like those in §2 to help explain the inverse relationship between powers and roots, for each case below:

(a) $4^2 = 16$ (c) $\sqrt{36} = 6$
(b) $5^4 = 625$ (d) $\sqrt[3]{64} = 4$

12.   A fellow pupil writes $\sqrt{5} = \sqrt{1+4} = \sqrt{1} + \sqrt{4} = 1 + 2 = 3$. How will you convince him of his error? Suppose he writes $\sqrt{a^2 + b^2} = a + b$. How will you straighten him out in this case?

13.   Evaluate:

(a) $\sqrt{2500}$ (c) $\sqrt{100 + 100 + 100 + 100}$
(b) $\sqrt{2^2 \times 3^4}$ (d) $\sqrt{25 \div 4}$

14.   Evaluate:

(a) $\sqrt[3]{16} \times \sqrt[3]{4}$ (c) $\sqrt[20]{4^{30}}$
(b) $\sqrt[4]{2500} \div \sqrt{2}$ (d) $\sqrt{10} \times \sqrt{10}$

In Problems 15–20, use the small square root table in §3, interpolating when desirable.

15.   Find the root to two figures:

(a) $\sqrt{3.2}$ (c) $\sqrt{320}$
(b) $\sqrt{32}$ (d) $\sqrt{.32}$ *Answers:* (a) 1.8; (d) .57

16.   Find the root to two figures:

(a) $\sqrt{87}$ (c) $\sqrt{.0087}$
(b) $\sqrt{87000}$ (d) $\sqrt{8.7 \times 10^7}$ *Answers:* (c) .093; (d) 9300

17.   A 20-ft. ladder leans against a wall, with its base 10 ft. from the base of the wall. (Add further assumptions to make this a right triangle problem.) How far up the wall does the ladder reach? Check your result by making a scale drawing.   *Answer:* 17 ft.

18.   A tunnel entrance is in the form of a rectangle 14 ft. wide and 6 ft. high surmounted by a semicircular arch. Can a truck 10 ft. wide and 10½ ft. high pass through?

19.   How large in diameter must a pipe be if it is to carry 40 gal. of water per minute at a speed of 40 ft. per second?   *Answer:* .64 in.

20.   An isosceles triangle of base 10 in. and height 12 in. is cut by a line parallel to its base so that the two pieces have equal areas. How far up is the cut made?   *Answer:* 3.5 in. above the base

§4.   THE SQUARE ROOT ALGORITHM

In §3 we noted that multiplying a number by 100 only multiplies its square root by 10. Adding two digits to a number only adds one digit to the root. In finding a square root is is therefore conventional to use primes (') to *point off* the digits of the number in pairs, called "periods."

This shows how many digits the root will have and also where they will be written (stars *) when the procedure for finding the root is carried out. *Examples:*

$$\overset{*}{\sqrt{25}} \qquad \overset{*\ *}{\sqrt{6'25}} \qquad \overset{*\ *}{\sqrt{15'42}} \qquad \overset{*\ *\ *}{\sqrt{4'27'30}}$$

The function of the algorithm is to locate the largest whole number whose square is either equal to or less than the given number. In the "less than" case, there will be a positive remainder. Thus if the given number is 14, the root is 3, the remainder 5: $14 = 3^2 + 5$.

Let the task be to find $\sqrt{590}$. Point off: $\overset{*\ *}{\sqrt{5'90}}$. We find root digits in left-to-right order. To find the tens digit, we must locate the largest multiple of ten whose square is less than or equal to 590:

$$0, 10, 20, 30, 40, 50, 60, 70, 80, 90.$$

Since the squares of these numbers end in two zeros, we may neglect the 90 of the 590 and just compare them with 500. But this is equivalent to comparing the squares of the ten digits 0, 1, 2, 3, . . . , 9 with 5. In other words, we look only at the first period, 5, of the given number, and mentally run though the squares of the digits: $0^2 = 0, 1^2 = 1, 2^2 = 4, 3^2 = 9,$ . . . . Since 2 is the largest number whose square is 5 or less, it is the root digit sought:

$$\overset{2\ \ *}{\sqrt{5'90}}$$

Next we deduct $2^2 = 4$ from 5, then bring down the second period, 90:

$$\begin{array}{r} \overset{2\ \ *}{\sqrt{5'90}} \\ \underline{4} \\ 1\ 90 \end{array}$$

In actuality, we have deducted $20^2 = 400$ from 590, leaving a "partial remainder" of 190. The next root digit must take care of this partial remainder, but its relationship to the remainder is not a simple one. To explore the relationship algebraically, denote that digit by x and also denote $a = 20$. Then the entire root which we are after will have the value $a + x$, and its square is to be compared with 590:

$$(a + x)^2 = a^2 + 2ax + x^2.$$

Since $a^2 = 20^2 = 400$ has already been deducted, it is the $2ax + x^2$ portion that must take care of the remaining 190. Write this in factored form:

$$2ax + x^2 = x(2a + x).$$

Our aim is now to build up this expression, then take it away from 190 (for the various possible values of $x = 0, 1, 2, . . . , 9$).

The $2a$ is obtained by *doubling* the root digit 2 already found and writing it to the left of the 190, as shown below. This double, 4, is regarded as in *tens position*, so that it is equivalent to $2a = 40$:

$$
\begin{array}{r}
2 \ * \\
\sqrt{5'90} \\
4 \\
\hline
4 \ * \ \ \big|\overline{1\ 90}
\end{array}
$$

When any value of x ($x = 0, 1, 2, \ldots, 9$) is inserted in the places indicated by the stars in the above, then the number now shown as "4 *" will have the value $2a + x$. When this number is multiplied by x, the desired value $x(2a + x)$ will be obtained. We wish to find the largest value of x for which $x(2a + x) \leq 190$.

The practical scheme is to estimate this x by dividing the 4 written on the left into 19 (a finger being held over the last digit of the 190). The result is $x = 4$. This is written in the starred places, the multiplication 4×44 [$= x(2a + x)$ for $a = 20$, $x = 4$] is carried out, and the product, 176, is taken from 190. (This estimating scheme may produce too high a value for x, so that the product $x(2a + x)$ exceeds the partial remainder. When this occurs, reduce the x value by 1 and multiply again, etc.)

The above method of estimation is based upon the observation that x is usually substantially less than $2a$, so that when x is such that $x(2a) \leq 190$, it is likely that $x(2a + x) \leq 190$. But $x(2a) \leq 190$ is equivalent to $x \leq 190/2a$, i.e. $x \leq {}^{190}\!/_{40} = 1\frac{3}{4}$.

The completed work is shown at the right. We have determined that

$$590 = 24^2 + 14.$$

Hence $\sqrt{590} \approx 24$. More precisely, the square root of 590 is 24, with a remainder of 14.

$$
\begin{array}{r}
2 \ \ 4 \\
\sqrt{5'90} \\
4 \\
\hline
44 \quad \big|1\ 90 \\
\big|1\ 76 \\
\hline
14
\end{array}
$$

The demonstration on the following page shows in detail the process of taking a square root.

The work may be carried on beyond the decimal point. Suppose that we wish to find $\sqrt{598.4}$ to *four figures*. Applying the algorithm to 598 gives but two figures ($\sqrt{5'98}$). To get two more, point off two periods to the right of the decimal point, as shown in the work at the right. The work is carried out just as though the given number had been 5984000. The root so found is 100 times that of 598.4. It is apparent that the decimal point in the root will always be properly located if placed just above the position of the point in the given number.

$$
\begin{array}{r}
2 \ \ 4. \ 4 \ \ 6 \\
\sqrt{5'98.40'00} \\
4 \\
\hline
44 \quad \big|1\ 98 \\
\big|1\ 76 \\
\hline
484 \quad \big|22\ 40 \\
\big|19\ 36 \\
\hline
4886 \quad \big|3\ 04\ 00 \\
\big|2\ 93\ 16 \\
\hline
10\ 84
\end{array}
$$

TAKING A SQUARE ROOT

Let us find $\sqrt{139,100}$. The first period is 13, and the largest square contained in it is 3. The first stage of the work is shown at the right, with the double of the 3 written in, in preparation for Stage 2.

Place a finger over the last digit of the 491, and divide 6 into 49, obtaining 8. This turns out to be too large. Try **7**. This works. Double 37 and write it in, in preparation for Stage 3.

Place a finger over the last digit of 2200, and consider dividing **74** into 220. To estimate the result, use a "one-step" rule, as in the case of long division. Deleting all divisor digits after the first and dropping the same number of dividend digits, divide 7 into 22, obtaining 3. This turns out to be too large. Try 2. This works.

Hence:

$$139,100 = 372^2 + 716,$$

whence

$$\sqrt{139,100} \approx 372.$$

```
           3
      √13'91'00
           9           (Stage 1)
    6  |  4 91
```

```
           3  8
      √13'91'00
           9              No!
   68  |  4 91
       |  5 44
```

```
           3  7
      √13'91'00
           9           (Stage 2)
   67  |  4 91
       |  4 69
   74  |    22 00
```

```
           3  7  3
      √13'91'00
           9              No!
   67  |  4 91         (But see
       |  4 69         the note
  743  |    22 00      at left)
       |    22 29
       |    - 29
```

NOTE. According to the abandoned part of the work shown in between Stage 2 and Stage 3 at right $139,100 = 373^2 - 29$. This negative remainder, -29, is smaller in absolute size than the positive remainder, 716. Hence we say that $\sqrt{139100} \approx 373$, with *least absolute remainder*. It may be shown algebraically that the root value with least absolute remainder is always the closer to the exact root value. (To show this, begin by writing out the squares of x, $x + \tfrac{1}{2}$, $x + 1$.) In the present instance, therefore, we know that $372.5 < \sqrt{139,100} < 373.5$. It is this *nearer* rather than always the *under* value (positive remainder) which we ordinarily cite as the answer to a practical problem (§8, Chapter 5).

```
           3  7  2
      √13'91'00
           9           (Stage 3)
   67  |  4 91         End
       |  4 69
  742  |    22 00
       |    14 84
       |     7 16
```

To illustrate how the occurrence of zero digits affects the work, four stages are shown in the extraction of the square root of 403 to four figures:

$$
\begin{array}{l}
\quad\ 2\quad .\\[-2pt]
\sqrt{4'03.00'00}\\[-2pt]
\quad\ 4
\end{array}
\qquad
\begin{array}{l}
\quad\ 2\ \ 0.\\[-2pt]
\sqrt{4'03.00'00}\\[-2pt]
\quad\ 4
\end{array}
\qquad
\begin{array}{l}
\quad\ 2\ \ 0.\ 0\\[-2pt]
\sqrt{4'03.00'00}\\[-2pt]
\quad\ 4
\end{array}
\qquad
\begin{array}{l}
\quad\ 2\ \ 0.\ 0\ 7\\[-2pt]
\sqrt{4'03.00'00}\\[-2pt]
\quad\ 4
\end{array}
$$

| 4 | 03 | 40 | 03 00 | 400 | 03 00 00 | 4007 | 03 00 00 |
| | | | | | | | 2 80 49 |

| (4 into 0 | (40 into 30 | (400 into 3000, i.e., |
| gives 0) | gives 0) | 4 into 30, gives 7) |

REMARKS.   The algorithm is modified slightly when an abacus or electric office machine is to be used. Successive squares are built up through *cumulative addition* of the *odd* natural numbers. This is justified by the relation $(n+1)^2 - n^2 = 2n + 1$. In the first few cases:

$$
\begin{aligned}
1 &= 1 = 1^2,\\
1 + 3 &= 4 = 2^2,\\
1 + 3 + 5 &= 9 = 3^2,\ \text{etc.}
\end{aligned}
$$

The procedure by which $\sqrt{139,100}$ may be found is shown in outline at the right. The odd numbers $1, 3, 5, \ldots, 17$ are cumulatively deducted from the first period, 13, so long as the remainder stays positive. In this case, there are three subtractions. This number, 3, is the hundreds digit of the root.

In the second stage of the work, it is not squares but expressions of form $2ax + x^2$ that must be built up by cumulative deduction. The first difference is $310^2 - 300^2 = (310 - 300) \times$

ABACUS WORK SCHEME

$$\sqrt{139,100}$$

Take Away	Remainder	
	13'91'00	
1'00'00	12'91'00 ⎫	
3 00 00	9 91 00 ⎬	3
5 00 00	4 91 00 ⎭	
61 00	4 30 00 ⎫	
63 00	3 67 00 ⎪	
65 00	3 02 00 ⎪	
67 00	2 35 00 ⎬	7
69 00	1 66 00 ⎪	
71 00	95 00 ⎪	
73 00	22 00 ⎭	
7 41	14 59 ⎫	2
7 43	7 16 ⎭	
Root:	372	
Remainder:	716	

$(310 + 300) = 6100$. The actual procedure is to deduct $1, 3, 5, \ldots, 17$ in second period position, with each augmented by $2 \times 3 = 6$ (twice the hundreds digit) on the left.

In the third stage, the first difference is $371^2 - 370^2 = 741$. The actual procedure is to deduct $1, 3, 5, \ldots$ in third period position, with each augmented by $2 \times 37 = 74$ on the left.

There is a routine for operating an office machine to do the above work mechanically. If there are many root digits to be found, a practical method is to determine three or four of them as above, then get twice as many by a single division operation, according to the scheme of §5.

§5. APPROXIMATING ROOTS BY DIVISION

We will describe the process, then explain why it works. Given a number, we first divide or multiply it by one or more hundreds in order to bring it within the 1 to 100 range. The square root of this related number lies between 1 and 10, and after finding it, we may multiply it or divide it by as many tens as needed to give the root of the original number (§3). So we need discuss only the approximation of the square roots of numbers lying between 1 and 100.

First, we find the whole number (1, 2, 3, . . . , 10) whose square is closest to the given number. Let us illustrate the procedure by finding $\sqrt{40}$. Mentally running through the squares of the digits, we note: $6^2 = 36 < 40 < 49 = 7^2$. The closer value is $6^2 = 36$. As the *first approximation* to the desired root, we write

$$A_1 = 6. \qquad \text{(First Approximation)}$$

In two steps, the key to the process, we get a second approximation from the first. In Step 1, we divide the first approximation, 6, into the number, 40, and round the result to the nearest *even* number of tenths:

(1) $$40 \div 6 \approx 6.6.$$

In Step 2, we *average* the two values, the 6 and the 6.6, by adding and halving. This average is the *second approximation* to the root:

(2) $$A_2 = \frac{6 + 6.6}{2} = 6.3 \qquad \text{(Second Approximation)}$$

Next we *repeat* the two steps, but with the new approximation, 6.3, in place of the old. In the division of Step 1, we carry out the work until we have *twice as many digits* (four) as make up the approximate value 6.3 (two), again rounding so that the last digit is *even:*

(1) $$40 \div 6.3 \approx 6.350.$$

(2) $$A_3 = \frac{6.3 + 6.350}{2} = 6.325. \qquad \text{(Third Approximation)}$$

Another repetition gives a fourth approximation:

(1) $$40 \div 6.325 \approx 6.3241106.$$

(2) $$A_4 = \frac{6.325 + 6.3241106}{2} = 6.3245553. \quad \text{(Fourth Approximation)}$$

Still another repetition would produce a fifth approximation, expressed to 16 "significant digits."

In the above example, each new approximation verifies the one before. Thus if $A_3 = 6.325$ is rounded off to two figures, $A_2 = 6.3$ is obtained (6.3|25). When such verification is obtained, the new approximation will be truly accurate (except that its last digit may be off by 1) to twice as many figures as those of the previous approximation. When the verification fails, the new approximation will be accurate to *one less* than twice as many figures. To illustrate this situation, we find a "worst" case by taking as large a number as we can that is nearer 1 than 4. Take 2.4. The first approximation to $\sqrt{2.4}$ is 1. The two steps give:

$$(1) \qquad\qquad 2.4 \div 1 = 2.4.$$

$$(2) \qquad A_2 = \frac{1 + 2.4}{2} = 1.7.$$

Already, A_2 does not round to A_1. Hence we round A_2 to *one less* figure, obtaining $A_2' = 2$, and continue:

$$(1) \qquad\qquad 2.4 \div 2 = 1.2.$$

$$(2) \qquad A_3 = \frac{2 + 1.2}{2} = 1.6.$$

Since A_3 rounds to A_2', we may safely keep twice as many digits at the next stage:

$$(1) \qquad\qquad 2.4 \div 1.6 = 1.500.$$

$$(2) \qquad A_4 = \frac{1.6 + 1.500}{2} = 1.550.$$

Since $A_4 = 1.550$ does round to $A_3 = 1.6$, even though barely, we may be sure that $\sqrt{2.4} = 1.550$ to within 1 in the last digit. (Try another repetition, obtaining $A_5' = 1.549194$.)

A handy feature about "iterative" processes is that they are generally self-correcting. Suppose that while finding $\sqrt{40}$, a student gets 6.9^+ instead of 6.7^- when he divides 6 into 40. Rounding 6.9^+ to the nearest even tenth gives 7.0. Averaging this with 6, he gets the false result $A_2 = 6.5$. Next he gets

$$(1) \qquad\qquad 40 \div 6.5 \approx 6.154.$$

$$(2) \qquad A_3 = \frac{6.5 + 6.154}{2} = 6.327.$$

Since this does not round to $A_2 = 6.5$, he replaces it with $A_3' = 6.33$ and continues:

$$(1) \qquad\qquad 40 \div 6.33 \approx 6.31912.$$

$$(2) \qquad A_4 = \frac{6.33 + 6.31912}{2} = 6.32456.$$

This nearly rounds to 6.33, hence should not be off by much more than 1 in its last digit. (Actually, it is correct in all six digits. Compare with our earlier eight-figure result.)

It is easy to see why the division method works. In the case of $\sqrt{40}$, our aim is to find the number which when multiplied by itself gives 40. Compare these relations:

$$\sqrt{40} \times \sqrt{40} = 40,$$
$$6 \ \times \quad ? \ = 40.$$

We regarded 6 as an approximation to $\sqrt{40}$. The number symbolized by the question mark has an equal right to be regarded as an approximation to $\sqrt{40}$. We find it by dividing 40 by 6 (Step 1 of the process). This gives 6.6 (to the nearest even tenth). The comparison becomes:

$$\sqrt{40} \times \sqrt{40} = 40,$$
$$6 \times 6.6 \approx 40.$$

Of the numbers 6 and 6.6, one must be *under*, the other *over*, $\sqrt{40}$. It seems reasonable that an *average* of the two (Step 2) should furnish a better approximation to $\sqrt{40}$ than does either one separately. And so it does.

Higher roots may be found by a similar division procedure. Setting out to find the cube root of 200, we determine the first approximation $A_1 = 6$ from the comparison

$$5^3 = 125 < 200 < 216 = 6^3.$$

Now we write:

$$\sqrt[3]{200} \times \sqrt[3]{200} \times \sqrt[3]{200} = 200,$$
$$6 \times 6 \times \quad ? \quad = 200.$$

We find the number symbolized by the question mark by dividing 200 by $6^2 = 36$. This gives 5.6 (nearest tenth), so that

$$6 \times 6 \times 5.6 \approx 200.$$

To get a second approximation, we average these *three* figures:

$$A_2 = \frac{6 + 6 + 5.6}{3} \approx 5.9.$$

The procedure is repeated:

(1) $$\frac{200}{(5.9)^2} = \frac{200}{34.81} \approx 5.74.$$

(2) $$A_3 \approx \frac{5.9 + 5.9 + 5.74}{3} \approx 5.85.$$

Repeating once more:

(1) $$\frac{200}{(5.85)^2} = \frac{200}{34.2225} \approx 5.8441.$$

(2) $$A_4 \approx \frac{5.85 + 5.85 + 5.8441}{3} \approx 5.8480.$$

Note that with each approximation beyond the second, we retained one less than twice the number of digits in the previous approximation. This is the rule to be followed in the case of the cube and higher roots.

NOTE (for advanced students only!). The following general rule may be established by algebraic analysis: Under the root approximation process described above, if the relative error in a given approximation to $\sqrt[n]{N}$ is r, then the relative error in the next approximation is approximately

$$\frac{n-1}{2} r^2$$

For a square root, $n = 2$, so that the new relative error is $r^2/2$. In the illustration concerning $\sqrt{40}$, the second approximation was $A_2 = 6.3$. A_2 being given to tenths, its absolute possible error is $\frac{1}{2}$ of .1, or .05, so that its relative possible error is $r = .05/6.3$. Computing $r^2/2$ and multiplying it by 6.3, we get the approximate absolute possible error e in the next approximation ($A_3 = 6.325$):

$$e \approx \frac{1}{2}\left(\frac{.05}{6.3}\right)^2 (6.3) = \frac{.00125}{6.3} < \frac{.001}{2}.$$

According to this inequality, e is less than the absolute possible error to which numbers expressed in thousandths are subject. Hence it is likely that the third approximation, $A_3 = 6.325$, actually does give $\sqrt{40}$ correct to thousandths. In practice, we by-pass these technicalities and just use the "doubling the number of digits" rule, which is itself based on this technical analysis.

PROBLEM SET 2 (§4–§5)

In Problems 1–6, find the integral root by the standard algorithm of §4. Write the result in the form: Given Number = (Root)^2 + Remainder. (Example: 45 = $6^2 + 9$, or 45 = $7^2 - 4$.) Cite the answer that corresponds to the least absolute remainder. (Example: $\sqrt{45} \approx 7$.)

1.	$\sqrt{500}$	3.	$\sqrt{1000}$	5.	$\sqrt{64387}$
2.	$\sqrt{676}$	4.	$\sqrt{3520}$	6.	$\sqrt{612000}$

7–12.* Set up abacus work schemes for finding each root in Problems 1–6.

In Problems 13–18, find the root to four digits. Check your answers by squaring them.

13.	$\sqrt{21.08}$	16.	$\sqrt{.6300}$	
14.	$\sqrt{4362}$	17.	$\sqrt{.0002432}$	
15.	$\sqrt{883.608}$	18.	$\sqrt{2.008}$	

19.   Check your answers to Problems 13–18 as directed, by the following division process. Round each four figure value to two figures. Divide this value into the original number, obtaining a four-figure quotient. Average this quotient with the two-figure divisor. [*Examples:* $\sqrt{21.08} \approx 4.6$; $21.08 \div 4.6 = 4.583^-$; $\frac{1}{2}(4.6 + 4.583^-) = 4.591$.]

20.* The theory underlying the square root algorithm was discussed in detail in §4, with respect to the case of $\sqrt{590}$. Repeat the discussion, using $\sqrt{4160}$.

In Problems 21–30 find the root to the number of figures requested, using the division method of §5.

21.	$\sqrt{20}$	(4 figs.)	26.	$\sqrt{883.60800}$	(7 or 8 figs.)
22.	$\sqrt{8}$	(8 figs.)	27.	$\sqrt[3]{10}$	(3 figs.)
23.	$\sqrt{3}$	(6 figs.)	28.	$\sqrt[3]{593}$	(5 figs.)
24.	$\sqrt{21.08}$	(4 figs.)	29.*	$\sqrt[5]{40}$	(3 figs.)
25.	$\sqrt{.6300}$	(8 figs.)	30.*	$\sqrt[10]{1.238}$	(5 figs.)

§6. ERRORS

Physical measurement, we have pointed out, can never be absolutely precise. Even in theory, a steel rule cannot have an exact length. Under an imaginary supermicroscope, its end would show up as a disorderly atomic swarm, so that one could not tell just where the metal left off and the air began.

Man's own personal measurement errors, however, are so much larger than those which are inherent in our physical conceptions that in ordinary discussion we may as well speak of the "true" lengths of steel rules, of the "true" speeds of moving bodies, and so on, just as though these quantities could be exactly defined.

Let a certain quantity have a true numerical value T. Let M denote the value found by "measurement" (M may be determined directly, or as the end result of a computation involving several direct measurements). Then we will regard M as an approximation to T and use it as a substitute for T in further work.

The **absolute error** (e) in using M as an approximation to T is defined as the *difference* between M and T:

$$e = M - T,$$
$$\text{Absolute Error} = \text{Measured Value} - \text{True Value}.$$

Ordinarily, we will just call the absolute error the *error*.

Illustration 1. A jar contains 75 nuts. A shopper estimates by eye that the jar holds 90 nuts. Here $T = 75$, and $M = 90$. The shopper's error is $90 - 75 = 15$ (nuts). Had she estimated 70, her error would have been $70 - 75 = -5$ (nuts).

RULE. *The error of a sum is the sum of the errors.*

In proving this rule, we use the e, M, T notation above, but tag the letters with the subscripts 1 and 2, so that they will refer respectively to the first and second of the quantities to be combined:

$$
\begin{array}{rccc}
 & e_1 & = & M_1 & - & T_1 \\
+ & e_2 & = & M_2 & - & T_2 \\
\hline
 & e_1 + e_2 & = & (M_1 + M_2) & - & (T_1 + T_2) \\
 & & = & M \text{ of sum} & - & T \text{ of sum} = e \text{ of sum.}
\end{array}
$$

Illustration 2. Let two jars contain 42 and 75 nuts, so that $T_1 = 42$ and $T_2 = 75$. Let estimates of their contents be $M_1 = 40$ and $M_2 = 80$. Then the true sum is $T = 42 + 75 = 117$, while the "measured" sum is $M = 40 + 80 = 120$. The various errors are: $e_1 = -2$, $e_2 = 5$, $e = e_1 + e_2 = 3$.

When the error is divided by the true value, the result is called the **relative error** (r) in using the measured value as an approximation to the true value:

$$\text{Relative Error} = \frac{\text{Absolute Error}}{\text{True Value}},$$

$$r = \frac{e}{T} = \frac{M - T}{T}.$$

The relative error is often stated as a percent. In the nut jar illustration, with $T = 75$ and $M = 90$, so that $e = 15$, the relative error is

$$r = \frac{15}{75} = .20 = 20\%.$$

RULE. *The relative error of a product is approximately equal to the sum of the relative errors of the factors.*

Proof. Let T_1, T_2, T stand for the true values of the first factor, second factor, and their product $(T = T_1T_2)$, respectively. Similarly M_1, M_2, and $M = M_1M_2$. Note that $e_1 = M_1 - T_1$ and $e_2 = M_2 - T_2$ may be written in the forms $M_1 = T_1 + e_1$, $M_2 = T_2 + e_2$. Then

$$M = M_1M_2 = (T_1 + e_1)(T_2 + e_2) = T_1T_2 + e_1T_2 + e_2T_1 + e_1e_2$$
$$e = M - T = M_1M_2 - T_1T_2 = e_1T_2 + e_2T_1 + e_1e_2.$$

To get r, divide through by $T = T_1T_2$;

$$r = \frac{e}{T} = \frac{e}{T_1T_2} = \frac{e_1}{T_1} + \frac{e_2}{T_2} + \frac{e_1}{T_1} \cdot \frac{e_2}{T_2} = r_1 + r_2 + r_1r_2.$$

If the relative errors r_1, r_2 are small, as is ordinarily the case, then their product will be much smaller. (If $r_1 = r_2 = .1$, then $r_1r_2 = .01$; if $r_1 = r_2 = .001$, then $r_1r_2 = .000001$.) Hence it is usually practical to neglect the product term r_1r_2 and use the *approximate* relation

$$r \approx r_1 + r_2.$$ (The curly equality symbol $\approx$ means "approximately equals.")

Example 1. The true dimensions of a rectangular field are 64 ft. by 80 ft. By pacing, a boy estimates the size at 68 ft. by 86 ft., then computes the area by multiplying these values. How far off will he be?

Work. We estimate the relative error:

$$r \approx r_1 + r_2 = \frac{4}{64} + \frac{6}{80} = .0625 + .0750 = .1375 \approx 14\%.$$

In actuality, $64 \times 80 = 5120$ and $68 \times 86 = 5848$, so the error is 728 sq. ft., and the relative error $728/5120 = 14\frac{7}{32}\%$.

Example 2. A balloon of radius 10 in. is inflated by further blowing to reach a radius of 11 in. What is the relative increase in its volume?

Work. The volume of a sphere is given by the formula $V = (\frac{4}{3})\pi R^3$, where R is the radius. Regard the 1-in. increase in radius as an "error." Then the relative error in the radius is $\frac{1}{10} = 10\%$. The volume is the product of five factors, $V = (\frac{4}{3}) \times \pi \times R \times R \times R$, whose relative errors are 0, 0, 10%, 10%, 10%. Adding these gives 30% as an approximation to the relative increase in the volume. (The exact value is about 33.1%.)

For a *difference* of estimated values: $e = e_1 - e_2$.
For a *quotient* of estimated values: $r \approx r_1 - r_2$.

The proof of the difference rule is like that for a sum. With regard to the quotient we note that

$$T = \frac{T_1}{T_2} \qquad \text{is equivalent to} \qquad T_1 = T_2 \times T.$$

Applying the product rule to the latter relation gives

$$r_1 \approx r_2 + r, \qquad \text{from which we get} \qquad r \approx r_1 - r_2.$$

Rules for powers and roots may also be derived from the product rule. For example, if $T = \sqrt[3]{T_1}$, then $T_1 = T^3 = T \times T \times T$, and the product rule gives $r_1 \approx 3r$, so that $r \approx \frac{1}{3}r_1$. A 6% relative error in measuring the capacity of a cubical box will therefore lead to about a 2% relative error in the estimate of its edge.

§7. POSSIBLE ERRORS

In practical application, "true" values are seldom known. Hence we are unable to compute exact errors. We deal instead with **possible errors:** positive numbers that numerically exceed the unknown true errors. Relative possible errors are estimated by dividing possible errors by measured or estimated values.

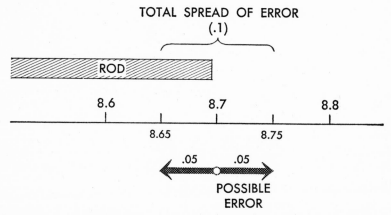

Fig. 33   The Possible Error in a Measurement Made to the Nearest Tenth

Suppose that a person measures the length of a rod and gives his answer as 8.7 in. The presumption is that he measured to the *nearest tenth* of an inch. The true length may then be any number of inches between 8.65 and 8.75 (Fig. 33). The true error may have any value between −.05 and +.05, as readily seen in the figure. The *possible error* is taken to be .05, for this is the smallest positive number that is sure to numerically exceed (or equal) the true error.

In computing with decimal values, we must ordinarily assume that the values are correctly given, with the last digit representing a "nearest" choice. *The possible error is equal to one-half the place value of that last digit.*

Illustrations. For 2., 2.6, 5.72, .034, .0340, the possible errors are .5, .05, .005, .0005, .00005, respectively. If the value of a piece of property is quoted as $20,300 and if we assume that the fact of the figure's being given as an even hundred means that it is correct to the nearest hundred dollars, then the possible error is $50.

With the direction of the error unknown, the rule for a difference merges with that for a sum, and the rule for a quotient with that for a product.

To see why this happens, consider a quotient, $T = T_1/T_2$. Let the relative possible error be 10% for both T_1 and T_2. Then the true relative errors r_1, r_2 may fall anywhere within the range from −10% to +10%. Hence their difference, $r_1 - r_2$, may fall anywhere between −20% and +20%. For example, the measurer may *overestimate* T_1 by nearly 10%, so that $r_1 \approx 10\%$, while *underestimating* T_2 by nearly 10%, so that $r_2 \approx -10\%$. Then $r_1 \approx r_1 - r_2 \approx 10\% - (-10)\% = 20\%$. The relative possible error in the quotient thus turns out to be the *sum* of the relative possible errors in the numerator and denominator, just as with the product.

COMPUTATIONAL ERROR RULES

1. *With a sum or difference combination of two or more estimated values, the possible error is the sum of the possible errors of the values.*

2. *With a product or quotient combination of two or more estimated values, the relative possible error is approximately equal to the sum of the relative possible errors of the values.*

Example 1. By pacing, a man estimates the dimensions of a rectangular field to be 60 ft. by 85 ft. He knows by past experiment that his estimates of distance by pacing are usually correct within about 8%. He figures that he can cut the grass on the field at the rate of 100 sq. ft. per minute, but recognizes that this estimate may be off as much as 10%. At worst, how long will the mowing job take?

Work. His time estimate is given by

$$t = \frac{60 \text{ ft.} \times 85 \text{ ft.}}{100 \text{ ft.}^2/\text{min.}} = \frac{5100}{100} \text{ min.} = 51 \text{ min.}$$

The terms 60, 85, 100 of the above product-quotient combination are subject to relative possible errors of 8%, 8%, 10%, respectively. According to Rule 2, the relative possible error r of t is approximately given by

$$r \approx 8\% + 8\% + 10\% = 26\%.$$

From this we estimate the (absolute) possible error e of t:

$$e \approx 51 \times 26\% = 51 \times (.26) \approx 13 \text{ (min.)}.$$

So to be on the safe side, the man may allow 64 min. for the task. (NOTE. An "exact" computation, with 60, 85, 100 replaced by 64.8, 91.8, 90, gives about 66 min.)

§8. ROUNDING DECIMAL VALUES

Bookkeepers are the only people who deal with decimal numbers in full digital array. The rest of us fill our scratch pads and stud our conversation with "rounded" values: "She must be over fifty." "He makes ten thousand a year." "Eight million live in New York City." "I bought a 4½-lb. roast." "I weigh 170."

To round a number, mentally place a vertical bar at the position where you wish to cut it off. The digits to the right of the bar are dropped, but it may be necessary to replace some or all of them by zeros so as to maintain the place values of the other digits. The number standing on the left of the bar is retained as is, or is increased by 1, according as the lopped-off portion is under or over the halfway value (|500000...). The 1950 population of the Continental United States was 150,697,361. In millions, this becomes:

rounds to

150|697 361 ⟶ 151 000 000.

There is no universal agreement upon handling the halfway cases. Should 2.25 when rounded to tenths become 2.2 or 2.3? Perhaps the *even* rule is best: *Of the two choices, select the one for which the digit just left of the imaginary bar is even.* (*Examples;* 2.2|5 rounds to 2.2; 45.75|55 to 45.76; 6|50 to 600; 77|500 to 78000; etc.)

One popular rule is to increase the digit in every halfway case. This has the disadvantage of introducing an accumulative error into sums. Also, when a rounded value is divided by 2, which frequently occurs, the final value may be thrown off. Under the increase rule, 2.25 rounds to 2.3. Dividing by 2 gives 1.15, which then rounds to 1.2. The even rule, on the other hand, leads to 1.1, which is closer to the "true" value, $2.25/2 = 1.125$.

Business firms usually drop a half-cent when paying a dividend or wage, but charge the full cent when billing.

Suppose that a number has been rounded, but that the imaginary vertical bar is still in position. Locate the first (leftmost) non-zero digit.

The digits from there to the bar are called the **significant digits** of the rounded number. (Any zeros that precede or follow this group of digits serve only to locate the decimal point.) *Examples:*

3.142	Significant digits: 3,1,4,2	Number of them: 4
151|000000	Significant digits: 1,5,1	Number of them: 3
.0000602	Significant digits: 6,0,2	Number of them: 3
27.20	Significant digits: 2,7,2,0	Number of them: 4

When a rounded number is a *whole number*, there is one chance in ten that it is "ambiguous." Thus if 23,962 is rounded to *hundreds*, the result is 24,000, which appears to be accurate only to *thousands*. Various notational devices for showing which digits are significant, and which are not, have been suggested. Inherently awkward, none have been commonly adopted. Scientists by-pass the difficulty by expressing numbers in the *standard form* explained in §4 of Chapter 9. In the case above, in which 23,962 was rounded to hundreds, the result would be written 2.40×10^4. The presence of the otherwise superfluous zero digit reveals it to be a third significant digit.

PROBLEM SET 3 (§6–§8)

1. According to the definition, which leads to a positive absolute error—an overestimate or an underestimate?

2. If it turns out that you have overestimated your income for the month by $40 and have underestimated your expenditures by $20, what is your net budget error?

3. Before setting out on a vacation jaunt with his family, Angus Snood made the cost estimates shown below. List each "error," estimated cost less actual cost, and verify that they sum to the total error.

	Estimated Cost	*Actual Cost*	*Error*
Car Costs	$120	$134.25	
Accommodations	90	98.00	
Food	75	68.20	
Other	50	82.15	

4. A candidate received 56,432 votes. He had expected 62,500 votes. What was the relative error in his prediction?   *Answer:* About 11% (10.75⁺).

5. The actual dimensions of a lot are 150 ft. by 270 ft. By pacing, a boy estimates the size at 160 ft. by 290 ft. Compute the relative error in each dimension. From the actual and the estimated area values, find the relative error in the area. Verify that the results satisfy the exact formula $r = r_1 + r_2 + r_1 r_2$. How closely do they satisfy the approximate formula $r \approx r_1 + r_2$?

6. Same as Problem 5, except that the actual and estimated dimensions are 150 ft. by 270 ft. and 140 ft. by 290 ft., respectively.

7. A carpenter measures the radius R of a circular disk, then computes the diameter and circumference from the formulas $d = 2R$, $c = 2\pi R$. If he was off

by 2% in his measurement of the radius, by what percents will his values of the diameter and circumference be off? (From now on, use the approximation $r \approx r_1 + r_2$.)

8.* The frequency of oscillation of a simple pendulum is inversely proportional to the square root of its length. To increase the frequency 2%, how should the length be altered?

9.* A ball-bearing, while still spherical, has been worn down from its initial diameter of .750 in. to .728 in. Originally it weighed 1.02 oz. About what does it weigh now? *Answer:* .93 oz.

10. For each value listed, give the possible error and the relative possible error (stated as decimals):

    (a) 23   (c) 20 lb.
    (b) $67   (d) 2.3 oz.
           Answers: (c) 5 lb., .25 [possibly .5 lb., .025]; (d) .05 oz., .022

11. As in Problem 10:

    (a) .004   (c) 21.63 cm.
    (b) 3800 ft. (d) 4 ft. 2 in.
           Answers: (a) .0005, .125; (d) .5 in., .01

12. To the nearest ten feet, the length and width of a field are 200 ft. and 80 ft., respectively. The computed perimeter and area values are thus 560 ft. and 16,000 sq. ft., respectively. Replacing 200 by 195 and 80 by 75, compute the least values that the perimeter and area may have. Replacing 200 by 205 and 80 by 85, compute the greatest values that the perimeter and area may have. Estimate these same extremes by combining possible and relative possible errors in length and width. Compare results. (Thus the estimated relative possible error in the area is given by $\frac{5}{200} + \frac{5}{80} = 8.75\%$, while $8.75\% \times 16,000 = 1400$, so that the estimated greatest possible area value is 17,400 sq. ft., which compares closely with 205 ft. $\times$ 85 ft. $= 17,425$ sq. ft.)

13. To the nearest foot, the length and width of a room are 20 ft. and 12 ft. Discuss the possible errors in perimeter and area values in the same way as directed in Problem 12.

14. The base diameter and the height of a cylindrical barrel are measured as 22 in. and 28 in., respectively, each to the nearest inch. Discuss the possible error in the volume, according to the directions of Problem 12. ($V = \pi R^2 H$).

15. A boy is clocked at $11\frac{1}{2}$ sec. in a hundred-yard dash. The time is thought to be correct to the nearest $\frac{1}{2}$ sec., while the 100-yd. measurement may be as much as 6 ft. off. Discuss the possible error in the speed, in feet per second, according to the directions of Problem 12. *Partial Answer:* $r \approx 4.2\%$

16. How many significant figures have each of these values?

    (a) 2.13   (c) 504.3   (e) 30.10
    (b) 762   (d) 2.008   (f) .0068   *Answers:* (e) 4; (f) 2

17. As in Problem 16:

    (a) 2.00   (c) 2.60×10^7
    (b) 2700   (d) 36 million   *Answer:* (b) Ambiguous, 2 to 4

18. Round each value to the nearest tenth:

(a)	20.72	(d)	6.25	(g)	.063
(b)	1.008	(e)	283.4739	(h)	.05
(c)	6.15	(f)	49.98	(i)	3.60

19. Round each value to have 3 significant figures:

(a)	29,374	(d)	6.065	(g)	2.937×10^{12}
(b)	6.045	(e)	6.095	(h)	.02937
(c)	6.055	(f)	29.37	(i)	.0083548

20.* Collect a number of adding-machine tape receipts from a grocery store, each with at least ten entries. (Discard tapes with items under 6¢, which may represent bottle deposits, corrections, etc. Eliminate any sales-tax items.) On each tape, round each entry to the nearest 10¢, add and compare with the machine total, computing the "absolute error," rounded total less machine total. (The class may study and discuss the distribution of a hundred such errors. See §9.)

§9.   ADDING AND SUBTRACTING

Two numbers rounded to the same decimal place are said to be equally *precise*. Since the possible error in a number is one-half the place value of the last significant digit (§7), two equally precise numbers will have equal possible errors. Thus 2.62 and 780.29 each have the possible error .005, and 23,700 and 9200 presumably each have the possible error 50. Of two numbers, the one with the smaller possible error is said to be the more precise: .07 is more precise than 3.6.

In adding or subtracting several numbers, it is pointless to attempt to gain more precision than is displayed by the least precise number in the group. For the possible error of the sum is the sum of those of the numbers, and the error of the least precise number will dwarf the others (being at least ten times as big). Hence before adding or subtracting, we ordinarily round all the values to have the same degree of precision as the initially least precise number.

STANDARD RULE

Before adding or subtracting, round all numbers to the same (decimal) place value. (The answer will then be automatically rounded to that place value.)

Even in adding a number of values, there is little chance that rounding errors will accumulate sufficiently to throw the answer off substantially. Occurring both positively and negatively, the true errors will tend toward cancelling out one another. Suppose, for example, that ten dollar-and-cent entries, chosen at random (like $2.43, $26.17, etc.), are rounded to the nearest dollar and added. The result will be more than a dollar away from the true sum in only about one-third of the cases, and will be more than four dollars off in less than one case out of ten thousand.

Example 1. In a news story, a man reads that the 1950 population of the "South" (16 states and the District of Columbia) was 47,197,088. He remembers that the 1950 population of the United States was about 151,000,000. What should be his estimate for the population outside the South?

Work. The U.S. Population figure is precise only to millions. Round the other value to millions, and subtract:

$$
\begin{array}{r}
151,000,000 \\
-\ \ 47,000,000 \\
\hline
104,000,000 \quad (Answer)
\end{array}
$$

Example 2. A team of three men measures the road distance between two intersections. Smith drives to a certain crossroad, reading 5.4 miles on his odometer. Jones goes from there to another crossroad, measuring 7.76 miles on a "fifth-wheel" device attached to his car. Barry lays a surveyor's tape along the final portion, finding it to be 3.478 miles. Estimate the total distance.

Work. Jones' and Barry's careful work is wasted. Round the numbers to *tenths*, and add. The estimate is 16.7 miles. (If the figures are added without rounding, the result is 16.638, which rounds to 16.6.) It is instructive to ask, "How short might the true distance be?" Smith's figure being 5.4, it may be presumed that the true length of his portion is at least 5.35 miles. Jones' portion must be at least 7.755 miles, Barry's 3.4775 miles. The true distance is at least their sum, 16.5825 miles. Similarly, the true distance must be less than 16.6935 miles. In view of these extreme possibilities, the "best" single answer is clearly either 16.6 or 16.7, with 16.6 just a shade the more preferable.

$$
\begin{array}{r}
5.4 \\
7.8 \\
3.5 \\
\hline
16.7
\end{array}
$$

§10. MULTIPLYING AND DIVIDING

Of two numbers, the one with the smaller relative possible error is called the more *accurate*. In multiplying or dividing several numbers, it is pointless to maintain a substantially higher order of accuracy in one or more numbers than in the others.

Given a number, consider the related whole number that is composed of its significant digits in sequence. We will call this whole number the **accuracy** of the original number. *Examples:*

23.072	has the accuracy	23072
.00730	has the accuracy	730
2900	presumably has the accuracy	29 (possibly 290 or 2900)

The relative possible error (r) of a number is half the reciprocal of its accuracy (α), in symbols:

$$ r = \frac{1}{2} \cdot \frac{1}{\alpha}. $$

Thus for 23.072, the absolute possible error is $(1/2)(.001)$ and the relative possible error is $(1/2)(.001/23.072) = (1/2)(1/23072)$. Halving the relative possible error doubles the accuracy, etc.

Example 1.   Compare the accuracies of the numbers 26.3 and 5.41.

Work.   The accuracies of the numbers are 263 and 541. Since 541 is a little more than twice 263, 5.41 is a little more than twice as accurate as 26.3.

Suppose two numbers are multiplied or divided. We know that the relative possible error of the resulting product or quotient is approximately given by $r \approx r_1 + r_2$. Denoting the accuracies of the numbers by α_1 and α_2 and substituting $r_1 = 1/2\alpha_1$, etc., we obtain

$$\frac{1}{\alpha} \approx \frac{1}{\alpha_1} + \frac{1}{\alpha_2}.$$

Here, α denotes the *theoretical accuracy* of the result. (We will wish to round the result so that its accuracy will agree with the theoretical accuracy, as nearly as possible.)

The relationship generalizes, in the obvious way, to apply to more than two numbers. Hence in any sequence of multiplications and/or divisions, *the reciprocal of the theoretical accuracy of the result is approximately equal to the sum of the reciprocals of the accuracies of the numbers.*

In illustration, take the product

$$.426 \times 158.3$$

The accuracies of the given numbers are 426 and 1583. Form the reciprocals and add:

$$\frac{1}{426} + \frac{1}{1583} \approx .002347 + .000632 = .002979 \approx \frac{1}{336}.$$

Hence the theoretical accuracy of the product is about 336.

Multiplying 158.3 by .426 in full gives 67.4358. How shall we round this result so that its accuracy will be close to 336? Here are the two possibilities:

(1)   67.4|358 $\longrightarrow$ 67.4.   Accuracy: 674
(2)   67.|4358 $\longrightarrow$ 67.   Accuracy: 67

The test of closeness is one of ratio: 674 is only just over twice as accurate as 336, while 336 is nearly five times as accurate as 67. So the proper choice is 67.4. We give this as the answer to the multiplication problem:

$$.426 \times 158.3 \approx 67.4.$$

Another way of analyzing is to compute the *extreme bounds* on the result (see the note to Example 2 below). The least and greatest values which the product could have are:

LOWER BOUND   UPPER BOUND

.4255 × 158.25 = 67.33...   .4265 × 158.35 = 67.53...

Clearly, 67.4 represents an appropriate choice for the answer. To retain a fourth figure, for example, citing the answer as 67.44 (67.43|58), would give a misleading impression with regard to the accuracy of the answer.

In casual computation, we would not wish to carry out exact analyses as set forth above. We usually depend upon "rough and ready" rules based on counting significant digits.

The number of significant digits provides a crude measure of accuracy. Thus a number with two significant digits has an accuracy between 10 and 99; a number with three significant digits has an accuracy between 100 and 999; etc. Cutting one significant digit away from a number drops its accuracy by a factor of 10. But multiplying a number by itself, say, drops the accuracy only by a factor of 2, because

$$\frac{1}{\alpha_1} + \frac{1}{\alpha_1} = \frac{2}{\alpha_1} = \frac{1}{\frac{1}{2}\alpha_1}.$$

So when several numbers are multiplied or divided, the theoretical accuracy of the result is less than the accuracy of any one of the given numbers, but usually not so much less as to cause the "loss" of a significant digit, and hardly ever so much less as to cause the loss of two such digits.

This reasoning leads to the following standard computational rules. In both cases, it is assumed that the computation is one that involves only multiplications and divisions or the taking of powers and roots.

SAFE RULE

In the given numbers, and throughout the computation, retain one more significant digit than is to be kept in the final answer.

COMMON RULE

First locate the number of least accuracy. Round each other number as far as possible without diminishing its accuracy below that of the least accurate number. As the computation proceeds, continue to round in this same way. Round the final answer to have just as many significant digits as the least accurate number.

The common rule is the more efficient, and is fairly satisfactory for ordinary computation. Where from two to six numbers are involved, the rule gives a "wrong" result about 30% of the time (one too few or one too many significant digits). The safe rule calls for lengthier computations, and the loss of accuracy caused by it (usually unnecessarily) cannot always be tolerated.

Example 2. The length and width of a long rectangular tape are measured. To the nearest tenth of an inch, the width is 3.2 in. and the length is 912.4 in. What is the area?

Work. We will use the common rule. The area A is given by:

$$\text{Area} = (3.2) \times (912.4) \text{ sq. in.}$$

The accuracies of the given numbers are 32 and 9124. The least accurate number is 3.2. We round 912.4 to 910, so that its accuracy is 91, still larger than 32. We round the result to two "figures" (significant digits):

$$A = 3.2 \times 910 = 2912 \approx 2900 \text{ (sq. in.)}   (Answer)$$

NOTE. Let us, for the practice, also compute the extreme bounds for the answer. Since 3.2 and 912.4 are accurate only to tenths, the *true* width and length may fall anywhere between these bounds:

$$3.15 < \text{True Width (in.)} < 3.25,$$
$$912.35 < \text{True Length (in.)} < 912.45.$$

The true area must therefore lie between these bounds:

$$3.15 \times 912.35 = 2873.9025 < \text{True Area} < 2965.4625 = 3.25 \times 912.45.$$
$$\text{(sq. in.)}$$

Apparently from the given information about the length and width, we can say of the area only that it falls somewhere between 2874 and 2965 sq. in. If we must cite some single figure for the area, 2900 represents a sound choice. (The apparent absolute possible error in 2900 is 50, while half the spread of error from 2874 to 2965 is 46, an unusually good agreement.)

Example 3. Divide 12,630 by 138. (Assume these to be rounded values.)

Work. Proceeding according to the common rule, we round 12,630 no further, since rounding one more place would reduce its accuracy to 126, less than 138. We carry out the long division to get three figures, as are in 138:

$$\frac{12630}{138} = 91.5|2... \approx 91.5.   (Answer)$$

NOTE. In computing extreme bounds for a quotient, take care. The upper bound is found by selecting the largest possible numerator and the smallest possible denominator:

$$\frac{12625}{138.5} \approx 91.2 < \frac{\text{True}}{\text{Quotient}} < 91.9 \approx \frac{12635}{137.5}.$$

Since the apparent absolute possible error in 91.5 is only .05, while half the error spread from 91.2 to 91.9 is .35, it would seem that this is a case in which the common rule is "wrong." A two-figure answer, 92, would be more appropriate.

Example 4. Find the value of 319.346 × 8.3029 correct to about three significant digits.

Work.

Safe Rule: 319.3 × 8.303 = 265|1.1479 ≈ 2650.
Common Rule: 319   × 8.30 = 264|7.7   ≈ 2650.

Example 5. Evaluate: $\dfrac{563 \times 607}{1234}$.

Work. With 563 the least accurate number, no initial rounding is needed:

$$\frac{563 \times 607}{1234} = \frac{341741}{1234} \approx \frac{341700}{1234} \approx 277. \quad (Answer)$$

Note that four digits were retained in 341700, because rounding another place would have reduced its accuracy to 342 < 563.

REMARK. Strictly speaking, what we have defined above as the "accuracy" of a numerical value should be called its "apparent accuracy" instead. The "true accuracy" of a value is related to its true relative error in the same way that its "apparent accuracy" is related to its possible relative error ($r\alpha = \frac{1}{2}$).

§11. THE ACCURACY RULE

The number of significant digits, as we observed in §10, provides only a crude measure of accuracy. It would therefore seem desirable to develop a simple computational rule that is based wholly upon the conception of accuracy. Such a one is given below. Note that it differs from the common rule of §10 only in the criterion used for rounding the final answer.

ACCURACY RULE

In multiplying or dividing several numbers, first locate the number of least accuracy. Round each other number as far as possible without diminishing its accuracy below that of the least accurate number. As the computation proceeds, continue to round in the same way. Round the final answer to have no more than twice the accuracy of the least accurate number.

Over the range for which the common rule is "wrong" about 30% of the time, the accuracy rule is "wrong" about 10% of the time.

The rule is based upon an evaluation of what happens "in the average," when several numbers are multiplied or divided. Consider the illustration of §10 in which the multiplication .426 × 158.3 was analyzed. Carried out in full, the multiplication process gave the result 67.4358, though the theoretical accuracy of the answer was only 336. In lieu of testing ratios, we may determine a "ten range" centered on 336 by dividing and multiplying it by $\sqrt{10}$, which is approximately equal to 3.16. Thus:

$$\frac{336}{3.16} \approx 106 \qquad \text{and} \qquad 336 \times 3.16 \approx 1060.$$

Then 67.4358 should be rounded so that its accuracy lies between those bounds: $106 < 674 < 1060$. In fact, only the upper bound, 1060, need be computed; then 67.4358 should be rounded to obtain as large an accuracy as possible which does not exceed this upper bound. In general, with a sequence of multiplications and/or divisions, we should round the final answer so that its accuracy is as large as possible, but not exceeding 3.16 times its theoretical accuracy.

To get a simple rule, we substitute the "accuracy of the least accurate number" for the "theoretical accuracy of the answer." But that is a larger value, so that the size of the 3.16 factor needs to be reduced in compensation. Consideration of the situation in the average shows 2 to be a good choice for the factor.

ILLUSTRATIONS

(1) $\quad \dfrac{98}{73} \approx 1.34.$ $\qquad\qquad\qquad$ (Accuracy: $134 < 2 \times 73 = 146$)

(2) $\quad \dfrac{152}{206} \approx .74.$ $\qquad\qquad\qquad$ (Accuracy: $74 < 2 \times 152 = 304$)

(3) $\quad \dfrac{(.238)(8.0371)(15.763)}{.9624} \approx \dfrac{(.238)(8.04)(15.76)}{.962}$

$$\approx \frac{(.238)(126.7)}{.962} \qquad\qquad (1267 > 238)$$

$$\approx \frac{30.2}{.962} \qquad\qquad (302 > 238)$$

$$\approx 31.4 \qquad\qquad (314 < 2 \times 238 = 476)$$

NOTE. A power is a "worst case" of a multiplication, each factor being equally inaccurate. Squaring halves the accuracy, cubing divides it by three, etc. On the other hand, accuracy is gained when a root is taken. Here is a special rule for powers and roots (the factor of 3 which appears in it being rounded from $\sqrt{10} \approx 3.16$).

SUPPLEMENTARY RULE FOR POWERS AND ROOTS

When taking an nth power of a base, round the answer so that its accuracy does not exceed $3/n$ times the accuracy of the base. When taking an nth root of a base, round the answer so that its accuracy does not exceed $3n$ times the accuracy of the base.

PROBLEM SET 4 (§9–§11)

In these problems, all numerical values should be taken as "rounded"—correct just to their last significant place value. Thus 2.73 is correct to the nearest hundredth, 3760 to the nearest ten, etc.

In Problems 1–5, add or subtract as directed, after initial roundings:

1.	24.372	2.	2700	3.	.0064	
	6.29		392		.0105	
	.8840		57.6		.0002	
	+ 162.096		+ 940		+ .073	

4.	36,000	5.	. 27.063
	− 8,827		− 8.4

Answers: (1)   193.64; (3)   .089; (4)   27,000

6.   Give the accuracies of these values:

    (a)   237   (d)   5.70   (g)   10,000
    (b)   23,700   (e)   .057   (h) 6.2×10^8
    (c)   2.37   (f)   5.07   (i)   1.002
                             Answers: (b)   237; (e)   57; (g)   1

7.   How accurate is 2.72 in comparison with 68?
8.   Any four-digit value is bound to be at least how much more accurate than any two-digit value?
9.   In the most extreme case, how much more accurate can a four-digit value be than a three-digit value?
10.   "On the average," how much more accurate is a four-digit value than a three-digit value?

In Problems 11–20, compute the theoretical accuracy of the result, then round your calculated result so that its accuracy is as "close" as possible to the theoretical accuracy. (Use a table of reciprocals if you have one.)

11.	2.4×8.7	*Answer:* 21	(Th. Acc. = 19)
12.	$1.02 \div 1.04$	*Answer:* .98	(Th. Acc. = 51)
13.	2.2×3.6	*Answer:* 8	(Th. Acc. = 14)
14.	$3.6 \div 2.2$	*Answer:* 1.6	(Th. Acc. = 14)
15.	$2.2 \div 3.6$	*Answer:* .6	(Th. Acc. = 14)
16.	72.3×908	*Answer:* 65,600	(Th. Acc. = 402)
17.	$908 \div 72.3$	*Answer:* 12.56	(Th. Acc. = 402)

18. $\dfrac{27 \times 52}{63}$ *Answer:*   22   (Th. Acc. =   14)

19. $\dfrac{271 \times 52}{63}$ *Answer:*   220   (Th. Acc. =   26)

20. $\dfrac{86.0 \times (73.2)^2}{2466}$ *Answer:*   187   (Th. Acc. = 232)

In Problems 21–30, compute the result (a) by the common rule (§10), (b) by the accuracy rule (§11). As your instructor requests, (c) compute extreme bounds for the answer.

21.	2.4×8.7	*Answer:* (a)	21;	(b)	21;	(c)	20.3275, 21.4375
22.	$2.2 \div 3.6$	*Answer:* (a)	.61;	(b)	.6;	(c)	.589, .634
23.	$98 \div 92$	*Answer:* (a)	1.1;	(b)	1.07;	(c)	1.054, 1.077

24.	6.4×8.235		*Answer:* (a)	52;	(b)	52
25.	6.4×3.164		*Answer:* (a)	20;	(b)	20
26.	$372 \div 8.234$		*Answer:* (a)	45.2;	(b)	45.2
27.	$36.0 \times 28.2 \times 61.44$		*Answer:* (a)	62,300;	(b)	62,000
28.	$(36.0 \times 28.2) \div 61.44$		*Answer:* (a)	16.5;	(b)	16.5
29.	$61.44 \div (36.0 \times 28.2)$		*Answer:* (a)	.0605;	(b)	.060
30.	$(234.73 \times 804.632) \div 4205$		*Answer:* (a)	44.91;	(b)	44.91

31.* Verify that the given answers satisfy the "supplementary rule for powers and roots" cited in the note at the end of §11:

(a)	$(7.4)^3 \approx 410$	(d)	$\sqrt{20.4} \approx 4.52$
(b)	$(2.0)^5 \approx 30$	(e)	$\sqrt[3]{1.500} \approx 1.1447$
(c)	$(2.0)^{12} \approx 4000$	(f)	$\sqrt[100]{2 \times 10^{103}} \approx 10.8$

*§12. ABRIDGED MULTIPLICATION AND DIVISION

After two numbers have been multiplied out in full, several digits usually must be lopped off the result to round it to have appropriate accuracy. The aim of *abridged multiplication* schemes is to avoid doing the part of the work that produces the unwanted digits.

Consider the product 174×238. We usually arrange the work in the form shown on the left below. The form on the right is an alternative arrangement (§5, Chapter 5) in which the multiplier digits are used in left-to-right order, 1, 7, 4, to get the partial products 238, 1666, 952. Depending on the computational rule used (§10, §11), the result should be rounded to 41,400 or to 41,000.

```
        238          238|
    ×   174       ×   1|74        Result rounds to
        952          238|         41,400 or to 41,000
       1666          166|6
        238            9|52
      ─────          ───────
      41412          414|12
```

We focus our attention upon the form on the right. The part of the work lying on the right of the vertical bar represents wasted effort. To abridge the process, we may just neglect the digit products 7×8, 4×8, and 4×3, the ones contributing to the portion of the work that is to be discarded.

One way to do this is as follows. Multiply 238 by 1, then place a dot over the units digit, 8, of 238, to indicate that this digit is now "used up." The 23 that remains is multiplied by 7, giving the partial product 161, written next to the bar, as shown at the right. Then the tens digit, 3, of 238 is dotted. Multiplying 2 by 4 gives the last partial product, 8. The partial products are summed, and zeros are filled into the missing places of the result (under each multiplier digit).

Of course the result is too small. The neglected digit products make a contribution on the left of the bar that is just a little too large to be wholly overlooked. The lost contribution, from 7×8, 4×8, and 4×3, is shown on the right. It amounts to about 7 units in the place just left of the bar.

To correct for the loss, we modify the above procedure by adding 2 (in the place just left of the bar) to each partial product as it is written down. We call this process *automatic abridged multiplication*.

The rule is based upon the observation that the uncorrected scheme will, on the average, give second and later partial products that are about 2½ units too small in the place just left of the bar. The rule is amply accurate for ordinary multiplying. A discrepancy in the final answer of 3 or more units in the place just left of the bar will occur infrequently. (Correct rounding will usually eliminate even these discrepancies.)

When one factor has fewer significant digits than the other, use it as the multiplier. (*Alternative:* Set the bar farther to the right and delay the dotting.) In the following illustrations, correctly rounded answers are shown boxed, while the bracketed numbers under them give the results of multiplying out in full.

$$
\begin{array}{r|l}
23\dot{8}| \\
1 & 74 \\
\hline
238|
\end{array}
$$

$$
\begin{array}{r|l}
23\dot{8}| \\
1 & 74 \\
\hline
238 \\
161|
\end{array}
$$

$$
\begin{array}{r|l}
23\dot{8}| \\
1 & 74 \\
\hline
238 \\
161 \\
8 \\
\hline
407 & 00
\end{array}
$$

$$
\begin{array}{rr|l}
7 \times 8 = & 5 & 6 \\
4 \times 38 = & 1 & 52 \\
\text{LOST} \longrightarrow & \textcircled{7} & 12
\end{array}
$$

AUTOMATIC ABRIDGED MULTIPLICATION

$$
\begin{array}{r|l}
23\dot{8}| \\
1 & 74 \\
\hline
240 \\
163 \\
10 \\
\hline
413 & 00
\end{array}
$$

$$
\begin{array}{r|l}
6\dot{2}8\dot{5}| \\
2 & 408 \\
\hline
12572 \\
2514 \\
50| \\
\hline
15136 & 000 \\
\end{array}
$$
$$\boxed{15140000}$$
$$[15134280]$$

$$
\begin{array}{r|l}
17\dot{8}\dot{5}| \\
4 & 67 \\
\hline
7142 \\
1070 \\
121| \\
\hline
8333 & 00 \\
\end{array}
$$
$$\boxed{833000}$$
$$[833595]$$

$$
\begin{array}{r|l}
4.0\dot{7}6\dot{3}| \\
8 & 9.036 \\
\hline
326106 \\
36686 \\
122 \\
26 \\
\hline
362.940| \\
\end{array}
$$
$$\boxed{362.94}$$
$$[362.9374468]$$

To abridge a division, set it up according to the usual arrangement, then draw a vertical bar *after the first quotient* digit (unless this digit is 1, in which case set the bar one place farther to the right and delay dotting one step). Curtail work at the bar, increase each partial product by 2 before subtracting it, and place dots over "used up" digits of the divisor after each step of the work.

$$\begin{array}{r} 2| \quad . \\ 17\dot{4})\overline{413|00.} \\ 350 \\ \hline 63| \end{array}$$

At the right are shown the successive steps in the division of 41,300 by 174. After the first step, we test 17 into 63, obtaining 3 for the second quotient digit. We increase the partial product $3 \times 17 = 51$ by 2 before putting it down, etc.

$$\begin{array}{r} 2|3 \quad . \\ 17\dot{4})\overline{413|00.} \\ 350 \\ \hline 63| \\ 53| \\ \hline 10| \end{array}$$

$$\begin{array}{r} 2|38. \\ 17\dot{4})\overline{413|00.} \\ 350 \\ \hline 63| \\ 53| \\ \hline 10| \\ 10| \\ \hline \end{array}$$

NOTE. Some textbooks on arithmetic describe abridged procedures arranged like those shown here, but requiring the computer to estimate mentally the corrections needed to compensate for the discarded digit products.

Further examples:

$$\begin{array}{r} 3|.08 \\ 2\dot{6}\dot{7})\overline{822|.} \\ 803 \\ \hline 19| \\ 18| \\ \hline \end{array} \qquad \begin{array}{r} .02|408 \\ 6\dot{2}\dot{8}\dot{5})\overline{151.36|00} \\ 125\ 72 \\ \hline 25\ 64| \\ 25\ 14| \\ \hline 50| \\ 50| \\ \hline \end{array} \qquad \begin{array}{r} 1.1|35 \\ 84\dot{3})\overline{957.0|} \\ 843 \\ \hline 114\ 0| \\ 84\ 5| \\ \hline 29\ 5| \\ 25\ 4| \\ \hline 4\ 1| \\ 4\ 2| \\ \hline \end{array}$$

*PROBLEM SET 5 (§12)

Use the automatic abridged methods to perform the indicated multiplications and divisions. Round each result according to the common rule (§10) or the accuracy rule (§11), as directed. (Results before rounding are shown in parentheses at the far right.)

1.	148 × 462	Answer:	68,400 or 68,000	(68,400)
2.	30.6 × .618	Answer:	18.9	(18.94)
3.	4.23 × 10.76	Answer:	45.5	(45.54)
4.	6.812 × 80.57	Answer:	548.9	(548.86)
5.	2.358 × 3.762	Answer:	8.869 or 8.87	(8.869)
6.	18.94 ÷ 30.6	Answer:	.617 or .62	(.617)
7.	18.94 ÷ .618	Answer:	30.6	(30.6)
8.	8.869 ÷ 3.762	Answer:	2.358	(2.358)
9.	708 ÷ 45.2	Answer:	15.7	(15.66)
10.	98 ÷ 96	Answer:	1.0 or 1.02	(1.02)

11.* Observe that the partial products occurring in the division of Problem 7 are the same as those appearing in the multiplication of Problem 2, likewise for Problems 8 and 5. Hence the two abridged processes are "inverse" to each other. Why do the partial products differ in Problems 6 and 2?

12.* In each of Problems 1–10, carry out the work without abridgment, but round according to either rule. In any case does the answer differ from the one obtained before? (*Partial Answer:* 548.8 in Problem 4. Two other cases, common rule only.)

*§13. THE SLIDE RULE

A pair of yardsticks furnishes a crude *slide rule* for adding and subtracting numbers. The method of operation is to slide one stick along the top edge of the other. Figure 34 shows the addition of 5 to 8. The upper stick is slid to the right until its left (zero) end is above the 8-in. mark on the lower stick. Then below the 5-in. mark on the upper stick is read the answer, **13** (13-in. mark on the lower stick). In this way, the abstract numerical operation 8 + 5 = 13 has been replaced by a physical operation of adding lengths: 8 in. + 5 in. = 13 in.

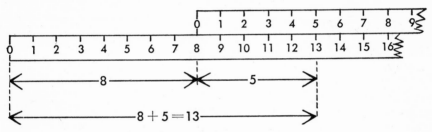

Fig. 34   An "Adding" Slide Rule

In subtraction, the procedure is reversed. To take 5 from 13, set 5 on the upper stick over 13 on the lower, then read **8** below the left end of the upper stick (Fig. 34 applies here too). The addition and subtraction of signed numbers may be demonstrated by replacing the yardsticks with strips of cardboard graduated with scales running from −10 to +10.

It is possible to graduate two strips with special scales so that the "adding" operation described above actually accomplishes the *multiplication* of the scale numbers, and the reverse "subtracting" operation accomplishes their *division*. The special scale is called a *logarithmic scale*, or "log" scale for short. Slide rules incorporating logarithmic, trigonometric, and other scales are extensively used by engineers, scientists, technicians, and industrial workers to expedite the many rough computations they must perform.

Children are often fascinated by the "magical" way in which the slide rule produces products, quotients, and roots. Many educators recommend the demonstration of the instrument in the middle or upper grades. Where time permits, it may be desirable that a child should make his own crude slide rule, as a mathematical experiment (in educational terminology: a "meaningful experience"). The needed logarithmic scale can be constructed without technical knowledge. We will call it a *multiplying scale*. To construct it, we will apply and reapply the principle that the length-adding operation earlier described must accomplish the multiplication of the scale values.

Take two strips of cardboard, about eleven inches long and an inch to an inch-and-a-half wide. Place two marks 10 in. apart along the edge of each strip (Fig. 13.2). Mark the 10-in. length so that it is divided into eight equal portions. In speaking of these marks, we will refer to their fractional positions: 0, ⅛, ¼, ⅜, ½, ⅝, ¾, ⅞, 1. Label the zero mark with the scale value 1 and the 1 mark with the scale value 10.

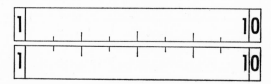

Fig. 35   Constructing a Slide Rule: First Stage

Henceforth we will refer to the 10-in. portions of the strips (scaled from 1 to 10) as upper and lower "scales," the left end of each scale (0 mark) being labeled 1 and the right end (1 mark) being labeled 10.

Now slide the upper scale to the position shown in Figure 36, so that its left end lies above the ½ mark on the lower scale. The ½ mark on the upper scale will then lie above the right end of the lower strip. With this "setting" of the rule we are adding two equal lengths: 5 in. + 5 in. = 10 in. By the principle of construction, this must accomplish the multiplication of the scale value that is to be placed at the ½ mark on the lower scale by the *same* scale value, to be placed at the ½ mark on the upper scale. Further, the product of these equals is read as 10 (right end of lower scale). Hence the square of the scale value in question is 10, and the value itself is $\sqrt{10}$. Extract the root by one of the procedures of §3–§5, finding the approximate value $\sqrt{10} \approx 3.162$. Label each ½ mark with this scale value.

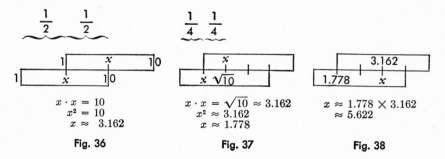

$x \cdot x = 10$	$x \cdot x = \sqrt{10} \approx 3.162$
$x^2 = 10$	$x^2 \approx 3.162$
$x \approx 3.162$	$x \approx 1.778$

$x \approx 1.778 \times 3.162$
≈ 5.622

Fig. 36   **Fig. 37**   **Fig. 38**

The quarter-marks are labeled by sliding the upper rule to the position shown in Figures 37 and 38. In Figure 37, it is seen that the value at the $\frac{1}{4}$ mark is the square root of $\sqrt{10}$, or $\sqrt[4]{10} \approx \sqrt{3.162} \approx 1.778$. Likewise, the value at the $\frac{3}{4}$ mark is $\sqrt[4]{10^3} = \sqrt[4]{10} \times \sqrt{10} \approx 1.778 \times 3.162 \approx 5.622$. The eighth-marks may be labeled by a similar procedure; we could continue to sixteenths, etc., were this desired.

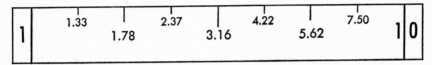

Fig. 39   Constructing a Slide Rule: Second Stage

Figure 39 shows the labeled lower scale at the present stage of construction. This is the multiplying scale that we want. But it is inconveniently labeled. We would like to have it marked to show where the whole-number scale values fall: 1, 2, 3, . . . , 10. At this point, it would be feasible to bring a standard slide rule into the classroom and point out how the 1, 1.33, 1.78, 2.37, etc. positions on its log scale match those shown on the homemade rule. The homemade rule could then be regraduated according to the slide rule scale.

But with the aid of a graph, we can finish the job on our own. In Figure 40, the scale values already found (1, 1.33, 1.78, etc.) are plotted against inch distances measured from the left end of the scale (0, 1.25, 2.50, etc.). A smooth curve is drawn through the nine plotted points. The distances corresponding to whole-number scale values are now estimated by drawing horizontal lines through these values to meet the curve, then vertical lines to the distance scale. Thus the dotted lines drawn in the figure show that the scale values 2, 3, 4 are to be placed at distances of 3.0, 4.8, 6.0 in. The work may be checked against the figures in the table at the right (distance = 10 $\times$ log of scale value).

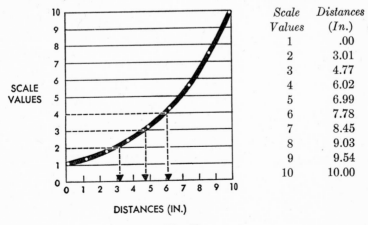

Scale Values	Distances (In.)
1	.00
2	3.01
3	4.77
4	6.02
5	6.99
6	7.78
7	8.45
8	9.03
9	9.54
10	10.00

SCALE VALUES

DISTANCES (IN.)

Fig. 40

Now the strips may be turned over and regraduated according to the distance readings. Figure 41 shows the result. (The 1.5, 2.5, etc., values are also marked in. To find the first four of these, set the scales for the divisions of 3 by 2, 5 by 2, etc.)

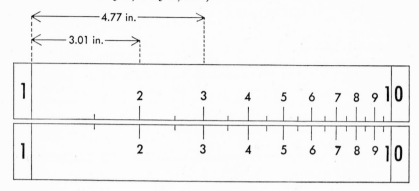

Fig. 41   The Slide Rule

When we give our new slide rule a tryout, we will soon face a troublesome situation. Trying 4×5, we find that the answer is "off the rule." One way of handling this situation is to join two lower scales end to end

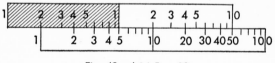

Fig. 42 $4 \times 5 = 20$

to make one twice as long, as shown in Figure 42. The values on the second scale are ten times those on the first, the two together forming a single scale graduated from 1 to 100. A second way is much simpler. After discovering that 4×5 lies off the rule, set the *right* instead of the left end of the upper scale above 5 on the lower. Below the 4 on the upper scale, read 2 on the lower. Multiply this by ten to get the answer: $10 \times 2 = 20$. To learn why this method works, study the relationship of the shaded scale in Figure 42 to the rest of the figure.

COMMON UNITS OF MEASURE (U.S.)

LENGTH

$$12 \text{ Inches} = 1 \text{ Foot}$$
$$3 \text{ Feet} = 1 \text{ Yard}$$
$$\left.\begin{array}{l}1760 \text{ Yards} \\ 5280 \text{ Feet}\end{array}\right\} = 1 \text{ Mile}$$
$$6076 \text{ Feet} \approx 1 \text{ Nautical mile}$$

1000 Microns = 1 Millimeter	2.540 Centimeters ≈ 1 Inch
10 Millimeters = 1 Centimeter	39.37 Inches = 1 Meter
100 Centimeters = 1 Meter	1.609 Kilometers ≈ 1 Mile
1000 Meters = 1 Kilometer	.6214 Miles ≈ 1 Kilometer

AREA

43,560 Square feet = 4,840 Square yards = 1 Acre
640 Acres = 1 Section = 1 Square mile
1,076 Square feet ≈ 100 Square meters = 1 Are

VOLUME

Liquid

8 Fluid ounces = 1 Cup
2 Cups = 1 Pint
2 Pints = 1 Quart
4 Quarts = 1 Gallon
31½ Gallons = 1 Barrel
(231 Cubic inches = 1 Gallon)

Dry

2 Dry pints = 1 Dry quart
8 Dry quarts = 1 Peck
4 Pecks = 1 Bushel
(2150 Cubic inches ≈ 1 Bushel)

1 Fluid ounce = 2 Tablespoons = 8 Fluid drams = 360 Drops = 480 Minims

1.057 Quarts ≈ 1000 Cubic centimeters = 1 Liter
35.31 Cubic feet ≈ 1 Cubic meter = 1 Stere

WEIGHT

60 Grains = 1 Dram   437½ Grains = 1 Ounce

$$\left.\begin{array}{l}7000 \text{ Grains} \\ 16 \text{ Ounces}\end{array}\right\} = 1 \text{ Pound}$$

2000 Pounds = 1 Ton   1000 Kilograms = 1 Metric ton
480 Grains = 1 Troy ounce   454 Grams ≈ 1 Pound
12 Troy ounces = 1 Troy pound   2.205 Pounds ≈ 1000 Grams = 1 Kilogram

TIME

60 Seconds = 1 Minute   12 Calendar months = 1 Year
60 Minutes = 1 Hour   10 Years = 1 Decade
24 Hours = 1 Day   100 Years = 1 Century
7 Days = 1 Week   1000 Years = 1 Millennium

365.2422 Days ≈ 1 Mean solar year

Index

Index

Abacus, binary, 106
  duodecimal, 103–104
  forms used by different peoples, 9, 15, 18, 19, 23
  line, 4–5, 7, 15–18, 69
  rod, 5–7
  See also Counting table
Abacus operations, adding and subtracting, 5, 74–75, 78
  multiplying and dividing, 17–18, 87–89
Abacus work scheme, 17, 18, 21, 88–89
Abridged processes, 87, 246–248
Absolute error, 231–233
Absolute value, 94, 172
Abstraction, 205–208
Acceleration, 200, 212
Accuracy, 239–244
  definition of, 239
Accuracy rule, 243
Acre, 211, 213, 214
Addition, of approximate values, 238–239
  law of, associative, 50–53
    commutative, 50–53
  of concrete expressions, 195–197
  of decimals, 157–158
  definition of, 46–47
  error rules, 231, 234
  of fractions, 145–148
  processes, 67–72
  scratch method, 72
  on a slide rule, 249
Addition fact, 47, 67–68
Additive measures, 192–197
Additive numeral system, 3, 8–15
  passim
Age cards, 109–111
Algebra, geometric, 184

  laws of, 57–58
Amen (=99), 119
Amicable numbers, 118, 120
Approximate computation, 159, 220–252,
Approximate equality sign, 200, 232
Approximate measurement, 182–183, 231–232
Approximation, decimal, 157, 187
  of roots, 219, 226–230
Arabian mathematics, 22–23
Area, 201–202
Arithmetic, Babylonian, 10
  binary, 105–107
  duodecimal, 102–105
  Egyptian, 9, 135–136
  fundamental theorem of, 126–127
  and geometry, 184, 188
  Greek, 22, 135, 184
  Hindu-Arabic, 21–23
  Mayan, 23–24, 98
  mental, 77
  Roman, 13–16, 135–136
Arrows, representing numbers, 179–180, 187
Associative law, 174
  of addition, 50–53
  for concrete expressions, 197
  of multiplication, 53–58

Babylonian mathematics, 9–13, 24, 98, 155
Base, of number system, 1–2, 97–111
  passim, 110 (table), 214–215
  of a power, 217
  of a rate, 166–168
Base set (fractions), 145–147
Base-two system (*see* Binary system)